ASHRAE Design Guide for Tall, Supertall, and Megatall Building Systems, Second Edition

This publication was written under the auspices of ASHRAE Technical Committee (TC) 9.12, Tall Buildings. TC 9.12 is concerned with the function, operation, energy, and human safety for buildings in excess of 300 feet in height. Also included is the determination of requirements related to hydraulics, airflow, infiltration, thermal insulation, water vapor retarders, environmental control, fire and smoke control, and maintenance.

ABOUT THE AUTHOR

Peter Simmonds is the retired managing director/principal of Building and Systems Analytics, LLC based in Marina Del Rey, CA and Hong Kong. He has Bachelor of Science degrees in Mechanical Engineering and Research and Development from Reading Technical College; a Master's degree from HTS, Den Bosch, the Netherlands; and a PhD from the University of Southern California. He is an ASHRAE Life Member and has twice chaired Technical Committee (TC) 9.12, Tall Buildings. Simmonds is a past President of the College of Fellows, he is a Fellow of The International Building Performance Association (IBPSA), and is a Fellow of the Façade Tectonics Institute. He has been involved in the design and operation of tall, supertall, and megatall buildings around the world for more than 30 years. He is a recognized authority in the field of façade performance. A main goal of his research and applications has been to understand the heat transfer and performance of radiant systems for both heating and cooling. His studies related to thermal performance of these systems led to a unique way to enhance these systems. Publications of his work led to the development of radiant systems in the United States and are included in *ASHRAE Handbooks*. He received the Carter Bronze Medal from the Chartered Institution of Building Services Engineers in 1993 and the Crosby Field award from ASHRAE in 2020.

He has authored or coauthored more than 60 technical papers, articles, and books and is a member of several ASHRAE Technical Committees.

ASHRAE

ASHRAE, founded in 1894, is a global society advancing human well-being through sustainable technology for the built environment. The Society and its members focus on building systems, energy efficiency, indoor air quality, refrigeration, and sustainability within the industry. Through research, standards writing, publishing and continuing education, ASHRAE shapes tomorrow's built environment today. ASHRAE was formed as the American Society of Heating, Refrigerating and Air-Conditioning Engineers by the merger in 1959 of American Society of Heating and Air-Conditioning Engineers (ASHAE) founded in 1894 and The American Society of Refrigerating Engineers (ASRE) founded in 1904.

1791 Tullie Circle, NE
Atlanta, GA 30329
1-800-527-4723
www.ashrae.org

CTBUH

The Council on Tall Buildings and Urban Habitat (CTBUH) is the world's leading resource for professionals focused on the inception, design, construction, and operation of tall buildings and future cities. Founded in 1969 and headquartered at Chicago's historic Monroe Building, the CTBUH is a not-for-profit organization with an Asia Headquarters office at Tongji University, Shanghai; a Research Office at Iuav University, Venice, Italy; and an Academic Office at the Illinois Institute of Technology, Chicago. CTBUH facilitates the exchange of the latest knowledge available on tall buildings around the world through publications, research, events, working groups, web resources, and its extensive network of international representatives. The Council's research department is spearheading the investigation of the next generation of tall buildings by aiding original research on sustainability and key development issues. The Council's free database on tall buildings, The Skyscraper Center, is updated daily with detailed information, images, data, and news. The CTBUH also developed the international standards for measuring tall building height and is recognized as the arbiter for bestowing such designations as "The World's Tallest Building."

The Monroe Building
104 South Michigan Avenue, Suite 620
Chicago, Illinois 60603
www.ctbuh.org
www.skyscrapercenter.com

ASHRAE Design Guide for Tall, Supertall, and Megatall Building Systems, Second Edition

Peter Simmonds

ISBN 978-1-947192-50-8 (paperback)
ISBN 978-1-947192-51-5 (PDF)

Published in cooperation with the Council on Tall Buildings and Urban Habitat

ASHRAE
1791 Tullie Circle, N.E.
Atlanta, GA 30329
www.ashrae.org

Cover image created by iCube for JAHN Architects. Used with permission.
Printed in the United States of America

Library of Congress Cataloging-in-Publication Data

Names: Simmonds, Peter, 1954- author. | ASHRAE (Firm)
Title: ASHRAE design guide for tall, supertall, and megatall building
    systems / Peter Simmonds.
Description: Second edition. | Atlanta, GA : ASHRAE, [2020] | Includes
    bibliographical references and index. | Summary: "The ASHRAE Design
    Guide for Tall, Supertall, and Megatall Building Systems, second
    edition, is concerned with HVAC, design, maintenance, and other factors
    for buildings 330 feet (100 m) or higher. The guide details the problems
    and possible solutions for tall, supertall, and megatall buildings"--
    Provided by publisher.
Identifiers: LCCN 2020014545 | ISBN 9781947192508 (paperback) | ISBN
    9781947192515 (adobe pdf)
Subjects: LCSH: Tall buildings--Design and construction--Handbooks,
    manuals, etc. | Megastructures--Design and construction--Handbooks,
manuals, etc. | Building, Iron and steel--Handbooks, manuals, etc.
Classification: LCC TH1611 .S53 2020 | DDC 720/.483--dc23
LC record available at https://lccn.loc.gov/2020014545

ASHRAE Staff	Special Publications	Cindy Sheffield Michaels, Editor
		James Madison Walker, Managing Editor, Standards
		Lauren Ramsdell, Associate Editor
		Mary Bolton, Assistant Editor
		Michshell Phillips, Senior Editorial Coordinator
	Publishing Services	David Soltis, Group Manager of Electronic Products & Publication Services
		Jayne Jackson, Publication Traffic Administrator
	Director of Publications and Education	Mark S. Owen

Updates and errata for this publication will be posted on the
ASHRAE website at www.ashrae.org/publicationupdates.

CONTENTS

CASE STUDIES

ASHRAE Design Guide for Tall, Supertall, and Megatall Building Systems, Second Edition, is accompanied by online content, which can be found at https://www.ashrae.org/tallbuildings. These files provide helpful spreadsheets. If the files or information at the link are not accessible, please contact the publisher.

FOREWORD

As the tall building industry moves into a new decade, it is appropriate to stand back and take stock of what we've accomplished, but also to be honest about where we have fallen short. The foreword to the first edition of this book, published in 2015, highlighted the critical issues of tall building design, especially concerning environmental footprint, in terms of both embodied and operational energy. We are duty-bound to continue to reiterate this as our highest priority. The fundamentals have not changed, though there have been some encouraging advances in the intervening five years.

First, let us review what remains the same. As always, architects and engineers determine how program, structure, and services will support each other efficiently. And, in each case, it falls to building services engineers to determine how a spatial arrangement of stacked floors will be ventilated, heated, cooled, and how it will interact with the envelope that surrounds it.

Tall buildings continue to require enormous amounts of energy to move their occupants from floor to floor, exhaust the heat they and their many electronics generate, and provide chilled air or heat to keep conditions comfortable. They require enormous skill and effort to seal envelopes and keep them airtight against the elements and to prevent unpleasant pressure changes as elevators hurtle up and down their lengths.

We are still faced with an overstock of tall buildings constructed following a protocol that dates from the 1950s—seal the building, cover it head-to-toe in glass, and air condition it 24 hours a day. For all of the advanced engineering work that goes into making these astounding structures stand up and function, from an MEP standpoint a large number of them are dinosaurs. For how iconic they are, many of these monoliths are not built for longevity.

It is commonplace to talk about a tall building's design life (or at least those of its critical constituent parts) as being 25, 50, or 100 years. It is particularly discouraging that one of the new "height records" from the past five years is that a tall building of greater than 656 ft (200 m), the Union Carbide/JP Morgan Chase headquarters building in New York, is now being dismantled for the first time. This 1960 office building fit the "dinosaur" paradigm to a tee, but it had been extensively retrofitted twice already, in 1982 and 2011, yet still the owners concluded it needed to be demolished and replaced to meet contemporary needs. We have to do better from the outset if we do not want to see buildings we construct today meet the same fate in 50 years.

Recladding in the conventional sense is enormously expensive and wasteful of materials. We should be designing not for 100 years, but for the ages, and that means designing envelopes and mechanical systems that can be replaced and improved over time as technology improves, or as human tolerance for adverse temperature conditions improves—and probably both.

That's why a design guide like this is so important, as is the practice of updating it with the latest developments in subsequent editions. There is so much research, so much unrealized potential in both passive and active systems—operable façades, dynamic façades, energy-generating façades, vertically vegetative façades, "breathing" façades, etc.—that embrace, rather than resist, natural environmental conditions. Of course, a solution for a one-story building is not going to work for a 100-story building if it is simply copied upwards 100 times. But the fact that tall buildings do require special engineering in order to achieve the same levels of environmental performance as their shorter peers is not a justification for not attempting it; rather it is a call to action to elevate the practice of tall building engineering to meet this challenge.

One of the more interesting opportunities for super- and megatall buildings is the stratification of climate that exists in any one location with height. Effectively, with the extreme heights now being achieved in tall buildings, we are designing one building that cuts across several climate zones. Significant temperature differences exist between the top of the building and the street level. Tall buildings should be exploiting this for their advantage—cool air is heavier and naturally drops, warm air rises—yet most continue to extrude the same vacuum-sealed façade upwards for hundreds of meters, with all of the energy expenditure that implies. Façades and building systems need to vary with height and reflect the climatic stratification that naturally occurs along their length.

This is already being done, and has been done for more than 20 years—it just hasn't been done nearly often enough. Double-skin façades like that pioneered in the 1997 Commerzbank Tower, Frankfurt, perform as environmental "switches" and provide for natural ventilation, while mediating the indoor temperature to a level that does not require 24/7 conditioning. Newer projects like the Shanghai Tower, with its large atria and communal sky gardens, take this idea to the next level, a social as well as a highly functional series of spaces.

Consider also the potential of those seemingly inexhaustible high-altitude resources—wind and solar. A handful of buildings have attempted to harness the wind and derive energy generation by directing it through sculpted gaps, towards turbines in their masses, and numerous skyscrapers now incorporate solar arrays. However, the implications of capturing wind energy at height have not been fully resolved, and is there the potential for high-rise façades to incorporate solar/thermal technologies, rather than just PV arrays.

Green walls offer a range of benefits, from increased energy efficiency to aesthetic appeal and the reduction of the urban heat island effect. The same exterior vegetation we find charming on low-slung collegiate buildings can also be exploited to great effect at height, providing significant cooling to the façade while blocking glare, enhancing the psychological well being of the occupants, and reducing impact on mechanical systems. Again, this is not a simplistic project of extrusion upwards, but it is being done, in places like One Central Park, Sydney, Oasia Downtown Hotel, Singapore, and the Bosco Verticale, in Milan, Italy.

We've also seen sophisticated mechanical, operable façades that adjust to solar conditions, such as at the Al Bahar towers in Abu Dhabi. Other cutting-edge façades, like the Doha Tower in Qatar, or the Shenzhen Energy Headquarters in China, incorporate historic building techniques to reduce thermal gain and thus improve efficiency. We should be seeing many more of these.

One of the most stunning innovations of recent years is also one of the simplest—a tall building in Tokyo, the NBF Osaki building, uses envirotranspiration to shed heat via rain-filled ceramic pipes that double as *brises-soleil*. In other words, it "sweats," and the microclimate surrounding it benefits from lowered temperatures. Multiply this across a whole city and the urban heat island phenomenon begins to seem less intimidating.

The superlative achievements of tall buildings in terms of height and stability have yet to be fully realized in the MEP department, but they can and must be if tall buildings are to be a positive force in urban environmental sustainability. Five years on from the first edition of this guide, it remains the case that there is much research and hard work ahead of us. Many one-off, bespoke solutions exist around the world, but there are few standardized sets of practices. In the work of our two organizations, ASHRAE and CTBUH, and in the pages before you, lie the bases for building that expertise.

Dr. Antony Wood
CTBUH Chief Executive Officer
Studio Associate Professor, Illinois Institute of Technology, Chicago
Visiting Professor of Tall Buildings, Tongji University, Shanghai

PREFACE

ASHRAE Technical Committee (TC) 9.12, Tall Buildings, has defined a tall building as one whose height is greater than 300 feet (91 m). At the time of the publication of the *HVAC Design Guide for Tall Commercial Buildings* in 2004, there were only about 300 buildings taller than 656 ft (200 m). This number had risen to 600 in 2010, and it was predicted that there would be 765 buildings taller than 656 ft (200 m) in 2012. Since 2004, there has also been an introduction of two new classes of tall buildings (CTBUH 2015):

- Supertall, which are buildings taller than 984 ft (300 m)

- Megatall, which are buildings taller than 2000 ft (600 m)

With the increasing migration of people into cities, tall buildings continue to be in demand. More specifically, at the time this document was going to press there were 1730 buildings already constructed around the world higher than 328 ft (100 m), the ASHRAE definition of a tall building in the previous design guide. 163 buildings have been constructed with designed heights of at least 984 ft (300 m) (CTBUH 2019), and there are 10 buildings either constructed or in design with heights more than 1980 ft (600 m). At press time there are seven buildings proposed with a height of more than 1980 ft (600 m) and 148 proposed with a height of more than 984 ft (300 m)

Tall commercial buildings present a series of design problems that differ from those found in other projects in the built environment. The previous *HVAC Design Guide for Tall Commercial Buildings* provided guidance in both understanding the HVAC design problems of tall commercial office buildings (with heights of 328 ft [100 m] or more) and in detailing their solutions.

This revision will be of interest to owners, architects, structural engineers, mechanical engineers, electrical engineers, firefighters, and other specialized engineers and consultants. The design guide not only focuses on the efforts of designers of the heating, ventilating, and air-conditioning (HVAC) systems, but also addresses the importance of the design team and their collective efforts and concerns that are the critical elements in determining the ultimate solutions to the projected needs of a tall building. This guide addresses design issues for tall commercial buildings, which are very often mixed use, consisting sometimes of low-level retail, office floors, residential floors, and hotel floors. Additionally, the matters discussed and the recommendations and comments that are developed, with various modifications, can be applied to other project types within the built environment. As buildings get taller, there are different climatic effects which vary over the height of a building. The façade becomes important, not only because of the building size, but also because of how it responds to ambient conditions and contributes to the building's heating and cooling loads. The façade also contributes to daylight harvesting.

Additionally, building intelligence presents a significant impact on tall building operation; how do the different building systems talk to each other and optimize their usage? What intelligence is provided for tenants? This is addressed in this guide.

Reflecting the addition of these subjects and the coverage of the newer classes of tall buildings, this new work is now the second edition of *ASHRAE Design Guide for Tall, Supertall, and Megatall Building Systems*.

Figure P.1 A tall building more than 984 ft (300 m) in height.

ACKNOWLEDGMENTS

This updated design guide would not have been possible without a whole army of experts who have generously contributed in one way or another.

First, there is ASHRAE Technical Committee 9.12, chaired by Luke Leung, who masterminded the revision and production of this design guide.

Second, we have a list of experts that really reads like who's who in tall, megatall and supertall buildings around the world:

Mehdi Jalayerian, ESD, Chicago

Tyler Jensen, ESD, Chicago

Russell Gilchrist, Gensler, Chicago

Sasha Zeljic, Gensler, Chicago

Richard Nemeth, KPF, New York

Rob Whitlock, KPF, New York

Peter Gross, KPF, New York

Wai Chu (John), KPF, New York

Tom Hartman, The Hartman Company, Georgetown

Ben Sun, ACCO, San Francisco

Duncan Philips, RWDI, Guelph, Canada

Vincent Tse, Parsons Brinkerhoff, Hong Kong

John Klote, Independent, Maryland

Bill Webb, Retired, Florida

Joe Huang, Whitebox Technologies, El Cerrito, CA

Tom Brady, Brady Enterprises, Beijing

Stuart Berriman, GB Architects, Playa Vista, CA

Wez Crutchfield, WEZBUILD, Hong Kong

Alan Lamb, Leighton, Hong Kong

Luke Leung, SOM, Chicago

Stephen Ray, SOM, Chicago

Kim Clawson, AON, Chicago

Robert Henderson, ARUP, San Francisco

Erin McConahey, ARUP, Los Angeles

Edward Tsu, Intelligent Technologies, Hong Kong

The primary author of the second edition of *ASHRAE Design Guide for Tall, Supertall, and Megatall Building Systems* was Peter Simmonds of Building and Systems Analytics, LLC. The first edition was supported by ASHRAE Research Project RP-1673.

CHAPTER 1
Introduction

INTRODUCTION

ASHRAE Design Guide for Tall, Supertall, and Megatall Building Systems was first published five years ago. It provided design information for tall (more than 300 ft [91 m] high) buildings and was written specifically for commercial buildings. The three current classifications of tall buildings are:

- Tall, more than 328 ft (100 m)
- Supertall, more than 984 ft (300 m)
- Megatall, more than 2000 ft (600 m)

A great deal has happened in the years since the first edition was published. Two megatall buildings are under construction, joining 86 constructed supertall buildings, 27 supertall buildings that have been architecturally topped out, and 44 supertall buildings that have been structurally topped out since 2015 (CTBUH 2019). There are also 97 tall, supertall, or megatall buildings under construction, and one proposed (see Figures 1.1 and 1.2). In this revised guide, we will only refer to *tall buildings*, but these include tall, supertall, and megatall buildings. Where there are any specific differences between tall, supertall, and megatall buildings, they will be fully described.

This book is accompanied by online content, which can be found at https://www.ashrae.org/tallbuildings. These files provide helpful spreadsheets. If the files or information at the link are not accessible, please contact the publisher.

The use of tall buildings has also changed in the last five years (see Figure 1.3). While the original design guide was specific to commercial buildings (office buildings), a modern-day tall building has many different functions. Many are "mixed use," where at ground level there may be retail and food and beverage space, the first section of the building may be commercial and/or offices, the second section may be residential, and the lucrative high-level section a hotel. Tall buildings are now not only taller but have many different functions and different code requirements. With specifics such as life safety, we sometimes venture into unknown territory.

The goals for this revision, based on discussions with some of the world's leading experts on HVAC designs for tall buildings, include the following aspects:

1. **The effect of ambient air temperature over the height of buildings, especially supertall and megatall buildings.** The ambient climatic conditions vary with altitude, and these changes in ambient conditions can seriously affect load calculations and performance of supertall and megatall buildings.

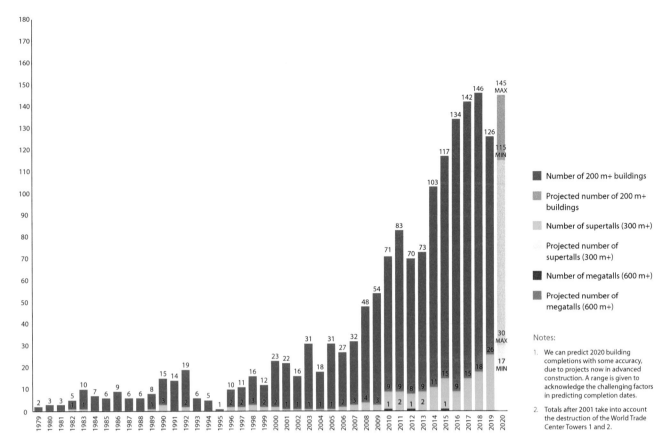

Figure 1.1   Increase in tall building construction from 1960 to 2019.

2. **Façades for tall buildings, leakage rates, and pressure resistance.** As the façade dimensions increase in proportion to the building's height, so too do the requirements for limiting leakage rates and increasing pressure resistance of façades.

3. **Natural ventilation for tall buildings.** There have been frequent requests for spaces to be naturally ventilated during recent years. Ambient conditions at higher levels are often complicated, and therefore natural ventilation design becomes critical.

4. **Energy calculations and consumption for tall buildings.** Nearly all new buildings are required to comply with some level of U.S. Green Building Council's Leadership in Energy and Environmental Design (LEED®) green building certification program. Many building codes require compliance with an energy code, in many cases based on ASHRAE Standard 90.1, *Energy Standard for Buildings Except Low-Rise Residential Buildings*, and therefore the energy performance calculations become critical. The newly harmonized International Green Construction Code (IgCC) and ASHRAE Standard 189.1 will also be referenced in the future (ICC 2018).

5. **Revised stack effect calculations for tall buildings.** As buildings become taller, the calculation and impact of stack effects become more critical.

6. **Green/sustainable tall buildings.** With both ASHRAE and the AIA issuing challenges for buildings to be net zero, the sustainability of tall buildings becomes more critical.

7. **Present-day trends in tall building HVAC systems, such as active beams and variable-refrigerant-flow (VRV) systems.**

This second edition provides information on the following aspects of tall building designs:

• Chapter 2, Architectural Design, does not address the aesthetics of buildings but does discuss possible core layouts and emergency egress routes and refuge floors from an architectural perspective. Floor efficiencies are also outlined.

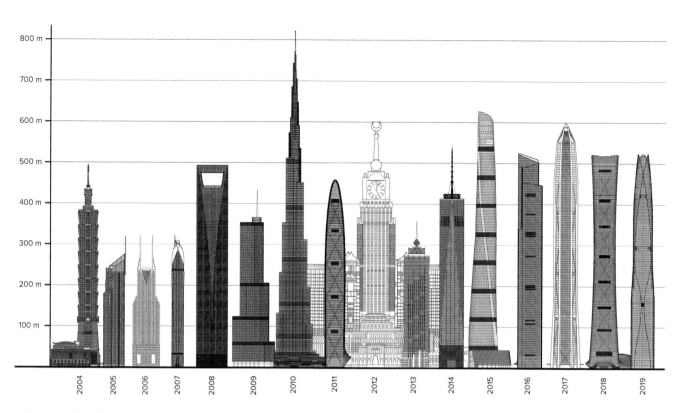

Figure 1.2 The world's tallest buildings completed by 2019.

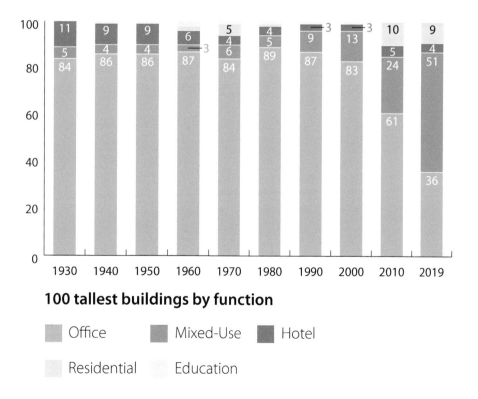

100 tallest buildings by function

Office   Mixed-Use   Hotel

Residential   Education

Figure 1.3 The world's 100 tallest buildings by function.

- Chapter 3, Climate Data, reviews different aspects of climatic data vertically over the height of a building.
- Chapter 4, Façade Systems, does not cover any structural engineering but does provide information on interpreting present-day energy codes that present some stringent challenges for tall buildings, and includes leakage rates and pressure resistance.
- Chapter 5, Stack Effect, is now a separate chapter including many new advances in stack effect calculations.
- Chapter 6, Heating and Cooling Loads, is a new chapter including vertical climate data.
- Chapter 7, Indoor Air Quality and Thermal Comfort, provides guidance on required ventilation aspects of tall buildings, especially when investigating the possibility of naturally ventilating residential and even office spaces. The thermal comfort of occupants is also important, not only because of the large number of occupants in these buildings but also in evaluating glazing and the mean radiant temperature (MRT) near it, specific HVAC systems, and the application of natural ventilation when assessing occupant comfort by the adaptive comfort method.
- Chapter 8, HVAC Systems, presents and traditional systems and some newer trends such as radiant systems and active and passive beams.
- Chapter 9, Central Mechanical Equipment, discusses essential mechanical, electrical, and IT equipment rooms.
- Chapter 10, Central Heating and Cooling, presents new specifics on traditional central plants.
- Chapter 11, Water Distribution Systems, has been revised to include specifics for modern-day tall buildings of heights over 2000 ft (600 m).
- Chapter 12, Energy Modeling and Authentication, is a revised chapter and provides information on how to model tall buildings and their systems and, most importantly, how to authenticate the proposed energy usage.
- Chapter 13, Vertical Transportation, outlines the dramatic improvement in this area over the last 15 years, not only because of the different building types in tall buildings but also because of improvements in elevator technology and the logistics of people movement
- Chapter 14, Plumbing Systems, includes information on traditional plumbing systems and also specifics such as gray and black water systems.
- Chapter 15, Life Safety Systems, contains new code requirements and solutions for life safety systems in tall buildings.
- Chapter 16, High-Rise Residential, is a new chapter with specifics for residential spaces in tall buildings.
- Chapter 17, Electrical System Interfaces, deals with difference between the landlord's electrical supply and tenants' electrical supply as well as the diverse requirements for standby power in a modern-day tall building and electrical distribution.
- Chapter 18, Intelligent Building and Controls, is a revised chapter that presents some of the many requirements of modern-day tall buildings and includes smart systems.

The design of any tall building is the result of the collaborative effort of owners, architects, structural engineers, mechanical and electrical engineers, and other specialized engineers and consultants.

Every building is a product of its location, the time during which the building is designed and erected, and the specific client for whom the building is being constructed. Although a building is constructed of multiple commercially available products, how these products are assembled will differ in its completed state. Accordingly, every building will usually differ in many ways from other buildings regardless of apparent similarities.

This design guide addresses design issues for tall commercial office buildings, but the matters discussed and the recommendations and comments that are developed, with various modifications, frequently can be applied to other project types within the built environment. This is particularly true in the matters discussed in the General Overview section of this chapter. However, it is necessary to cover these matters to lay the groundwork for matters discussed

Figure 1.4 The Burj Khalifa, the current tallest structure in the world.

subsequently in this design guide, many of which are more exclusively applicable to the tall commercial office building.

GENERAL OVERVIEW

The design of mechanical and electrical systems for large commercial office buildings is a continually evolving art form that progressively responds to the local market economic and political concerns, the space utilization needs and requirements of the specific user who will occupy the building, and the building's geographic location.

The techniques and design alternatives for a tall commercial office building, because of its inherent size, physical location in major urban areas, and typically sophisticated group of owners, occupants, architects and engineering designers, are subject to a particularly intense response to the complex requirements of any building. The HVAC design engineer, as a significant member of the design team, must complete the design with due consideration of first cost, operating expense for the completed building, the present and future needs of the building occupants, the resiliency of the building, as well as environmental issues and the conservation of energy, regardless of source, in the completed project. The architectural profession responds to the same pressures, but, in addition, is subject to the requirement to create buildings that are attractive to the public at large, the real estate industry, and, most importantly, the owner of the building.

The purpose of mechanical and electrical systems in commercial office buildings has not changed, in any fundamental sense, over the history of the construction of buildings used for such occupancy. Clearly, the primary purpose of these systems was and is to provide space in the building that will permit the occupants to conduct their business in a productive, comfortable, and safe atmosphere.

In addition to the important advent of air conditioning, a series of changes have significantly modified the basis of the design of the air-conditioning systems for the tall commercial office building.

These changes include the following:

- The evolution of energy-conserving building designs that consume significantly less energy than energy code requirements.
- Expanding and changing zoning and building codes, which have impacted the architectural designs of buildings, the internal energy systems that can be used in buildings, and the enlarged life safety systems mandated to protect both the occupants and the contents of the building.
- The changing real estate market, particularly in the area of developer buildings (as contrasted with owner-occupied buildings). Potential tenants have become more knowledgeable and demanding with regard to the various proposed solutions capable of meeting their perceived needs.
- The altered utilization of buildings, largely driven by the personal computer and alternative telecommunication systems.
- The availability of new or modified air-conditioning designs and the commercially manufactured equipment to allow an altered response to the needs of buildings.

Figure 1.5 A rendering of a 2000 ft (600 m) high tower.

- Resiliency in tall buildings as occupants may stay in the building for a prolonged period.
- Finally, and of major impact, the recognition of the design profession that buildings must respond to environmental and green building concerns including, but not limited to, energy conservation as an end unto itself, indoor air quality (IAQ), sustainable design considerations, and new technology that will better address the global environment of both the present and the future (Figure 1.6).

This is a significant list of altered perceptions and design requirements to which the design community must respond. Nowhere is it of greater import than to the HVAC design professionals who are responsible for the documents that define the basis of the installations that are provided for any large commercial office building. How that response is determined and framed is a matter that must be given the full focus and the intellect of the HVAC designer of tall buildings, regardless of the location of the building.

Building Codes and Standards for Tall Buildings

The relevance of these codes and standards to this design guide is that they all invoke specific design requirements as a result of their definition of a tall building. This includes all codes and relevant standards, not just the model codes. The design of any building must respond to the requirements of the code that is applicable for the building and to the interpretation of that code by the local authority having jurisdiction over the project. All codes affect the design of any building in that they mandate specific design responses to environmental conditions such as solar heat gain, building envelope thermal opaqueness, air transport efficiency criteria, and pipe and duct insulation performance. They also detail the project seismic requirements for all building equipment with specific emphasis on life safety equipment, including the need for restraint of the sprinkler piping, emergency generators, and fire pumps. The codes address the

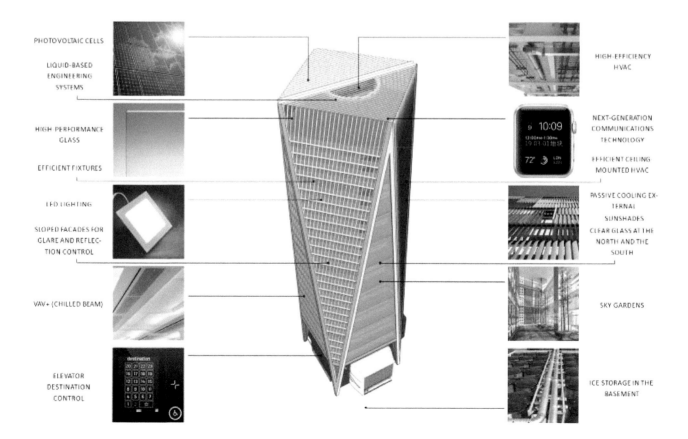

Figure 1.6 Various sustainable systems that can be applied to tall, supertall, and megatall buildings.

tall commercial building in detail regarding smoke management needs and the venting of elevator shafts. Many of these matters are discussed in more detail by topic in later chapters of this design guide.

ENERGY STRATEGIES

The fundamental strategy is to minimize energy usage, resource consumption, and plant space. Several factors affect this strategy, including the following:

- Minimization of solar energy gain to occupied areas through the façade/envelope
- Use of daylight to minimize lighting, and reduction of lighting when levels rise above the required level
- Maximizing re-use of 60% or more of the building energy use
- Minimize fan and pump energy use, possibly by floor-by-floor service
- Utilization, if possible, of wind-driven ventilation and cooling, as well as passive technologies.
- Low-energy terminal devices on occupied floors
- Allowing indoor temperature and humidity to fluctuate within comfort limits

We first propose a framework for understanding the energy consumption differences between tall and low-rise buildings. This framework is then mapped onto city-wide energy consumption data from New York City to discuss differences between tall and low-rise buildings. Finally, correlations between the data and framework are highlighted as well as additional noteworthy trends.

CHAPTER 2
Architectural Design

REAL ESTATE CONSIDERATIONS

Every designed and constructed building must respond to real estate considerations if the project is to be successful. These considerations include ownership issues as well as matters that are more appropriately a concern of the building use. While these matters are important in all buildings, they are of even greater importance in tall commercial office buildings because of their size and the need to meet the additional occupant requirements. It is difficult to fundamentally alter a large building after it is finished and available for use. Therefore, the building usage and performance criteria should be defined at the outset of design. An example of the information that may be included in the detailing of the design criteria for a tall building project is included in the Preface.

An initial real estate consideration that must be recognized and dealt with is the nature of the ownership of the building. The ownership entity for whom a building is being constructed falls into several distinct categories. These categories may overlap, but generally do not. There is often more than a single ownership category, and the alternative categories may well affect the design solutions developed for any project.

Many tall commercial office buildings are corporate headquarters developed within a customized program, typically by the architect and owner with significant input from a real estate consulting firm retained by the owner. The developed program will establish the specific requirements for the design team. For example, will the building contain a data center? If so, how large and with what potential for expansion? What dining facilities are to be included? Are there executive dining area requirements that are separate from the general employee dining? Are the telecommunication requirements and possible technology vendors established? What areas beyond the data center will operate on an extended time schedule or on a 24/7 basis? The answer to these and similar programmatic questions will all have a direct impact on the HVAC solutions that will need to be developed for the project. In addition, there may be other significant issues, such as built-in redundancy to allow for future flexibility, that will have a major effect on the final design solution.

It is not unusual for a corporation anticipating growth to meet their future needs by one of two means. The first method is to build a building that is larger than presently needed and to lease the extra space for given periods to other business firms unrelated to the developing corporate owner. In the future, as the need for expansion develops, the corporation will move into these spaces as outside tenants' leases expire.

The second means of providing for future corporate growth is to design the building to allow for future building expansion. This is often not a viable alternative for a tall commercial building. Tall buildings are almost always built in major cities on constricted sites that are fully utilized at the time of the construction. Moreover, the height and size of the building is typically built to the maximum dimensions allowable by the local zoning board. This (in the absence of a zoning code modification) restricts the expansion option for a tall commercial office building in an urban location.

There are isolated cases where a corporate headquarters has been built with the first phase of the project completed to meet a present need of the corporation, but the structure was also designed to handle the addition of floors in a second phase. This solution is rare because roof-located equipment on the top of the original set of floors presents costly and logistically difficult relocation problems that tend to preclude this approach. The necessary relocation requires moving equipment including cooling towers, general and toilet exhaust fans, elevator machine rooms, and any other roof-located equipment such as emergency generators or dry coolers for data center or telecommunication equipment.

Other than corporate headquarters, tall commercial office buildings are usually erected by developers. At least three alternative types of developers exist.

The first is a developer who erects a building for a specific single user. The building will be a "build-to-suit" building that does not substantively differ from the corporate headquarters in that a very specific program must be prepared for the occupying user by its staff, the architect, and the real estate advisors providing a detailed definition of the tenant's exact requirements. The needs and requirements of the occupying user must be fully defined in any contract, because any modification of these needs and requirements that may develop during the actual design and construction of a build-to-suit building can result in substantial, unanticipated costs to the occupying user.

Figure 2.1 A 1312 ft (400 m) high tower.

The other two types of developers are motivated largely by their ownership intention with regard to the building upon completion. First, there are developers who historically plan and build for long-term ownership of their buildings. Many of these portfolio owners own and keep all of their developed properties, passing them on to future generations of their family or successor corporations. Alternatively, there are developers who construct a building with the expressed intent to dispose of the building some time after the building is completed, potentially in the very short term. The time they retain ownership is rarely defined and, more often than not, is controlled by the fluctuations in the price of real estate in the local market,. A fully rented building with high rents will obtain a higher purchase price than one partially leased at low rents—the exception being if the leases are due to expire and the rental prices for space in the geographic area are increasing.

In large part, the reaction of a developer to the specific real estate issues in the design of large commercial office buildings is affected by whether the developer is building to suit a single user, has long-term ownership intentions, or has short-term ownership intentions. A partial summary of these considerations is as follows:

- Market forces that include prospective tenant perceptions and expectations
- The developer's target market (e.g., financial services sector, general corporate market, unknown and unspecified business entities)
- Large multifloor tenant occupiers versus multiple-tenant single-floor occupants
- Core to exterior wall dimension requirement to meet the needs of perspective tenants
- Clear ceiling height desired on each office floor
- Code-mandated building height or building massing limitation
- Overtime building usage
- Available alternative energy sources and their costs
- Allowable utility metering arrangements
- Green building issues

This list is generally self-explanatory and, in part, beyond the scope of this design guide. Several of these issues are discussed in detail in other chapters (e.g., large multifloor tenant occupiers versus multitenant single-floor occupancy, overtime building usage, available energy sources and their costs, and allowable utility metering arrangements). There are several listed items for consideration that would usually be architectural design matters but that are also affected by the HVAC design solutions and therefore warrant discussion in this introductory chapter.

ARCHITECTURAL CONSIDERATIONS

Although the architect must respond to many of the real estate considerations outlined previously, there are concerns, primarily architectural in nature, to which the architect must respond that require input from other members of the design team. These certainly include aesthetic considerations, such as the inclusion of a large atrium or the location of louver areas on the exterior of the building that can modify the appearance of the building. The architect must also address any request to include a below-grade parking area, the provision of significant retail area on the lowest level of the building, or the inclusion of rental apartments or condominiums in the project. Any of these possibilities raise a whole variety of HVAC requirements as well as alter the electrical, plumbing, and vertical transportation systems for the project. They affect the mechanical design and the massing solution of the structure as well as the resulting limitation of possible locations for mechanical and electrical space. Several of these matters are discussed subsequently in this design guide, but two other architectural considerations require further discussion at this time. These are the design of the core areas and the determination of the project's floor-to-floor height. The resolution of both matters affects both the building cost as well as the architectural and HVAC designs.

Core Design and Location

The architectural design of the core areas of any building is much more difficult than might appear at first glance. The core design is also extremely critical in that it must meet the needs of the occupants while also simplifying the provision of mechanical and electrical services to the occupied floor. Assuming the space on the floor beyond the core has been developed to meet the needs of the floor occupant, the core is fine-tuned and organized by the architect and the consulting engineers. Moreover, the cost of the core and its content can be substantial. Finally, the configuration of the core impacts the usable area on a given floor and the resultant rent for that floor, so it should be arranged in the most efficient area possible, resulting in the highest possible efficiency of the floor.

Most tall commercial buildings are designed with a center core that provides maximum flexibility in the architectural subdivision of the floor. This is particularly true in the case of a multiple-tenant floor. In addition, the use of a central core allows for the potential to improve the distribution of air-conditioning ducts, because they can be extended to the floor from both sides of the core. This both reduces their size and shortens their length.

The central core also offers structural advantages, with the stiff core providing a means to resist wind loads. A central core can also simplify the construction of the building in that it forms a central spine for the building with radial construction being added in all four directions, which can be accomplished more efficiently than if construction were more limited in how it could proceed.

In some cases, (with small floors or with a building that is located against an existing building party wall), a side core will be designed for a building. As is discussed in Chapter 8, this can offer opportunities for introducing outdoor air directly to the floor if floor-by-floor air-conditioning units are planned for the building.

In buildings with very large floor plates, multiple or decentralized cores may be necessary to reduce the travel distance to stairs or toilets. A cost disadvantage of multiple cores is the potential need for additional elevators.

Service Cores

The position of service cores is important in any building but even more so in tall buildings. The core can be used for structural support and is also related to the building exterior, as most often ventilation air supply and exhaust systems are routed to and from the exterior to the core, where most mechanical rooms are situated. There are three types of commonly used cores (Figure 2.2):

- Central core.
- Double core
- Single-sided (or offset) core

In locations where the climate is hot or hot and humid, it is suggested that the core(s) be located on the east and west façades to insulate the interior zones from the ambient conditions. There are studies that show that cooling loads have been kept at a minimum when using a double-core configuration with glazing on the north south and south façade and cores on the east and west façades. The same designs can be applied in temperate climates.

Core Components

As a minimum, the core must incorporate the following entities:

- Fire escape stairs
- Vertical transportation elements, which is an arrangement of elevators and possibly escalators, including both passenger elevators and one or more service or freight elevators.
- Restrooms for both the male and female population and with provision to meet the Americans with Disabilities Act (ADA) requirements for both sexes
- Electrical closets
- Communication closets for multiple telecommunication providers

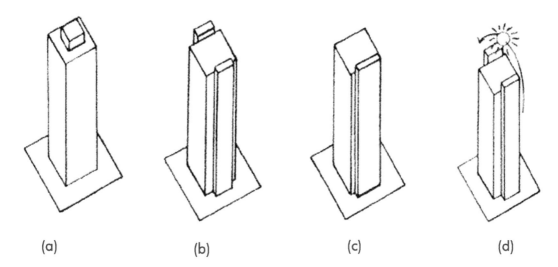

(a)   (b)   (c)   (d)

Figure 2.2 (a) Central core, (b) double core, (c) single-sided core, and (d) east and west sides.

- Local fan rooms (if floor-by-floor air-conditioning equipment is the selected approach for the project) or large supply air and return air shafts (if central fan rooms are the selected approach for the project)
- Shaft space for other HVAC risers, beyond those for the local fan rooms or the supply and return ducts for the central fan rooms, such as toilet exhaust, general exhaust or dedicated smoke exhaust risers, and possibly kitchen exhaust risers
- Space for risers for the piping of the HVAC system and plumbing system as well as riser space for electrical distribution cable and the building management and fire alarm systems distribution cabling

The number, location, and arrangement of the stairs is an architectural issue driven by local building codes. A minimum of two exit stairs are always required and the maximum travel distance for any occupant on the floor is defined within every building code, but the specific maximum travel distance can vary from code to code. Moreover, for very large floor areas, there may be a need for more than two stairs to meet maximum travel distance requirements. Although the entries to the stairs should be located as remotely from each other as possible, the project design must conform to the maximum code-defined distance from any occupied area on a floor to a stair.

The details of alternative vertical transportation systems are discussed in Chapter 13. The effect of the elevators on the core design can involve not only the elevators serving the floors but also the elevator shafts that contain elevators that bypass specific floors and serve floors above those for which the core is being designed. This would be the case in buildings in excess of approximately 15 to 20 floors where multiple banks of elevators are usually included to meet the design criteria for interval and waiting time, which is critical in the selection of the elevator system.

A second consideration in the core design as a result of the use of multiple banks of elevators is that the alternative core, as it changes because of the elimination of elevators, must address the shaft locations for HVAC ductwork and piping and electrical risers with minimal, if any, offsets in these shafts. If the core is designed in a manner that requires offsets in the service risers, it must be understood that any transfers are likely to be expensive as well as consumptive of space.

Finally, the elevator system for a first-class commercial tall building usually includes service or freight elevators which are used to move material, goods, or equipment, in addition to people, within the building. Typically, in smaller buildings, one of the passenger elevators can be used as a "swing car" that is used for passengers most of the time but converts to handle goods and materials on an as-needed basis. This issue is discussed in Chapter 13.

Restrooms are driven by the applicable building code. The code will mandate the minimum number of fixtures (water closets, urinals, and lavatories) for each sex. The Federal Americans with Disabilities Act (ADA) and the building code also address the number of toilets for the handicapped. These handicapped toilets can be provided in the male and female restrooms or can be located in a separate handicapped restroom, which could be a unisex space used by both males and females. Separate restrooms for the handicapped are solely used in the retrofitting of an existing building where the original design did not consider the matter of the handicapped. Newly constructed buildings must, under all codes and under the ADA, include within each restroom a defined number of fixtures for the handicapped of both sexes.

The building code definition addresses a minimum number of each type of fixture required for males and females. These quantities are derived from the floor area of the specific floor and a defined number of males and females based on that area. For a corporate headquarters or a developer building catering to a higher level of occupiable density (person per unit area), the number of fixtures mandated by the code is frequently increased due to the sense that the code-dictated number of fixtures is marginally insufficient for a corporate tenant. Moreover, on very large floor plates, two restrooms may need to be provided for each sex to limit the travel distance of any occupant to a reasonable length. This can further complicate the design of the overall core required for a project and frequently results in a separate auxiliary core smaller in area and remote from the main core that will contain the added restroom and additional stairs if they are required.

Electrical closets are also a major issue in core design. Their location on any floor must be such as to permit diverse routing of electric cable at the utilization voltage appropriate for the geographic location of the building to any area of the floor to meet the agreed-upon design criteria in watts per unit area for the project. There are limits to the distance that the floor distribution cable can be extended on any given floor without a cost penalty. In general, on a floor in excess of approximately 25,000 ft^2 (2400 m^2), more than one electrical closet will be required to serve that floor. On floors smaller than 25,000 ft^2 (2400 m^2), a second closet may still be included if needed for tenant planning.

The communication closet has gone through a major change over the past decade. Currently, corporations may each use four or more telecommunications companies, In a large developer building with unknown multiple tenants, provision must be made in the risers for as many as 12 different telecommunication companies. Not all will be used on every tenant's space, but all may be required for a multiple-tenant building. The communication risers may not be installed during construction. Instead, riser space and empty sleeves may be installed in the communication closet, with the empty risers being filled as specific tenants request specific telecommunication providers for their space. In a developer building currently under design in New York City, forty empty sleeves are being provided in each of two closets on every floor to meet anticipated but unknown demands from yet to be determined tenants. The service for each vendor to a specific tenant will be independently routed in each of the two closets. Moreover, in the below-grade levels, space will be needed for multiple points of entry from each telecommunication provider to allow its service to be brought to two separate service rooms from at least two different streets to ensure continuity of service under any possible emergency contingency.

A further change in telecommunication system design has occurred in that rack-mounted equipment is used to interface with the desktop data services equipment, including telephones, being used by the occupant. This requires much more space than was previously required when the telephone equipment distribution wiring terminated at terminal strips in the telephone closet. The rack space used today is typically located away from the core on the floor, which allows full front and back access (a requirement) and, just as important, provides the degree of security mandated by many tenants. This need for security is particularly critical with large corporations or enterprises that serve the financial markets. They will insist that the actual telecommunication equipment be installed within their demised premises with access limited to their staff. With the arrangement outlined, even the base building operating staff will not have access to the tenant's proprietary telecommunication switches and equipment.

A final but separate involvement of the telecommunication closet in the core is that it is frequently used to house the fire alarm system and building management system risers and floor equipment. This is logical in that it is space present on all floors, can be easily accommodated in a new building with multiple risers, and can be accessed by the building owner's operating personnel or the fire alarm or building management system maintenance people for servicing.

The need for shaft space for HVAC ductwork and piping and the space requirements for local floor-by-floor fan rooms is discussed in Chapter 8.

In summary, the complication of the design of the core of a tall commercial office building becomes clearer when the disparate elements that must be integrated are considered. The architect is appropriately challenged to meet the goal of an efficient core (i.e., one that uses the least amount of the gross floor area). The definition of an efficient core is not simple in that the percentage of the gross area that will be used is a function of the size of the floor. For example, on larger floor plates (i.e., those with areas greater than 20,000 gross ft^2 [1800 gross m^2]), the core will often take less than 15% to 20% of the total floor area of a typical floor. This core usage will be possible while still meeting the demands of travel distance to stairs, provision for and access to all vertical transportation elements, an appropriate number of toilet fixtures, and the needs of the mechanical and electrical consulting engineers providing for the electrical equipment and access from these services in the core to meet the requirements of the diverse tenant occupants. There are other possible design details that would alter these approximate percentages. For example, if a floor grows beyond a certain size or has internal loads with high cooling requirements, it can become necessary to add a second local floor air-handling unit and fan room, which will cause a reduction in the usable area.

Core Design Example

Figure 2.3 shows the several elements in a core as they might be assembled for a building. The core in Figure 2.3 is of interest because it shows that there are three passenger elevator banks in the drawing. Passenger elevators PE1 through PE6 serve the lower stories of the building. The passenger needs for the mid-levels of the building are served by passenger elevators PE7 through PE12. The passenger needs for the uppermost building floors are served by passenger elevators PE13 through PE17. Above the floors that the low-rise bank of elevators serve, that bank is dropped, decreasing the size of the core and increasing the usable space except for the approximately two floors immediately above the floors served by the elevators,

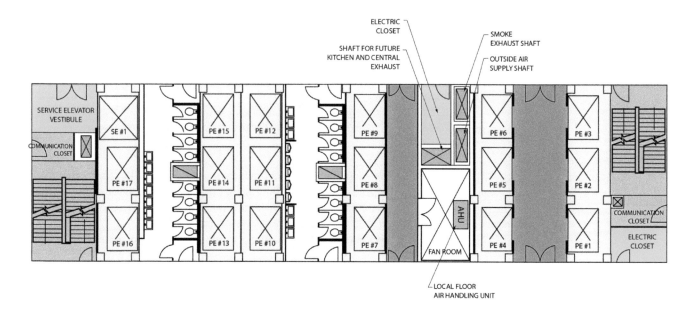

Figure 2.3 A typical core layout.

which contain the elevator machine room for the low-rise bank. Higher in the building, the midrise bank of elevators is dropped, further decreasing the core area. Also note the service elevator (SE1), which serves all floors from the basement to a mechanical equipment room on the uppermost level of the building. The service elevator is provided with an adequately sized vestibule to permit the movement of large office equipment, furnishings, and other equipment from the service elevator to the floor.

The area between the mid-rise elevator banks is used for the men's restroom, and the space between the high-rise elevators and service car is used for the women's restroom. This area usage increases the overall efficiency of the core but may create a relocation problem for stairs as well as for piping, ductwork, and other mechanical and electrical services because the low-rise and mid-rise elevator banks are eliminated.

The project for which this core is shown used local floor-by-floor fan rooms. The floor for which the core is shown could contain a package chilled-water or a direct-expansion air-handling unit.

The selection of local fan room or central fan rooms is discussed in detail in Chapter 9. Note that the local fan room solution will use more space on the individual floor, therefore affecting the core design but will usually need less space in the overall building when the reduction of the double-height central mechanical equipment room required in the alternative solution for the large air-conditioning supply systems is taken into consideration.

Floor-to-Floor Height

An important issue that fundamentally involves the architectural design of the building is the floor-to-floor height. The overall cost of a tall building is affected by the floor-to-floor height of the individual floors. A small difference in this height, when multiplied by the number of floors and the area of the perimeter length of the building, will result in an increase in the area that must be added to the exterior skin of the building. The exterior skin of the building can cost in excess of $100 per ft^2 ($1100 per m^2). In addition to the increase in the cost of the skin, an increase in the floor-to-floor height will increase the length of the vertical structural elements as well as all of the building's other vertical elements, such as shaft enclosures, HVAC, plumbing, electrical power distribution and telecommunication risers, elevator components, stairs and the length of the interior partitions. Accordingly, a small reduction in the floor-to-floor height in a tall building can be a matter of importance when the overall cost of the building is being determined. In addition, where zoning regulations exist that limit the bulk and height of a building, a small increase in the vertical dimension of each floor may result in fewer floors in the developed building.

The final floor-to-floor height of the office occupancy floors of any building will involve decisions by the owner, architect, structural engineer, and both the HVAC and electrical engineer. All will influence the ultimate determination of this key dimension. The discussions in the sections of this design guide on floor-to-floor height that are contained immediately after this introductory paragraph are concerned with normal office floor occupancy areas. Floors in the building that contain data centers, dining facilities, or other special areas with special requirements need separate considerations beyond those discussed.

The Owner's Involvement

The owner will make judgments on many of the issues discussed in this section of this design guide that will influence the floor-to-floor height of the building, but the owner will be the primary entity in determining whether to include a raised floor for the general office occupancy areas of the project.

The single most important change in building occupants' needs in the past decade has been the development of the electronic workplace. The need to satisfy the expanding and continually changing electronic needs in tall commercial buildings has led to the inclusion of raised floors to increase the horizontal distribution of both power wiring and information technology cabling, including telecommunication cabling and any interconnection of personal computers, printers, and the like. Typically the raised floors in general office spaces will be between 4 and 6 in. (between 100 and 150 mm) above the concrete slab when the raised floor is used exclusively for the distribution of power wiring and information technology cabling. Floor tiles are included above the slab to provide the walking surface in the office space and in turn are covered by carpet tiles of the same size as the floor tiles. The carpet tiles and then the floor tiles can easily be lifted to provide the needed access to allow modification of the wire and cable as the needs of tenants change.

The use of raised floors for general occupancy office areas has largely been limited to corporate headquarters or owner-occupied buildings but is becoming common for developer buildings as a competitive advantage in leasing the building. For most projects in Europe, a raised floor is a standard feature, regardless of whether the building is being constructed for owner occupancy or unspecified tenants.

One cost benefit that accrues to projects using a raised floor exclusively for wire and cable distribution is that neither the wire nor the cable installed within the raised floor cavity need be plenum rated or installed in conduit. As noted in Chapter 8 in the discussion of underfloor air distribution systems, this cost benefit cannot be obtained on a project using the raised floor as a plenum for air distribution. Nonetheless, the application of raised floors with under-the-floor air-conditioning distribution systems is becoming more common with the increased use of raised floors.

Irrespective of the type of air-conditioning system used on a project, it is expected that the use of raised floors in the United States will increase in the future, as they can provide substantial occupant savings in the completed building as the need for information technology cabling and power wiring modifications change. The cost of the occupancy changes or churn over the life of a building is significant as frequent changes can occur. The use of a raised floor allows the relocation of electric outlets and information technology connections at a relatively low cost when compared to the cost of these relocations without a raised floor.

The inclusion of a raised floor must be viewed as a factor in the floor-to-floor height of the building. The inclusion of the raised floor will increase the floor-to-floor height, but the integration of a raised floor with an underfloor air-conditioning distribution system may also be beneficial and minimize the increase in the floor-to-floor height for a given project.

The Architect's Involvement

The architect, with the active involvement of the owner, will determine the floor-to-floor dimension to provide space that, in their judgment, is aesthetically attractive. While tall commercial office buildings have been designed to provide different floor-to-ceiling heights, the minimum clearance is 9 ft, 0 in. (2.75 m). On floors with an area of more than approximately 30,000 ft^2 (3000 m^2) with longer lease spans from the exterior wall to the core elements, a higher ceiling height of 10 ft (3.05 m) is often provided. Larger or deeper lease span floors require additional daylighting and aspect (views), so the increased height is beneficial to building occupants.

Once the floor-to-ceiling height has been determined and the decision to include or not include a raised floor has been made, the floor-to-floor height largely falls to the joint coordination efforts of the structural engineer and the HVAC design engineer.

STRUCTURAL COORDINATION

The structural engineer must make his selection of the structural design and floor slab system for a project with the active involvement of the mechanical, electrical, and fire protection (sprinkler) members of the design team, because the structural systems must be fully integrated with the ductwork, the HVAC piping (if any), the lighting, the electrical distribution system, and the sprinkler piping. This integration of the structural, mechanical, and electrical designs will determine the space requirements between the top of the ceiling and the bottom of structural slab of the floor above, which will be the starting point of the next floor.

Most, but not all, tall commercial buildings in the United States have a steel structure rather than reinforced concrete. The reasons for the use of steel include the following:

- Careful scheduling of the contractors will allow structural steel to be designed and ordered in advance of the final completion of architectural and mechanical, electrical, and plumbing designs. This facilitates fast-track construction, which allows the steel to be erected as soon as the foundations are complete, with a resultant reduction in the total construction time of the building.

- Structural steel construction is more readily and economically adapted to the long-span, column-free space desired by interior space designers and occupants, thus allowing for more flexible space designs and an increase in the building's potential marketability.
- Structural steel construction provides the flexibility to alter the capacity or configuration of the structure to handle changes in loading by reframing or reinforcing the structural steel so that future occupant requirements may be accommodated. Such changes could be required by the introduction of floor-to-floor communicating stairs, elevators, dumbwaiters, or by the need to increase the load capacity of portions of a floor to support compact files, libraries, telecommunications equipment, or mainframe computer components.
- Structural steel will result in a lighter weight construction than reinforced concrete. This allows savings in the cost of the foundations. The reduction in weight will also lower the seismic forces that the building will experience.
- The temporary shoring of a concrete floor for some time after the casting of a concrete floor is not required in structural steel construction, allowing the other construction trades to commence work earlier.

The structural engineer designs the floor for the dead loads of the building (the self-weight of the structure, partitions, floor finishes, ceilings, mechanical and electrical equipment, etc.) and code-prescribed live loads. Additionally, the girders and beams that frame from column to column are designed to resist lateral loads from the wind or the seismic forces imposed on a building. The floor must be designed so that code-mandated allowable stresses are not exceeded (strength) and vibrations or deflections are not excessive (serviceability).

The structural design of the building core presents challenges to the structural engineer because the core is usually designed to resist a large part of the wind and seismic forces to which the building will be exposed. This design requirement can be achieved by introducing bracing or deep girders or a combination of bracing and girders between columns at the edge of the core. This is where the supply and return ductwork leave or enter the shaft or the local floor-by-floor fan room. It is also the location where the ducts are at their maximum dimension and where extra height will be required for fire dampers where they exit a fire-rated shaft.

If the structural engineer concerned himself only with structural criteria, the floor members would have an optimal depth at the least cost while providing the required strength and serviceability for the project. As a design reality, however, the structural engineer will coordinate with the other design team members to ensure the optimum overall solution for the project. This collaborative effort will result in a design that will produce a dimensioned zone between the underside of the ceiling and the underside of slab of the floor above that will minimize the floor-to-floor height to a point that is appropriate for the project. The design process for this space will involve compromises by both the architectural and several engineering disciplines to provide the necessary structural openings without compromising overall structural rigidity. All parties must focus on the goal of reducing the vertical dimension of the ceiling cavity to its lowest possible dimension.

The collective effort starts early in the design process and is continuous, because the decisions that are made will affect the ongoing design outcomes of the several disciplines. An early start and the continuity of the effort is even more critical if the project is being subjected to fast-track construction as the structural steel may well be in fabrication before the HVAC designs are completed.

The HVAC design engineer can, in conjunction with the architect and the design of the core elements, start by locating the supply and return air shafts (in the case of a central air-conditioning supply system solution) or the local fan room (in the case of a floor-by-floor air-conditioning supply system solution) at a location where the distribution of the mechanical and electrical elements are able to be extended to the occupied floor in the smallest vertical dimension when integrated with the structure. The HVAC engineer can also design the ductwork to have the highest possible aspect ratio, which may nominally increase the cost of the ductwork but which will also result in a shallower duct that can more readily be accommodated to the structural design.

There are several alternative approaches to an integrated design by the architectural and engineering professionals:

- The structural engineer can determine the shallowest depth of beams and girders that will satisfy the strength and serviceability requirements. The HVAC designer will then utilize ductwork, possibly with a greater aspect ratio, and pass the ductwork and other mechanical and electrical services between the fireproofing on the bottom of the steel framing and the top of the ceiling.

  The structural engineer can leave the girders at their optimum depth or make them deeper than required while providing strategically located openings in the webs of the structural members (near the center of the span) or notches near the ends of the members. It is possible to provide small round holes in the structural element to allow the passing of small mechanical or electrical elements through the steel. Examples of these alternatives are shown in Figure 2.4. Any of these approaches will result in the ductwork and structure occupying the same vertical space.

- The structural engineer can provide a stub girder system where the girders are dropped so that beams can be supported by bearing on the top flange of the girder. This alternative creates a void within which ductwork and other crossover services can go over the girder's top flange and beneath the concrete floor.

- It is also possible to modify the location of the intermediate girders to create a usable void as is shown in Figure 2.5. In Figure 2.5a, the girder is upset into the floor above, and in 2.5b the girder is lowered into the floor below. Either approach requires the involvement of the architect. Both these solutions will result in projections of the beam into the shaft or fan room, which may create interferences requiring careful coordination and a possible decrease in future flexibility. Where the girder is lowered to create a void above it, the approach is further limited in that girder cannot be lowered to the point that it would be lower than the height of any door located beneath the girder in the floor below.

- A alternative approach is shown in Figure 2.6. This solution involves the use of V-shaped bracing which will be framed between the columns. The bracing provides support for the girder

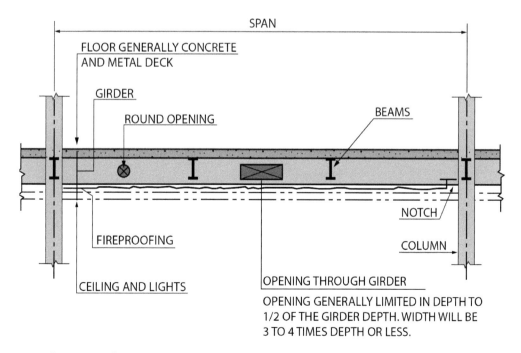

Figure 2.4 Typical structural openings in steel girder for ducts and other services.

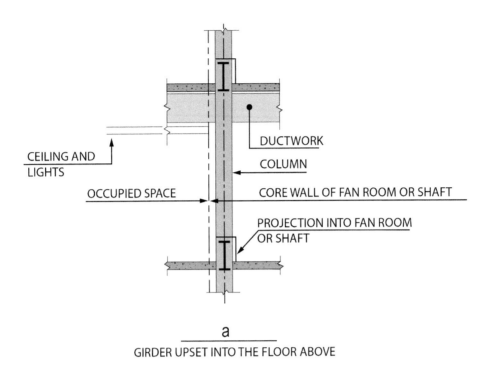

Figure 2.5 Two options, a and b, for girder construction.

while creating a void for the ductwork. The girder size will decrease in depth, because its bending moment will be less than the moment of a girder without the brace as a support. The bracing sizes and connections and their costs will be greater than they would if the bracing were used for lateral support only.

Other means of minimizing the floor-to-floor height that involve the structural engineer and the HVAC engineer have been tried with varying success. The possible means of integrating the structure and the mechanical, electrical, and plumbing services are an important challenge to the designers and must be addressed collectively, because the ultimate integrated design will have an economic effect on the total project cost beyond their specific engineering discipline installed cost. The goal of the design team is, therefore, to provide the most cost-efficient integration of the structural system with mechanical and electrical systems.

A final approach is to lower the ceiling around the core, as this area will frequently be used as a circulation corridor when the interior spaces are laid out, and an 8 ft, 0 in. (2.45 m) ceiling height the width of a possible corridor in this location will not be considered obtrusive.

STRUCTURAL RULES FOR BEAM PENETRATIONS

The following is an excerpt from "Design for Openings in the Webs of Composite Beams" by CIRIA/SCI (Lawson 1987). Note that the advice from most steel fabricators is that generally it is more efficient to avoid stiffened openings.

1. Openings should preferably be positioned at mid-height of the section. If not, the depths of the upper and lower sections of web should not differ by more than a factor of two.

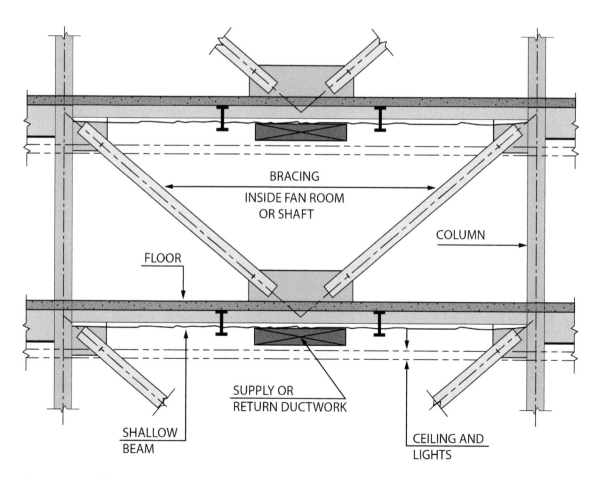

Figure 2.6 A typical bracing void for ducts and other services.

2. No opening should be located closer than two times the beam depth D to the support or 10% of the span, whichever is the greater.

3. The best location for any opening is between 1/5 and 1/3 of the span from a support in uniformly loaded beams, or in the lower shear zone of beams subject to point loads.

4. Openings should not be less than the beam depth, D, apart.

5. Unstiffened openings should not generally be deeper than $0.6D$ nor longer than $1.5D$. The instability of the web should be checked using Equation 1.1.

$$\ell_e = 0.45h_o \text{ (for circular openings)}$$
$$\ell_e = \ell_o - 0.55h_o \text{ (for elongated openings)} \tag{2.1}$$

where
ℓ_o = length of the elongated opening and
h_o = length of the circular opening or the ends of an elongated opening

6. Stiffened openings should not generally be deeper than $0.7D$ or longer than $2D$.

7. Point loads should not be applied at less than D from the side of the adjacent opening.

8. If the above criteria are followed then the additional deflection resulting from each opening could be taken as 3% of the mid-span deflection without openings.

9   Stiffeners would generally be of the form as shown in Figure 2.7 Their projection past the opening and the strength of the connecting welds should be sufficient to develop the full strength of the stiffener at the opening.

ALTERNATIVE DUCTWORK DESIGNS

A further means of reducing the vertical height of ductwork, the ceiling void, and the floor-to-floor height is to have multiple points of duct entry to the floor from the core. This can

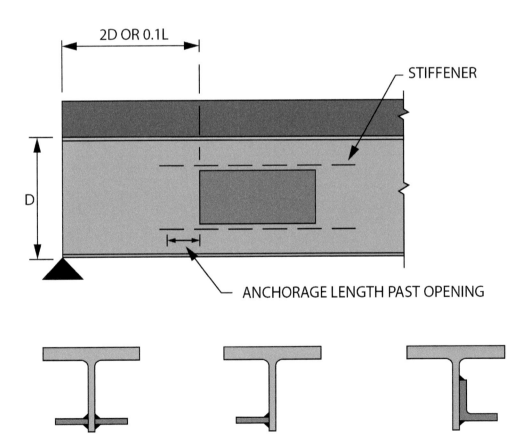

Figure 2.7 Various stiffening options.

be arranged only with the active participation of the architect, because this arrangement will affect other core areas.

Floor-by-floor air-conditioning system alternatives are achieved by placing the local floor fan room at the end of the core, which will provide a minimum of two and as many as three entry points for the supply and return ducts.

Beyond these duct arrangements and their integration with the structural systems, the choice of the HVAC system itself can have a significant effect on the overall HVAC system integration with the structural system. This is discussed in Chapter 8.

A final consideration with a central fan room solution is the reduction of the number of possible vertical supply and return ducts. A project in Europe, which was a large expansion of an existing building, provides a dramatic example of this design technique. The existing building was not air conditioned and had 10 ft, 10 in. (3.3 m) floor-to-floor heights with 8 ft, 6 in. (2.60 m) floor-to-ceiling heights. The request was to provide floor integration so that a person walking from the existing building to the expansion area would neither step up nor down. To satisfy the need for flexible power and information technology cable distribution, a 5 in (125 mm) raised floor was also to be included. These requests were accommodated by the use of two HVAC design details and one detail that involved the ultimate architectural layout of the interiors of each floor. The first HVAC detail involved multiple duct drops from the central mechanical equipment room to the occupied floor and routing the floor supply ducts between the lighting fixtures. The second was to include fan-coil units on the exterior wall to reduce the volume of air required on each floor. The lighting fixtures, while shallow, were located beneath structural beams, creating a limitation on the location of partitions and the resultant space layouts. The ceiling void with this arrangement was 12 in. (300 mm).

LIGHTING SYSTEMS

One development that has taken place in the recent past is the availability of lighting fixtures for office illumination that provides an acceptable level of illumination of 55 to 65 foot candles (600 to 700 lx) of lighting but are only 5 in. (125 mm) to 5.5 in. (138 mm) deep. When integrated with the ceiling system, the overall height of both elements will be approximately 5.5 in. (138 mm) deep. These lower-height fixtures assist in the routing of both the ductwork and sprinkler piping within a given ceiling cavity.

It should be stressed that, contrary to the project in Europe just discussed, the ductwork and lighting fixtures should not be in the same plane, because the interior design of the floor is not usually known at the time the shell and core project is being designed and, even if it were known, it would change over the life of the building. When these changes occur, it will usually be necessary to move the lighting fixtures and the air-distribution devices, but the major distribution ductwork, short of a significant increase in air-conditioning capacity requirements, will remain in place.

CONCLUSIONS CONCERNING FLOOR-TO-FLOOR HEIGHT

The floor-to-floor height required to meet the needs of a tall commercial office building with general office occupancy can vary with a floor-to-floor height of 13 ft to 13 ft, 6 in. (3.9 to 4.1 m). if very carefully coordinated with all disciplines. This floor-to-floor height is achieved, for example, with the dimensions shown in Figure 2.9. The space from the bottom of the ceiling to the bottom of the slab of the floor above is 4 ft, 0 in. (1.2 m). This 4 ft, 0 in. (1.2 m) space would contain the lighting fixtures, ducts, sprinkler piping, and structural steel system supporting the slab. An increase (or decrease) in any of the elements shown in Figure 2.9 will result in an increase (or decrease) in the floor-to-floor height.However, heights of between 14 to 15 ft (4.2 to 4.5 m) are more typical to achieve Class A office floor specifications.

These conclusions do not include special areas in buildings such as data centers, trading floors, or dining facilities. A data center or trading floor will require a raised floor of as much as 24 to 30 in. (600 to 750 mm). Trading floors are normally open, partitionless spaces and very much call for a floor-to-ceiling height in excess of 9 ft (2.75 m) to allow line-of-sight communication between traders in various areas of the floor.[1]

Figure 2.8 A rendering of a typical office floor.

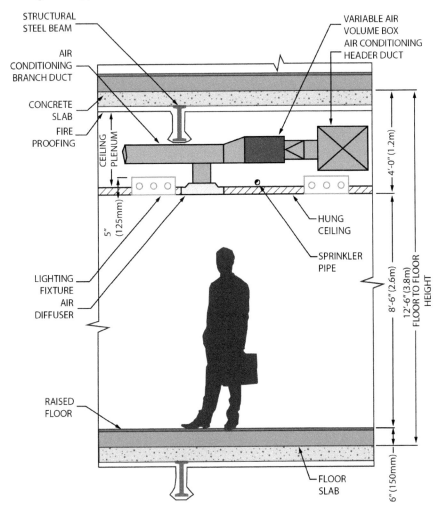

Figure 2.9 A typical section floor-to-floor height.

This brief overview is intended to highlight the issues involved in determining the floor-to-floor height, a significant determination that has a major impact on the building cost because of the effect it has on the area and cost of the exterior wall of the building and the other vertical elements in the building. Accordingly, the entire design team must focus considerable effort on reducing the floor-to-floor height to a practical minimum for any tall commercial office building.

SUPER SLENDER RESIDENTIAL TOWERS

The particularities of New York City's building code, developers' rights, and an extreme high-end residential market has led to the evolution of a new building type—super slender high-rise residential towers. While this is mirrored to some extent in high wealth, high density cities such as Hong Kong and London, the New York phenomenon of gaming of plot ratios, appropriation of adjoining properties' underdeveloped air rights, and the lack of discretionary restrictions has spawned this new tower type, which is characterized by slenderness ratios of between 12:1 to 24:1, small plot sizes, and heights of up to 1450 ft (440 m). This building type seems likely to be more pervasive as megacities evolve, and pose unique engineering challenges.

The primary issue is structural—providing adequate stability to lateral loading. This is exacerbated by the small footprint that limits the span of bracing elements and the added sensitivity to account for all the valuable usable floor area. Some towers are further challenged by having large volume space requirements on the lower floors, such as the 53W53 tower by Jean Nouvel, which has three levels of art galleries that require free span space and a transfer structure located at the 5th and 6th levels to carry internal columns from the tower above.

The structural response requires an integrated approach to manage wind loading. The resultant towers are analyzed through 3-D computational models and wind tunnel tests to create forms that break the edge vortices and so reduce the loads of wind gusts, which can reach up to 100 mph. Abrupt building edges, intermittent voided floor plates, and careful façade detailing are used to break up high-pressure points. The internal structure often relies on high-strength concrete and steel reinforcement (up to 14,000 psi, Grade 97 steel) to minimize the size of structural members. Shear walls, central cores with out-riggers, and "diagrid" external façade supports have all been used to resolve the structural challenge.

To date, all of these super-slender towers have also resorted to some form of damper to minimize the sway effects that may cause motion sickness for occupants. The accelerations caused by sway can be reduced by as much as 50% by dampers located in the tower's upper levels. Tuned mass dampers, which use suspended weights of between 300 to 800 tons with active or passive shock absorbers or pistons, or slosh dampers, which use hydraulic tanks, have been employed. These are not required to maintain the tower's structural integrity but are deemed a necessary requirement for the super-wealthy inhabitants.

The reduced floor plates of the towers (between 2000 to 8000 ft^2 [200 to 800 m^2]) and the demand for high ceilings adds complexity for mechanical design. The typical 15.5 ft (4.5 m) ceiling height is driven by the efficiency of using a switchback stair that entwines two separated escape stairs within a single stair core. The pressure to minimize core space limits risers and plant room locations and is exacerbated by the lack of the ceiling space that might otherwise be used if the tall loft volumes were not a prerequisite of the market. At 432 Park Avenue, by Rafael Vinoly and WSP, the tower was split into six vertical zones to reduce the effect of vertical distribution of power and water. Air distribution within the units needs careful handling to ensure all zones meet comfort levels with minimal ductwork. This is further challenged by the use of large, full-height glazing. The effect of large temperature differences on cold winter days leads to a cold air curtain sliding vertically down the large window areas. These are managed with trickle vents at the top and/or bottom to limit condensation issues and

1.   Current tall buildings in China are increasingly using a clear floor to ceiling height of 9 ft, 10 in. (3.0 m) as the minimum standard. This results in floor-to-floor heights of between 14 ft, 3 in. to 14 ft, 7 in. (4.40 to 4.50 m) as the accepted market standard for all new Class A (tall commercial) buildings.

mix the resulting cool air before it spills into the main spaces. The vertical stack and external pressure differential further restrict bringing in natural air at leach level with restricted operable windows and limited access to the external envelope.

The tall floor-to-ceiling height does help with the vertical transportation, not just for the escape stairs. Elevator strategies have to balance speed and availability demands of the high-end users with the restricted core space. The number of levels the elevators need to serve is reduced by the high ceiling design, while the vertical distance traveled can be managed by high-speed cabs and vertical zoning.

The value of residential units rises with elevation and lower floor levels often have restricted views blocked by adjoining towers. In New York the building height is not restricted, only the floor area, so many developers fill the lower levels with more utilitarian uses such as nanny flats, mechanical space, storage, gyms, pools, and spas.

The controversy generated by new building types continues and the main push back, beyond the social issues of wealth disparity and absentee ownership, has been the impact of shadows on public spaces. The concentration of these towers along 57th Street to the south of Central Park only adds sensitivity to the debate between faster moving tall shadows cast from these super-slender towers versus wider, slower shadows of existing buildings.

MIXED-USE/STACKED TOWERS

The development of super- and mega-high-rise towers has also come with the increase in mixed-use towers combining more than one user type. While the utopian ideals of vertical cities with fully integrated communities that follow the horizontal village model has yet to be fully realized, there is an increasing proportion of mixed-use, multiuse, or stacked towers that still offer the promise of reduced transportation and the associated benefits of well-planned increases of urban density. These hybrid tower types offer a mix of advantages and disadvantages over single-use towers.

Developers safeguard return on investment by diversifying their property, as the markets for office, hotel, residential and commercial are often cyclical and trend counter to each other. The mix of uses provides a varied portfolio that can hedge against market changes, as opposed to a single-use tower. In addition, the development of high-value items such as retail to the ground levels can have significant effect on related office or hotel rates because of increased street presence and points of differentiation between competing venues.

There are inherent planning challenges as the floor plate size, core configuration, and optimum grid size between two uses (offices and hotels, for example) can be conflicting. The typical strategy for this is the stratification of building use that changes both in height an in relation to the tapering floor plate as a tower rises. This stratification of use plays into the typical zoning of high rises, which become compartmentalized vertically to serve the constraints of mechanical, fire safety and vertical transportation needs.

The varying uses can be fully separated within a tower, but the highest earnings in mixed-use buildings are made by shared facilities such as pools, gyms, spas, clubs, and cafes. These further benefit by having an offset peak demand for each building user (office workers versus hotel guests) that allows a more efficient provision of space. This offset peak or *smoothed demand curve* can increase the efficiency of utilitarian factors like parking, vertical transportation loads, and energy management if planned into fully integrated schemes.

Some developers demand separate metering and management of utilities, requiring multiple central plant spaces within a tower, each dedicated to a self-contained user. However, the main synergy of having a tower with multiple occupancy types is found in harnessing the varied energy demand cycles in an integrated management system that allows for reduced energy consumption and equipment sizing. An integrated energy plant can offset heating/cooling loads and power distribution can be combined with on-site energy storage through batteries or thermal cycling. On-site power cogeneration can be run on waste heat from an absorption cooling plant, smoothing peak demand. Similarly, variable refrigerant flow systems and heat recovery allow high efficiency when running heating and cooling loads simultaneously in different parts of the building.

Vertical use zoning, or *stacking*, is typically limited to groups of 15 to 20 levels. This helps reduce vertical water and power risers, provides refuge floors, allows for the reduction of stack effect issues, and allows local distribution of intakes and exhaust air. These mechanical subdivisions or strata are often expressed externally, allowing the breakup of wind vortices to cut wind loading to the structure. Internally too, they can be transformed into terraces for relaxation of interaction between users, forming communal nodes along the vertical "street."

Multiple users often require separate and identifiable lobby spaces and vertical access, both for security and to establish the "front door" for the tenant. This puts high demand on ground floor space and often results in multilevel entrances. Hotels in particular favor sky lobbies, located remotely from the building entrance and separated by dedicated express elevator links.

Vertical transportation management helps resolve security and efficiency for the stacked uses. The Shanghai Tower, by Gensler, splits the building into nine separate elevator zones, served by 106 separate elevators including an uninterrupted super express elevator that reaches speeds of up to 4000 fpm (20.5 m/s) to reach the visitors' viewing deck at level 119. It has four double-deck lift cars to the hotel sky lobby at level 101 and benefits from the latest efficiencies of regenerative energy condensers and group controls.

Current elevator controls, such as the use of destination dispatching systems that group users' floor levels to reduce wait times and limit cab travel and stops, reduce energy use and smooth passenger flows and queuing. Smartphone apps and RFID chip cards manage security access to multiple levels. Advances in cable materials reduce motor loads and vastly increase the range of traditional steel rope systems. In the future, the use of multi systems such as rope-free electromagnetic levitation systems offer the promise of further reduced energy use and the use of more than a single cab per shaft to reduce the overall shaft area.

The difference in peak demand for parking can also allow for the overall reduction of parking bays by the use of swing spaces that can satisfy the offset demand profiles of different user groups. For example, office parking can be used for retail and leisure uses on weekends and evenings and hotel valet parking can compress spaces in tandem or mechanically stacked arrangements that would not work for the high-volume beginnings and ends of office days. The scale of these developments typically attracts colocation of transportation nodes that may further reduce the reliance on private transportation and parking.

As cities further densify, people are increasingly pushed into high-rise lifestyles. The growth of mixed-use towers reflects the maturity of this trend and echoes back to the complexity of the previously horizontal past. The added challenge of multiple tenant types can be harnessed to drive efficiencies of transportation and energy use and, perhaps, a well-integrated design can add to the overall quality of a convivial city.

CASE STUDY
CITIC Headquarters

Beijing

Name: CITIC Tower

Location: Beijing, China.

Description: The design of the 1732 ft (528 m) tall office tower draws inspiration from the form of a traditional Chinese ritual wine vessel, the *zun*, and is popularly called the China Zun. The design is an abstraction of the *zun* that balances aesthetics with the structural requirements and leasing needs. Transforming articulation design is applied throughout the tower from exterior envelop to the lobby and observation deck interiors. The building is a tapered rectangular prism with rounded corners. Its width changes vertically from its 256 ft (78 m) wide base to its 177 ft (54 m) wide "waist" to its 226 ft (69 m) wide top.

Building Function: CITIC Group and TD Bank headquarters, as well as leased office spaces and a multipurpose business center.

Building Height: 1732 ft (528 m)

Building Floor Area: 4,600,000 ft^2 (437,00 m^2)

Architects: TFP Farrells (Concept), Kohn Pedersen Fox Associates (Design), Beijing Institute of Architectural Design (Architect of Record)

Structural Engineers: Arup (Design), Beijing Institute of Architectural Design (Engineer of Record)

MEP Engineers: WSP (Design), Beijing Institute of Architectural Design (Engineer of Record)

Adapted from a report originally published at WorldArchitecture.com—
https://worldarchitecture.org/architecture-news/eezev/citic-tower-by-kohn-pederson-fox-is-beijing-s-tallest-building.html

CHAPTER 3
Façade Systems

Present-day energy compliance code requires the base-case window-to-wall ratio to be around 40% of the façade (this may vary based upon location and orientation), but many modern designs have window-to-wall ratios of 65% or more. Therefore, the façade load is critical in ensuring an energy-efficient building.

This chapter highlights current façade choices and designs to maintain a low-energy heat gain or heat loss from the interior space.

BUILDING ORIENTATION

Though the building orientation is normally determined by the available real estate and the architectural design, the tall building HVAC designer must remember to consider increased or decreased infiltration rates and solar loads affected by the planned building orientation. This can be especially important for megatall and supertall buildings, because infiltration from wind loads may be significant for very tall buildings, particularly for sites that may not have adjacent buildings or landscape that mitigates high winds.

Existing (adjacent) buildings can provide significant shading for a newly constructed tall building, though not for most super- and megatall buildings that project high above most traditional buildings. Though an adjacent tall building can reduce the peak and annual cooling load on the new proposed building, it must be considered that depending on the building's life span, an adjacent building may be demolished at some point in the future, thereby realizing the true cooling peak demand for the new building. Hence, future construction or demolition of adjacent buildings should also be considered to determine their effects upon cooling and heating loads. The cooling and heating systems must be sized to account for these possible future changes.

Solar loads may be significant in buildings even with reflective glass because of the lack of shading from adjacent structures. Adjacent structures with reflective glass may also reflect solar radiation to exterior portions of the building that normally would have small or no solar load. The worst case solar load should be considered based upon current adjacent structures and possible future adjacent structures in the calculation of cooling and heating loads.

FAÇADE SYSTEMS

A high-performance façade design is essential to minimize the solar cooling load and allow for efficient performance of air-conditioning systems while enhancing indoor comfort and maintaining views. In general, the façade (building envelope and glazing) performs several functions:

- Protection from external environment of wind and rain

- Insulation of heat in summer and cold in winter
- Reduction of solar radiation transmission
- Elimination of glare
- Minimizing infiltration and exfiltration
- Controlling levels of daylight
- Providing daylight beyond perimeter zone
- Aesthetic design
- Ease of cleaning and maintenance
- Allowing occupants to control their environment
- Provision of natural ventilation
- Mitigation of exterior to interior sound transmission
- Accommodation of daylighting design strategies to minimize electricity demand for lighting and reduce associated cooling loads
- Security considerations, especially and lower floors
- Blast design, especially at lower floors
- Impact-resistant design in high-wind areas as predicted by future climate modeling

The façade should be designed to minimize the solar gain to 10% to 20% of the incident radiation. Methods that can be used to achieve these levels include minimizing window area, ventilating the glazing, and/or articulation of the façade (e.g., placing the windows at a forward angle).

A double-skin façade (as shown in Figure 3.1) could be used with fan-coil, chilled ceiling, and chilled-beam cooling systems and would have the return air directed to the floor of the perimeter and up between exterior and interior windows. The characteristics of the design are as follows:

Figure 3.1 A section through a double-skin climate façade.

- Reduction of solar transmission to 10% to 15%
- Outdoor air supplied at high level
- Return air through internal layer in which solar shades are located
- Solar shades and daylight level can be automatic or controlled by occupants
- The heated return air can be used to preheat ventilation (outdoor) air
- Minimal use of internal space

Multi-skin façades (MSF) can provide a variable control of solar radiation and inside surface temperature as well as natural daylighting and noise. Through their construction, MSFs provide a higher level of acoustical insulation. MSFs can be designed to facilitate natural ventilation via the cavity. When natural ventilation is utilized by ventilating from the cavity of the MSF, openings in the façade are mitigated and improve the security of the building, as there are no direct openings in the façade. By utilizing natural ventilation, air-conditioning systems' energy requirements can be reduced.

Definition of a Double-Skin Façade

A façade covering one or several stories constructed with multiple glazed skins. The skins can be airtight or not. In this kind of façade, the air cavity situated between the skins is naturally or mechanically ventilated. The air cavity ventilation strategy may vary with time. Devices and systems are generally integrated in order to improve the indoor climate with active or passive techniques. Most of the time such systems are managed in semiautomatic way via control systems. (Loncour et al. 2004)

The layers of the façade are described by Poirazis (2006):

- *Exterior glazing* usually refers to a hardened single glazing. This exterior façade can be fully glazed.
- *Interior glazing*. Insulating double glazing unit (clear, low-E coating, solar control glazing, etc. can be used). Almost always this layer is not completely glazed.
- *Air cavity between the two panes*. It can be totally natural, fan supported, or mechanically ventilated. The width of the cavity can vary as a function of the applied concept between 8 in. to more than 80 in. (200 mm to more than 2 m). This width influences the way that the façade is maintained.
- The interior window can be opened by the user. This may allow natural ventilation of the offices.
- Automatically controlled solar shading is integrated inside the air cavity.
- As a function of the façade concept and of the glazing type, heating radiators can be installed next to the façade.

Double-skin façades are classified by BBRI (2002) as follows:

- Ventilation type
  This relates to the ventilation in the air cavity situated between the two glazed façades which can consist of the following:

  1. Natural ventilation
  2. Mechanical ventilation

- Partitioning of the air cavity
  The partitioning of the air cavity refers to the physical division of the air cavity. Distinction is first made to separate windows from façades.

  1. Airflow windows
  2. Double-skin façades

- Ventilation mode
  This area of the classification relates to the origin and the destination of the air circulating in the cavity.
  Five ventilation modes are distinguished:

  1. Outdoor air curtain,
  2. Indoor air curtain

3. Air supply
4. Air exhaust
5. Air buffer

Further design characteristics that focus the classifications are noted:

• Naturally ventilated façades change operational mode depending on conditions.
• Mechanically ventilated façades are generally not equipped with inlets and are most of the time characterized by only one ventilation mode.
• Double-ventilated façades are composed by two glazed skins, generally one single glazing and one insulating glazing. Façades ventilated with indoor air tend to have the insulated glazing placed at the outside layer, whereas those ventilated with outdoor air have it placed at the inside.
• Climate façades—Ventilation is mechanical and air flows from inside to outside.
• Double-skin façades—Ventilation is natural and air flows from exterior to exterior.
• Interactive façades—Ventilation is natural/mechanically assisted and from either interior/exterior to interior/exterior.

SHADING

Shading strategies are an important consideration in cooling-load-dominated climates or those with a hot season, including northern North America and northern Europe. There are many types of glazing constructions available due to the many types of spectral and low-e coatings available. Blinds can be installed in cavity between the glass layers. There are also electrochromic, thermochromic, and photochromic materials available, albeit they are very expensive. Fritted glass can also be used, but special care must be taken as most often the inside surface temperature of the glazing is increased due to the high solar absorption of the fritt.

Exterior shading is always preferred, as a portion of solar radiation is not permitted to enter the space, although maintenance of exterior shading can be higher than shading installed on the inside of the glass. For south orientations, horizontal shading is recommended, but for east and west façades, vertical shading is recommended (for the northern hemisphere).

Interior shading such as shades and blinds can be utilized for glare control, but do not remove solar radiation to the space as they merely convert short wave radiation to long wave radiation, which is heat. It is often suggested that the shading devices can be in two parts, the upper part to admit light deeper in to the space, the lower part is used for solar control. When interior shades are used, the radiation energy trapped between the inside glazing and the shade or blind must be considered, as it is converted to longwave radiation that increases the internal space temperature.

Table 3.1 Types of Multi-Skin Façades

One-Story Façade Modules	The air cavity is divided horizontally and vertically at the level of each façade module. Naturally ventilated double façades with one-story façade modules are also known as a *box window* type.
Corridor Façade	Corridor façades are characterized by a wide air cavity partitioned at the level of each story. Essentially, this is a one-story module that forms a corridor which can cover either a whole-story or several adjacent zones.
Multiple-Story Façade	Multiple-story façades are not partitioned vertically or horizontally. The air cavity extends a large height with metallic maintenance grids at the level of each story allowing circulation. In extreme cases, the air cavity can envelop the whole of the building without any partitioning.
Shaft Box Façade	Shaft box façades are very similar in nature to the one-story height module. However, the modules are linked with building high vertical by means of a bypass opening. The stack effect draws the air from the box windows into the vertical shafts and from there up to the top, where it is emitted.

GLAZING AND FAÇADE ANALYSIS

In most contemporary designs, the proposed building's energy consumption is compared to one that is base-case-compliant; many designers also strive for net zero status, meaning the proposed design should consume a minimum of energy. However, there are a few obstacles in the design path. Firstly, as previously stated, the base case building has typically a 40% window-to-wall ratio and modern buildings can have window-to-wall ratios as high as 65%. Secondly, the location of the building could be anywhere in the world—the closer to the equator, the higher the sun, and thus external shading can be accomplished with a minimal fin, but the farther away from the equator designers must accommodate low sun angles. Thirdly, the climate in which the building is to be designed for—heating- or cooling-dominated (or both)—must be accounted for.

To illustrate this, we use a hypothetical building situated in New York City (climate zone 4A). The building is 1980 ft (600 m) tall, has 144 floors each with a floor area of 20925 ft^2 (1944 m^2), and a total floor area of 2,799,360 ft^2 (279,936 m^2).

Designing the building from the beginning with energy-efficiency in mind is the surest way to reduce energy consumption. The skin of the building acts as a barrier between the indoor and outdoor environments. The thermal performance of a building depends upon the skin and the façade design to a large extent, ranking second to the local climate characteristics.

The calculations consist of three major components:

- Conduction through opaque wall
- Conduction through window glass
- Solar radiation through window glass

For a given location or latitude, assuming that the climatic factors and the local parameters such as acclimatization levels do not vary, the interaction of the architectural parameters (such as building orientation, window glazing type, and shading devices) and the climatic parameters (such as solar radiation intensity and wind speed) are the main factors upon which the calculations depend.

Climate Data

During summer design conditions the outside dry-bulb temperature decreases by about 10°F (6K) over the height of a 1980 ft (600 m) building. The same is also true, but inverted, during the winter scenario where the outside temperature further decreases over the height of the building. These scenarios are shown in Figure 3.2.

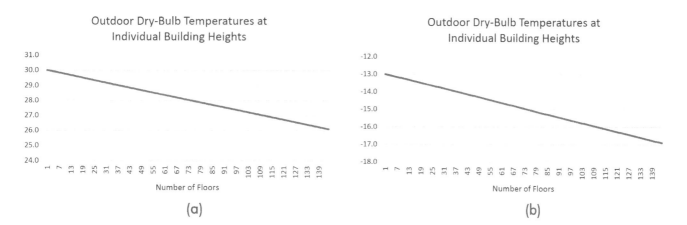

Figure 3.2 The variation in outdoor dry-bulb temperature as a function of the building height in (a) summer and (b) winter.

Traditional heat loss calculations would assume the winter design outside temperature would exist over the height of the building. This is also helpful for the selection of a suitable HVAC system for the building as the conditioning system must be capable of providing a variable cooling load.

As the building height increases, the wind speed and pressure also increase. The increase in wind speed over the vertical height of the building can be calculated from weather data. Figure 3.3 shows the wind speed against a façade. The wind speed at ground level is given at 1 m/s and this is extrapolated upwards. For a 1980 ft (600 m) megatall building the wind speed at the top of the building is approximately 2560 fpm (13 m/s). As wind speed increases with height, so does the pressure against the façade and façade leakage rates need to be critically assessed. Figure 3.4 shows the wind pressure against a façade when the ground speed is 3.3 ft/s (1 m/s). See the Façade Leakage Rates section for further details.

Calculation Techniques

The heat loss and heat gain calculations are:

$$Q = U * A * \Delta T$$

where

Q	=	Btu/h (W)
U	=	construction U-factor, Btu/ft^2/°F (W/m^2·K)
A	=	area, ft^2 (m^2)
ΔT	=	the temperature difference between indoors and outdoors (at different vertical heights)

Solar radiation is calculated by using a sunpath diagram for the site location and orientation of the glazing, this is calculated as:

$$Q_s = SR * SHGC * A$$

where

Q_s	=	the solar load through the glass, Btu/h (W)
SR	=	the solar radiation to the glass, Btu/ft^2 (Btu/m^2)
SHGC	=	the solar heat gain coefficient of the glazing

Figure 3.5 shows a typical section of the façade with exterior shading elements

To illustrate a design methodology, we show calculations for façades with 40% and 65% glass, respectively. Both façades have U-factors of 0.104 Btu/h/ft^2/°F (0.592 W/m^2·K) and the U-factor of the glass is 0.419 Btu/h/ft^2/°F (2.38 W/m^2·K). These values are taken from ANSI/ASHRAE/IES Standard 90.1 (ASHRAE 2016).

Table 3.2 shows the difference in heat gain to the space behind the façade for both a 40% and 65% window-to-wall ratio. The 65% façade allows a further (8907 Btu/h) 2290 W to a typical floor and therefore increases the energy consumption.

The difference in heat gain for the whole building is 5,021,757 Btu/h (964,334 W) for the 40% window-to-wall ratio and 6,935,689 Btu/h (1,294,090 W) for the 65% window-to-wall ratio. The difference is an increase in heat gain of 1,282,667 Btu/h (329,756 W) for the whole building.

Table 3.3 shows the difference in heat loss from the space through the façade for both a 40% window-to-wall ratio and a 65% window-to-wall ratio. The 65% façade allows a further 47,148 Btu/h (13,029 W) heat loss from a typical floor and therefore increases the energy consumption.

The difference in heat loss for the whole building is 19,791,391 Btu/h (5,486,726 W) for the 40% window-to-wall ratio and 26,580,679 Btu/h (7,362,925 W) for the 65% window-to-wall ratio. The difference is an increase in heat gain of 6,789,288 Btu/h (1,876,198 W) for the whole building.

The next step is to determine the solar load to the space through the façade. Using sunpath diagrams we can find the orientation with the highest solar gain. For this example, we are using the south façade.

Table 3.4 shows the heat gains to a typical floor for 40% window-to-wall ratio glazing and 65% window-to-wall ratio glazing. These are 5.28 and 8.23 Btu/h·ft^2 (16.3 and 25.5 W/m^2), respectively.

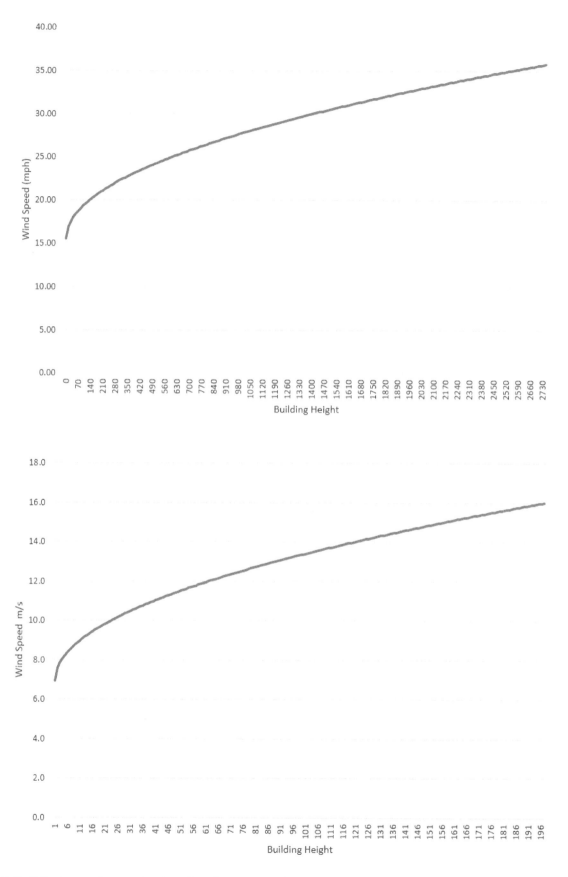

Figure 3.3 Wind speed over the height of a megatall building when the ground speed is 3.3 ft/s (1 m/s).

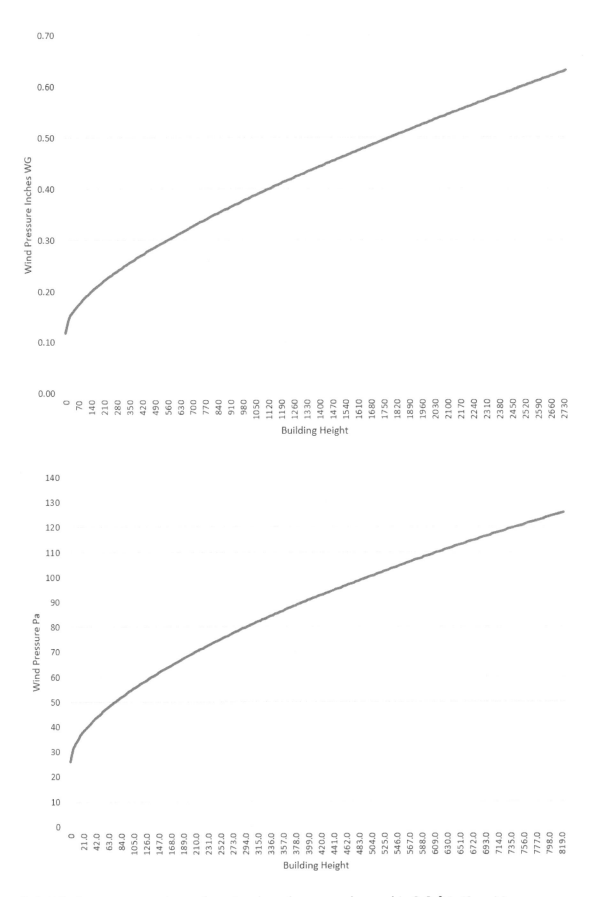

Figure 3.4 Wind pressure against a façade when the ground speed is 3.3 ft/s (1 m/s).

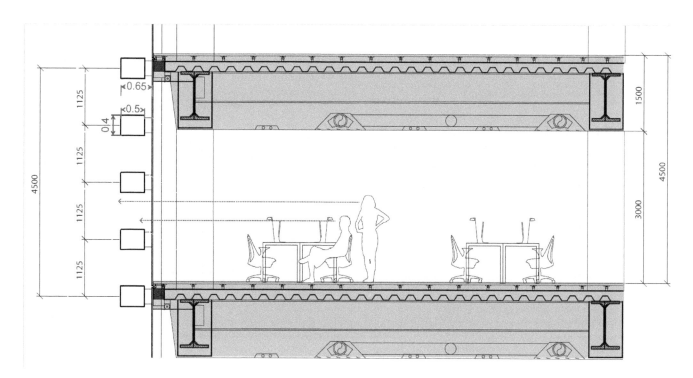

Figure 3.5 A typical section of the façade with exterior shading elements.

Table 3.2 Transmission of Heat Gain to the Space via the Façade for a Typical Floor, Summer (I-P)

Summer		Code—40% Glazing						Proposed Design—65% Glazing					
		Area, ft²	U-Factor, Btu/h·ft²/°F	Outdoor Temp., °F	Indoor Temp., °F	ΔT, °F	Energy, Btu/h	Area, ft²	U-Factor, Btu/h·ft²/°F	Outdoor Temp., °F	Indoor Temp., °F	ΔT, °F	Energy, Btu/h
North elevation	façade	2243	0.104	85.6	74	11.6	2706	1308	0.104	85.6	74	11.6	1578
North elevation	glass	1495	0.42	85.6	74	11.6	7284	2430	0.42	85.6	74	11.6	11,839
East elevation	façade	672	0.104	85.6	74	11.6	811	392	0.104	85.6	74	11.6	473
East elevation	glass	448	0.42	85.6	74	11.6	2183	728	0.42	85.6	74	11.6	3547
South elevation	façade	2243	0.104	85.6	74	11.6	2706	1308	0.104	85.6	74	11.6	1578
South elevation	glass	1495	0.42	85.6	74	11.6	7284	2430	0.42	85.6	74	11.6	11,839
West elevation	façade	672	0.104	85.6	74	11.6	811	392	0.104	85.6	74	11.6	473
West elevation	glass	448	0.42	85.6	74	11.6	2183	728	0.42	85.6	74	11.6	3547
Total		9716					25,966	9716					34,873

Figure 3.6 shows the percentage of the heat gain from the glazing and the percentage of heat gain from the façade for (a) 40% and (b) 65% window-to-wall ratio façade, respectively. For the 40% window-to-wall ratio, the percentage of heat gain to the space through the glazing is 112,689 Btu/h (31.66 kW) and is 83% of the load to the space. The total external load for the whole building is 2,591,846 Btu/h (759,993 W). For the 65% window-to-wall ratio, the percentage of heat gain to the space through the glazing is 175,794 Btu/h (49.54 kW) and is 85% of the load to the space. The total external load for the whole building is 4,043,255 Btu/h (1,139,435 W).

From Table 3.5 it is clear to see that 65% window-to-wall ratio glazing requires a higher heating and cooling load, in steady state and assuming a constant outside temperature for the building.

We know that outside temperature and air density decreases while wind speed increases over the height of the building in both summer and winter, but how do these phenomena affect building designs?

Table 3.2 Transmission of Heat Gain to the Space via the Façade for a Typical Floor, Summer (SI)

Summer				Code—40% Glazing					Proposed Design—65% Glazing					
		Area, m²	U-Factor, W/m²·K	Outdoor Temp., °C	Indoor Temp., °C	ΔT, °C	Energy, W	Area, m²	U-Factor, W/m²·K	Outdoor Temp., °C	Indoor Temp., °C	ΔT, °C	Energy, W
North elevation	façade	204	0.592	29.8	24	5.8	700	119	0.592	29.8	24	5.8	408
North elevation	glass	136	2.38	29.8	24	5.8	1876	221	2.38	29.8	24	5.8	3049
East elevation	façade	61	0.592	29.8	24	5.8	210	36	0.592	29.8	24	5.8	122
East elevation	glass	41	2.38	29.8	24	5.8	562	66	2.38	29.8	24	5.8	914
South elevation	façade	204	0.592	29.8	24	5.8	700	119	0.592	29.8	24	5.8	408
South elevation	glass	136	2.38	29.8	24	5.8	1876	221	2.38	29.8	24	5.8	3049
West elevation	façade	61	0.592	29.8	24	5.8	210	36	0.592	29.8	24	5.8	122
West elevation	glass	41	2.38	29.8	24	5.8	562	66	2.38	29.8	24	5.8	914
Total		883					6697	883					8987

Table 3.3 Transmission of Heat Gain to the Space via the Façade for a Typical Floor, Winter (I-P)

Winter				To Code—40% Glazing					Proposed Design—65% Glazing					
		Area, ft²	U-Factor, Btu/h·ft²/°F	Outdoor Temp., °F	Indoor Temp., °F	ΔT, °F	Energy, Btu/h	Area, ft²	U-Factor, Btu/h·ft²/°F	Outdoor Temp., °F	Indoor Temp., °F	ΔT, °F	Energy, Btu/h
North elevation	façade	2243	0.104	8.6	70	−61.4	−14,323	1308	0.104	13.5	70	−56.5	−7686
North elevation	glass	1495	0.42	8.6	70	−61.4	−38,553	2430	0.42	13.5	70	−56.5	−57,664
East elevation	façade	672	0.104	8.6	70	−61.4	−4291	392	0.104	13.5	70	−56.5	−2303
East elevation	glass	448	0.42	8.6	70	−61.4	−11,553	728	0.42	13.5	70	−56.5	−17,275
South elevation	façade	2243	0.104	8.6	70	−61.4	−14,323	1308	0.104	13.5	70	−56.5	−7686
South elevation	glass	1495	0.42	8.6	70	−61.4	−38,553	2430	0.42	13.5	70	−56.5	−57,664
West elevation	façade	672	0.104	8.6	70	−61.4	−4291	392	0.104	13.5	70	−56.5	−2303
West elevation	glass	448	0.42	8.6	70	−61.4	−11,553	728	0.42	13.5	70	−56.5	−17,275
Total		9716					−137,440	9716					−169,857

Table 3.3 Transmission of Heat Gain to the Space via the Façade for a Typical Floor, Winter (SI)

Winter				To Code—40% Glazing					Proposed Design—65% Glazing					
		Area, m²	U-Factor, W/m²·K	Outdoor Temp., °C	Indoor Temp., °C	ΔT, °C	Energy, W	Area, m²	U-Factor, W/m²·K	Outdoor Temp., °C	Indoor Temp., °C	ΔT, °C	Energy, W
North elevation	façade	204	0.592	−13	20	−33	−3983	119	0.592	−13	20	−33	−2324
North elevation	glass	136	2.38	−13	20	−33	−10,676	221	2.38	−13	20	−33	−17,348
East elevation	façade	61	0.592	−13	20	−33	−1193	36	0.592	−13	20	−33	−696
East elevation	glass	41	2.38	−13	20	−33	−3199	66	2.38	−13	20	−33	−5198
South elevation	façade	204	0.592	−13	20	−33	−3983	119	0.592	−13	20	−33	−2324
South elevation	glass	136	2.38	−13	20	−33	−10,676	221	2.38	−13	20	−33	−17,348
West elevation	façade	61	0.592	−13	20	−33	−1193	36	0.592	−13	20	−33	−696
West elevation	glass	41	2.38	−13	20	−33	−3199	66	2.38	−13	20	−33	−5198
Total		883					−38,102	883					−51,131

Table 3.4 Transmission Heat and Solar Radiation Gain to the Space Through the Façade, Summer (I-P)

Summer			Energy Code 40% glass SHGC = 0.4					65% glass SHGC = 0.4				
Height, 0–350 ft	Area, ft²	U-Factor, Btu/ft²·°F	Outdoor Temp., °F	Indoor Temp., °F	ΔT, °F	Energy, Btu	Area, ft²	U-Factor, Btu/ft²·°F	Outdoor Temp., °F	Indoor Temp., °F	ΔT, °F	Energy, Btu
North elevation wall	2243	0.104	85.6	74	11.6	2706	1308	0.104	85.6	74	11.6	1578
South elevation wall	2243	0.104	85.6	74	11.6	2706	1308	0.104	85.6	74	11.6	1578
East elevation wall	672	0.104	85.6	74	11.6	811	392	0.104	85.6	74	11.6	473
West elevation wall	672	0.104	85.6	74	11.6	811	392	0.104	85.6	74	11.6	473
North elevation glass	1495	0.42	85.6	74	11.6	7285	2430	0.42	85.6	74	11.6	11,837
South elevation glass	1495	0.42	85.6	74	11.6	7285	2430	0.42	85.6	74	11.6	11,837
East elevation glass	448	0.42	85.6	74	11.6	2183	728	0.42	85.6	74	11.6	3547
West elevation glass	448	0.42	85.6	74	11.6	2183	728	0.42	85.6	74	11.6	3547
Total						25,967						34,871

Height, 0–250 ft	Area, ft²	SHGC	Solar, Btu/ft²	Energy, Btu	Total	Area, m²	SHGC	Solar, Btu/ft²	Energy, Btu	Total
South elevation glass	1495	0.4	145	86,722	112,689	2,430	0.4	145	140,923	175,794

Table 3.4 Transmission Heat and Solar Radiation Gain to the Space Through the Façade, Summer (SI)

Summer			Energy Code 40% glass SHGC = 0.4					65% glass SHGC = 0.4				
Height, 0–100 m	Area, m²	U-Factor, W/m²·K	Outdoor Temp., °C	Indoor Temp., °C	ΔT, K	Energy, W	Area, m²	U-Factor, W/m²·K	Outdoor Temp., °C	Indoor Temp., °C	ΔT, K	Energy, W
North elevation wall	204	0.592	29.8	24	5.8	700	119	0.592	29.8	24	5.8	408
South elevation wall	204	0.592	29.8	24	5.8	700	119	0.592	29.8	24	5.8	408
East elevation wall	61	0.592	29.8	24	5.8	210	36	0.592	29.8	24	5.8	122
West elevation wall	61	0.592	29.8	24	5.8	210	36	0.592	29.8	24	5.8	122
North elevation glass	136	2.38	29.8	24	5.8	1,876	221	2.38	29.8	24	5.8	3,049
South elevation glass	136	2.38	29.8	24	5.8	1,876	221	2.38	29.8	24	5.8	3,049
East elevation glass	41	2.38	29.8	24	5.8	562	66	2.38	29.8	24	5.8	914
West elevation glass	41	2.38	29.8	24	5.8	562	66	2.38	29.8	24	5.8	914
Total						6,697						8,987

Height, 0–100 m	Area, m²	SHGC	Solar, W/m²	Energy, W	Total	Area, m²	SHGC	Solar, W/m²	Energy, W	Total
South elevation glass	136	0.4	459	24,970	31,666	221	0.4	459	40,554	49,541

INFILTRATION

The quality of construction is important as the joints between windows and masonry or concrete façade of the building must be properly sealed to minimize infiltration and exfiltration, which is of particular concern in buildings. Ventilation can be used to control infiltration by pressurizing the lower floors during the heating season and the upper floors during the cooling season. The use of heat recovery or enthalpy heat recovery between the ventilation air and exhaust air should be considered in energy simulations.

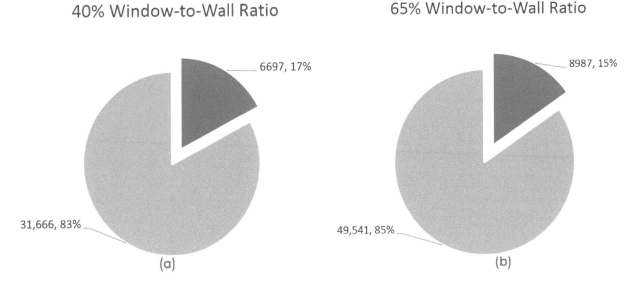

Figure 3.6 Percentage heat gain from the glazing and the percentage of heat gain from the façade for (a) 40% and (b) 65% window-to-wall ratio façade.

Table 3.5 Steady-State Load Calculations for Summer and Winter (I-P)

		Floor Area, ft^2	Window-to-Wall Ratio, %	Solar Radiation, Btu/h	Transmission, Btu/h	Total, Btu/h	Envelope Load as a Function of Floor Area, Btu/ft^2
To code	Summer	21,360	40	86,722	25,967	112,689	5.28
Proposed	Summer	21,360	65	140,923	34,871	175,794	8.23
To code	Winter	21,360	40		−137,448	−137,448	−6.43
Proposed	Winter	21,360	65		−184,576	−184,576	−8.64

Table 3.5 Steady-State Load Calculations for Summer and Winter (SI)

		Floor Area, m^2	Window-to-Wall Ratio, %	Solar Radiation, W	Transmission, W	Total, W	Envelope Load as a Function of Floor Area, W/m^2
To code	Summer	1944	40	24,970	6,697	31,666	19.73
Proposed	Summer	1944	65	40,554	8,987	49,541	25.48
To code	Winter	1944	40		−38,449	−38,449	−19.78
Proposed	Winter	1944	65		−51,596	−51,596	−26.54

FAÇADE LEAKAGE RATES

Envelope leakage in commercial buildings depends on HVAC system operation. Often, commercial buildings and their HVAC systems are in operation during normal daytime business hours but switch into "unoccupied" operation at night and on weekends and holidays. If pressurized while their HVAC systems operate, infiltration is often very low or even eliminated in buildings with tight envelopes. However, in unoccupied mode, this pressurization is often lost, so infiltration and potentially moisture intrusion may sometimes be significant.

There has been very little information made available regarding the vertical climatic effects on a building's heating and cooling loads by infiltration. How do these effects affect the performance of the building?

The 2012 IECC includes several requirements related to air sealing. The analysis in this section is based on IECC Section 502.4.1.2.3—Building Test. The IECC requires an air leakage test of the completed building having a leakage rate of not more than 0.40 cfm/ft^2 at 0.3 in. w.g. (2.0 L/s·m^2 at 75 Pa).

A report by Pacific Northwest National Laboratory (PNNL) (Gowri et al. 2009) documents information from the Envelope Subcommittee of ASHRAE SSPC90.1. This committee also investigated the possibility of including an air sealing requirement in Standard 90.1. The Envelope Subcommittee recommended a value of 1.8 cfm/ft^2 at 0.3 in. w.g. (9.0 L/s.m^2 at 75 Pa) as a baseline leakage rate (the "before" case). Gowri et al. state that this rate corresponds to the base infiltration rate used in the DOE Benchmark buildings.

Thus, we have two different recommendations:

- 0.40 cfm/ft^2 at 0.3 in. w.g. (2.0 L/s·m^2 at 75 Pa)
- 1.8 cfm/ft^2 at 0.3 in. w.g. (9.0 L/s.m^2 at 75 Pa)

It is possible to convert miles per hour (mph) (kph) to pressure and then calculate the leakage associated with that pressure. Figure 3.7 shows the calculated leakage rates for a 2700 ft (800 m) megatall building façade, calculated for 0.40 cfm/ft^2 @ 0.3 in. w.g. and 1.8 cfm/ft^2 at 0.3 in. w.g. (2.0 L/s·m^2 at 75 Pa and 9.0 L/s·m^2 at 75 Pa) at about 560 ft (273 m) for a façade specified at 0.40 cfm/ft^2 (2.0 L/s·m^2) leakage. The maximum leakage rate is reached, at any height above this the façade leakage rate will exceed the specified limit.

This is important because the actual outside air infiltration will be much higher than specified, and someone will need to be responsible for the increase in infiltration in the designs. They must decide to what pressure should the façade be tested to and determine what outside air infiltration rate should be included in the heating and cooling load calculations.

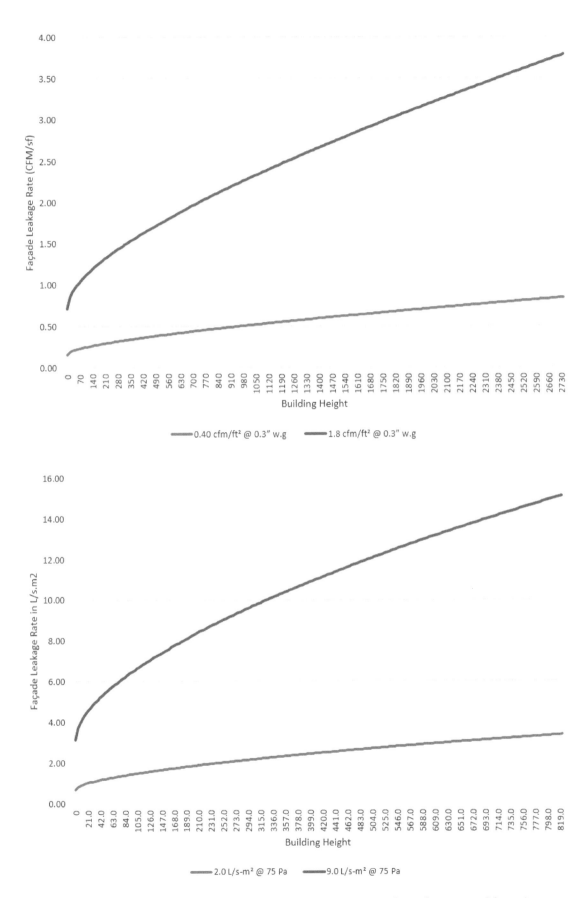

Figure 3.7 Equivalent leakage rates calculated from the wind speed in cfm (L/s) of façade area.

CHAPTER 4
Climate Data

CLIMATE AND THE ATMOSPHERE

The design of tall buildings has historically relied on ground measurements for climate data. In some cases, the climate information at grade has been extrapolated upwards. However, as buildings have become taller the need for elevation-specific meteorological data is becoming more important. This is especially relevant when the balance between sustainability and cost depends on good climate data to correctly size the HVAC equipment. The climate at 328 ft (100 m) above grade is not the same as 2000 ft (600 m). However, rarely does the design of the upper level of the building capitalize on that difference. Further, wind conditions at the top of a tall building are different. If sufficient data are known about this difference, it can be accounted for the design.

EXTRAPOLATING GROUND DATA UPWARDS

ASHRAE Handbook—Fundamentals, Chapter 14, Climatic Design Information, describes the U.S. standard atmosphere, which is used to estimate properties at various levels based on sea level conditions (ASHRAE 2017a). In this document, pressure is described as having a polynomial relationship with altitude, and temperature is linear. The linear parameter on temperature is referred to as *lapse rate* and it is approximately –0.35°F per 100 ft (–0.65°C per 100 m) altitude gain.

For wind engineering, the relationship between wind speed and elevation above ground is reasonably well understood for the first several hundred feet (meters). That relationship is typically described as a *power* or *log relationship* with parameters defining the ground roughness. Terms such as *open terrain* and *suburban* describe the different shapes of the wind speed profile as shown in Figure 4.1.

However, often this wind speed relationship is not appropriate, such as during thunderstorms or other wind events. In addition, the presence of terrain will make this extrapolation invalid.

The challenge with using extrapolations for temperature, pressure, and wind is that it is not clear that they are appropriate simultaneously. For example, rain will change the conditions through the atmosphere. Hence, the use of simple parameters is not viable for accurate analysis of conditions at altitude.

GENERATING CLIMATE DATA AT UPPER ELEVATIONS

One means to generate climate data above the ground for building design is to do one of the following:

- Measure it through remote sensing technologies or balloon releases
- Model it using weather forecasting techniques

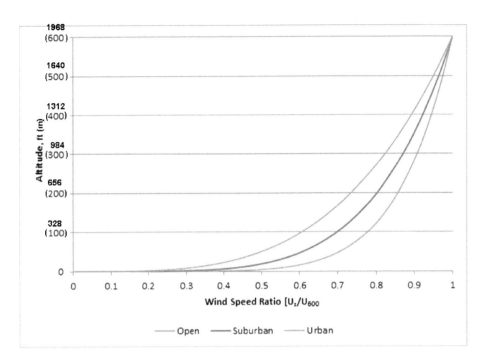

Figure 4.1 Wind speed profile for different ground roughness.

The use of remote sensing offers direct measurements, and the measurement protocol can be established to take simultaneous ground and elevated measurements. The options for sensing climate variables above grade include lidar, weather balloons, and satellites although some methods (e.g., satellites) measure temperature indirectly.

Climate modeling, such as that conducted by weather services, can also be used to generate climate data for the past. The advantage of this is that measurements at different weather stations can be used to seed the simulations. This means that the climate modeling tool is used to fill in the spaces between weather stations. The advantage of this approach for building design is that it can be used to recreate weather records for any location on the planet, including different elevations. Through the use of measured climate variables, the data generated by the simulations is based on actual measurements.

CLIMATE MODELING USING MESOSCALE NUMERICAL TECHNIQUES

There are different modeling tools available, typically referred to as mesoscale numerical weather prediction systems. They serve for both operational weather forecasting and atmospheric research needs. They are based on solving the fundamental equations of atmospheric motion on a 3-D grid, which includes representations of terrain and land use in the modeling.

The modeling can incorporate parameterizations for various grid scale and subgrid scale physical processes that influence atmospheric conditions, such as boundary layer turbulence, deep convection and cloud formation, precipitation, radiation, surface heat transfer, and moisture flux. Thus, various weather conditions, including sea breeze events, ground-level fog, and vertical wind shears can be detected. Further, the models contain physics for resolving turbulence structures in the atmospheric boundary layer. The modeling is not exactly the same as computational fluid dynamic (CFD) modeling, because of the scales involved, but the process is similar.

The results in Figures 4.2 and 4.3 present a comparison for Dubai and Toronto at grade and 2000 ft (600 m) in the air. The comparison shows how the temperatures and wind conditions vary.

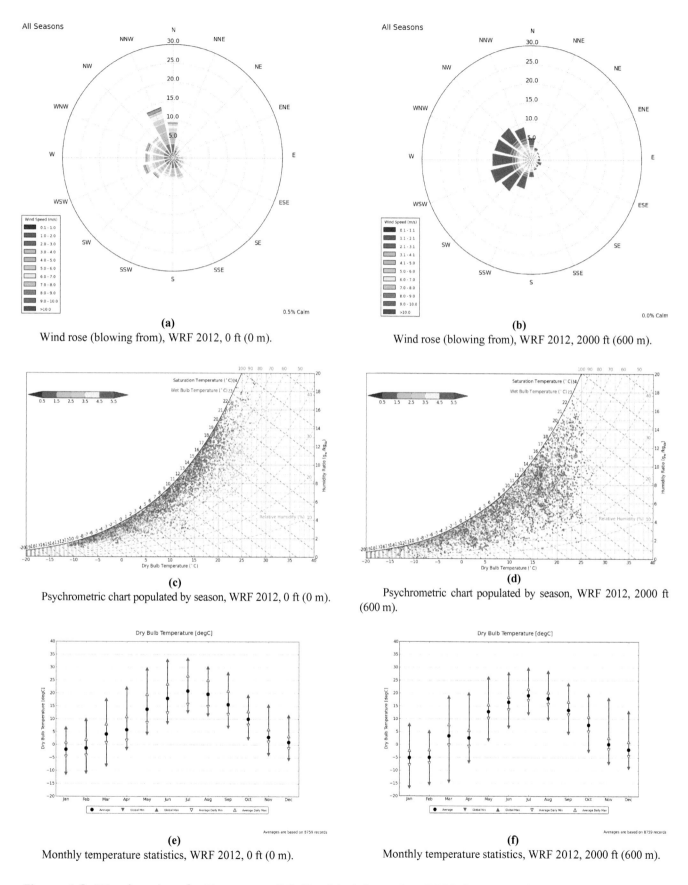

(a)
Wind rose (blowing from), WRF 2012, 0 ft (0 m).

(b)
Wind rose (blowing from), WRF 2012, 2000 ft (600 m).

(c)
Psychrometric chart populated by season, WRF 2012, 0 ft (0 m).

(d)
Psychrometric chart populated by season, WRF 2012, 2000 ft (600 m).

(e)
Monthly temperature statistics, WRF 2012, 0 ft (0 m).

(f)
Monthly temperature statistics, WRF 2012, 2000 ft (600 m).

Figure 4.2 Weather data for Toronto at 0 ft (0 m) height and at 2000 ft (600 m) height.

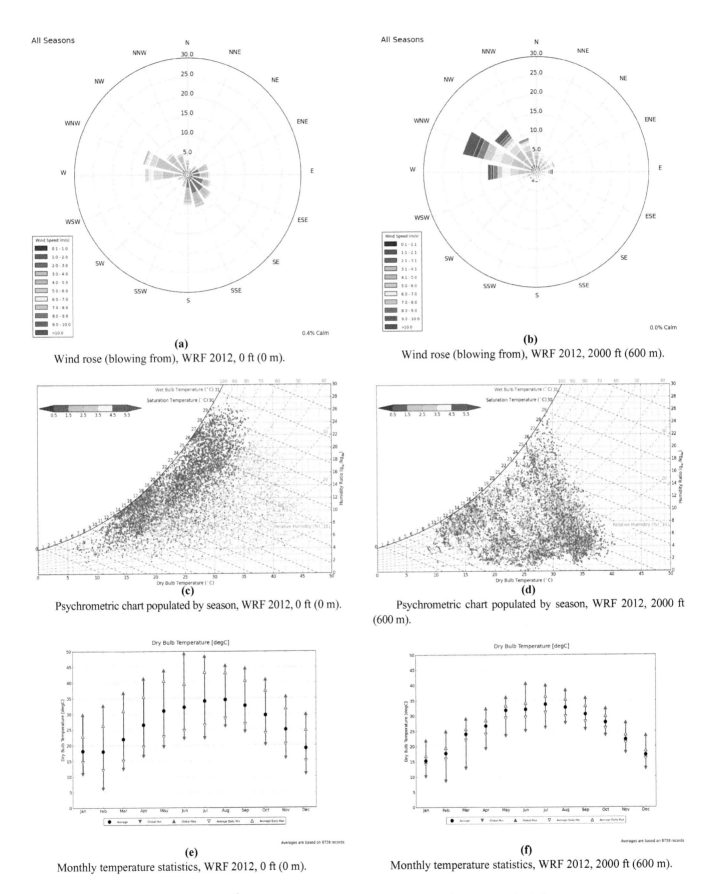

(a)
Wind rose (blowing from), WRF 2012, 0 ft (0 m).

(b)
Wind rose (blowing from), WRF 2012, 2000 ft (600 m).

(c)
Psychrometric chart populated by season, WRF 2012, 0 ft (0 m).

(d)
Psychrometric chart populated by season, WRF 2012, 2000 ft (600 m).

(e)
Monthly temperature statistics, WRF 2012, 0 ft (0 m).

(f)
Monthly temperature statistics, WRF 2012, 2000 ft (600 m).

Figure 4.3 Weather data for Dubai at 0 ft (0 m) height and 2000 ft (600 m) height.

CLIMATE ANALYSIS CASE STUDY

Outdoor and Indoor Air Temperature

Heating and cooling design temperatures can be identified using meteorological trends, such as ASHRAE weather data (ASHRAE 2017a).

For this example (Table 4.1), we have chosen the 99.6% range for winter (11.5°F [–11.4°C]) and the 0.4% range for summer (89.8°F [32°C]).

For most calculations in the chapter we will use absolute temperatures; therefore, –11.1 + 273.1 = 262 K (470.77 R) for the winter and 32 + 273.1 = 305.1 K (549.47 R) for the summer.

The height of the building under consideration must also be extrapolated. To obtain external temperatures we use the following formula:

$$T = T_G - 0.0033h \tag{4.1a}$$

$$T = T_G - 0.00649h \tag{4.1b}$$

where

T = temperature at height h, ft (m)

Table 4.1 Climate Data for Seoul, South Korea

SEOUL CITY, Korea, Republic of   WMO#: 471080

Lat: 37.567N   Long: 126.967E   Elev: 285   StdP: 14.54   Time Zone: 9.00 (JPN)   Period: 90-14   WBAN: 99999

Annual Heating and Humidification Design Conditions

Coldest Month	Heating DB		Humidification DP/MCDB and HR						Coldest month WS/MCDB				MCWS/PCWD to 99.6% DB	
	99.6%	99%	99.6%			99%			0.4%		1%			
			DP	HR	MCDB	DP	HR	MCDB	WS	MCDB	WS	MCDB	MCWS	PCWD
(a)	(b)	(c)	(d)	(e)	(f)	(g)	(h)	(i)	(j)	(k)	(l)	(m)	(n)	(o)
1	11.5	15.2	-8.7	3.5	16.8	-4.9	4.3	19.3	16.3	26.6	14.4	26.2	6.4	290

Annual Cooling, Dehumidification, and Enthalpy Design Conditions

Hottest Month	Hottest Month DB Range	Cooling DB/MCWB						Evaporation WB/MCDB						MCWS/PCWD to 0.4% DB	
		0.4%		1%		2%		0.4%		1%		2%			
		DB	MCWB	DB	MCWB	DB	MCWB	WB	MCDB	WB	MCDB	WB	MCDB	MCWS	PCWD
(a)	(b)	(c)	(d)	(e)	(f)	(g)	(h)	(i)	(j)	(k)	(l)	(m)	(n)	(o)	(p)
8	11.3	89.8	75.4	87.6	73.9	85.5	72.9	78.6	85.5	77.2	83.7	76.1	82.4	6.6	270

Dehumidification DP/MCDB and HR									Enthalpy/MCDB						Extreme Max WB
0.4%			1%			2%			0.4%		1%		2%		
DP	HR	MCDB	DP	HR	MCDB	DP	HR	MCDB	Enth	MCDB	Enth	MCDB	Enth	MCDB	
(a)	(b)	(c)	(d)	(e)	(f)	(g)	(h)	(i)	(j)	(k)	(l)	(m)	(n)	(o)	(p)
76.7	140.5	82.1	75.3	134.0	81.0	74.1	128.7	80.1	42.4	85.9	40.9	83.6	39.8	82.6	84.4

(I-P)

SEOUL CITY, Korea, Republic of   WMO#: 471080

Lat: 37.567N   Long: 126.967E   Elev: 87   StdP: 100.28   Time Zone: 9.00 (JPN)   Period: 90-14   WBAN: 99999

Annual Heating and Humidification Design Conditions

Coldest Month	Heating DB		Humidification DP/MCDB and HR						Coldest month WS/MCDB				MCWS/PCWD to 99.6% DB	
	99.6%	99%	99.6%			99%			0.4%		1%			
			DP	HR	MCDB	DP	HR	MCDB	WS	MCDB	WS	MCDB	MCWS	PCWD
(a)	(b)	(c)	(d)	(e)	(f)	(g)	(h)	(i)	(j)	(k)	(l)	(m)	(n)	(o)
1	-11.4	-9.3	-22.6	0.5	-8.4	-20.5	0.6	-7.0	7.3	-3.0	6.4	-3.2	2.9	290

Annual Cooling, Dehumidification, and Enthalpy Design Conditions

Hottest Month	Hottest Month DB Range	Cooling DB/MCWB						Evaporation WB/MCDB						MCWS/PCWD to 0.4% DB	
		0.4%		1%		2%		0.4%		1%		2%			
		DB	MCWB	DB	MCWB	DB	MCWB	WB	MCDB	WB	MCDB	WB	MCDB	MCWS	PCWD
(a)	(b)	(c)	(d)	(e)	(f)	(g)	(h)	(i)	(j)	(k)	(l)	(m)	(n)	(o)	(p)
8	6.3	32.1	24.1	30.9	23.3	29.7	22.7	25.9	29.7	25.1	28.7	24.5	28.0	3.0	270

Dehumidification DP/MCDB and HR									Enthalpy/MCDB						Extreme Max WB
0.4%			1%			2%			0.4%		1%		2%		
DP	HR	MCDB	DP	HR	MCDB	DP	HR	MCDB	Enth	MCDB	Enth	MCDB	Enth	MCDB	
(a)	(b)	(c)	(d)	(e)	(f)	(g)	(h)	(i)	(j)	(k)	(l)	(m)	(n)	(o)	(p)
24.8	20.1	27.8	24.1	19.1	27.2	23.4	18.4	26.7	80.7	30.0	77.3	28.7	74.8	28.1	29.1

(SI)

T_G =   temperature at ground level, °F (°C)

h =   height from ground level, ft (m)

The next step is to determine the external pressure vertically with the building height.

$$P = 14,696(1 - 6.8754 \times 10^{-5} \times Z)^{5.2559} \tag{4.2a}$$

$$P = 101,325(1 - 2.25577 \times 10^{-5} \times H)^{5.25588} \tag{4.2b}$$

where

P =   pressure, psi (kPa)

Figure 4.4 shows the decrease in external temperature for an 2000 ft (600 m) building in summer, when the outside temperature is 89.6°F (32°C) at the building base. Figure 4.5 shows the decrease in external temperature with building height for an 600 m (2000 ft) tall building in winter, when the outside temperature is 42°F (6°C).

Figure 4.6 shows the decrease in external pressure in psia (kPa) with building height for an 2000 ft (600 m) tall building in summer, when the outdoor temperature is 89.6°F (32°C). Figure 4.7 shows the decrease in external pressure in psia (kPa) with building height for an 2000 ft (600 m) tall building in winter, when the outdoor temperature is 42°F (6°C).

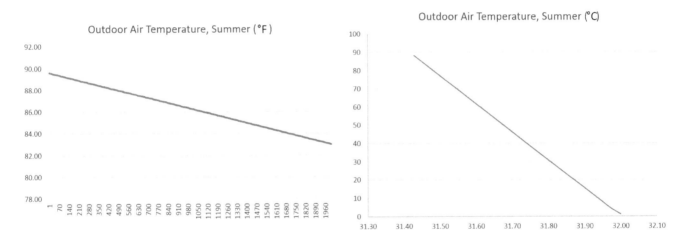

Figure 4.4 Decrease in external temperature for a 2000 ft (600 m) building when the outdoor temperature is 89.6°F (32°C) at the building base.

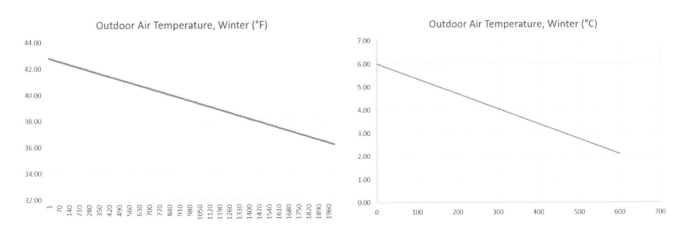

Figure 4.5 Decrease in external temperature for a 2000 ft (600 m) building when the outdoor temperature is 42°F (6°C) at the building base.

Now that the external pressure is known, it is possible to determine the density of the air vertically with the height of the building. For this we use the following formula:

$$\rho = P_{abs} / [0.2869(T + 273.1)] \qquad (4.3)$$

where

T =   absolute temperature, K

P_{abs} =   absolute pressure, Pa

ρ =   air density, lb/ft^3 (kg/m^3)

Figure 4.8 shows the external air density at different heights over the building height of 2000 ft (600 m) in summer. Figure 4.9 shows the external air density at different heights over the building height of (600 m) in winter.

The indoor air temperature for this example is assumed to be a constant 297.1 K (24°C)

Wind Speed and Pressure

Wind data are generally obtained from a meteorological station located away from an urban environment. In general, this wind speed must be corrected for terrain conditions and for the height of the building relative to the height of wind measurement (usually 10 m [66 ft]). An approximate correction is given as (CIBSE 2015):

$$V_z = V_m \, k \, z^a \qquad (4.4)$$

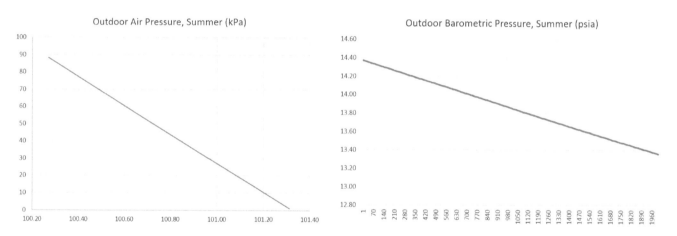

Figure 4.6 Decrease in external pressure in psia (kPa) with building height for an 2000 ft (600 m) tall building when the outdoor temperature is 89.6°F (32°C).

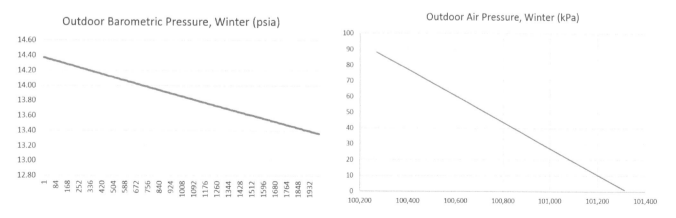

Figure 4.7 Decrease in external pressure in kPa (psia) with building height for a 2000 ft (600 m) tall building when the outdoor temperature is 42°F (6°C).

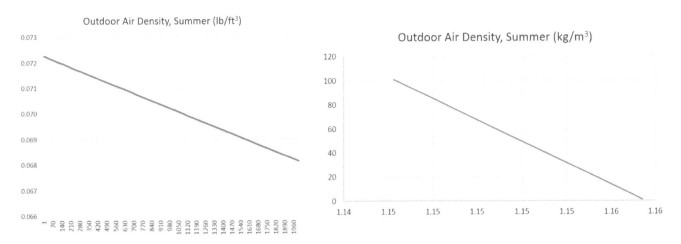

Figure 4.8 External air density at different heights over the height of a 2000 ft (600 m) tall building in the summer.

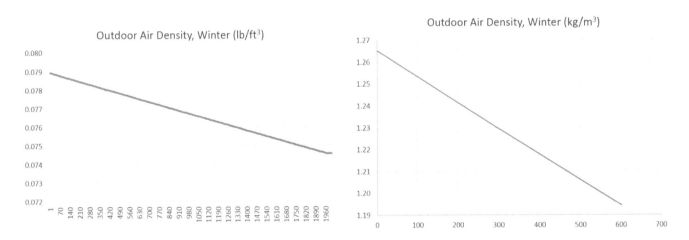

Figure 4.9 External air density at different heights over the height of a 2000 ft (600 m) tall building in the winter.

Table 4.2 Wind Speed Terrain Constants

Terrain Category	k	a
Open, flat country	0.68	0.17
Country with scattered wind breaks	0.52	0.20
Urban	0.35	0.25
City	0.21	0.33

where

V_z =   wind speed at the building height, fpm (m·s-1)

V_m =   wind speed measures in open country at a height of 33 ft (10 m), fpm (m·s-1)

z =   building height, ft (m)

k and a=   constants dependent on the terrain (see Table 4.2)

Figure 4.10 shows the wind speed at different heights of the 290 ft (88 m) tall building

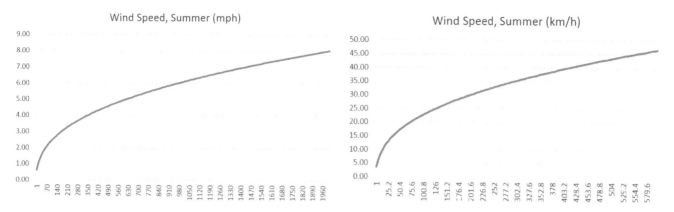

Figure 4.10 Wind speed at different heights of the 2000 ft (600 m) tall building in the summer.

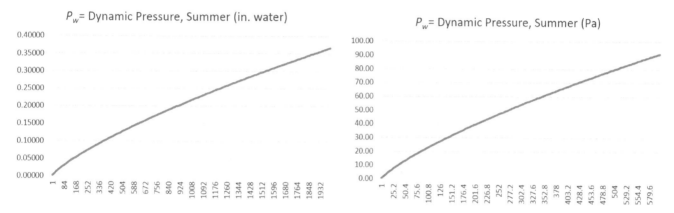

Figure 4.11 Dynamic pressure (in. water [Pa]) as a result of the outdoor air speed increasing with building height.

When impinging the surface of a rectangular building, wind deflection induces a positive pressure on the upwind face. The flow then separates at the corners, resulting in negative pressure regions being developed along the sides of the building. A negative pressure distribution is also developed along the rear facing or leeward façade (CIBSE 2015).

The magnitude of the wind pressure coefficient at any point for any given wind direction can generally be regarded as independent of the wind speed. Relative to the static pressure of the free wind, the time-averaged pressure acting on any point on the surface of a building may be represented by the following equation:

$$P_w = 0.5\,\rho V_z^2 \tag{4.5}$$

Figure 4.11 shows how the dynamic pressure as a result of the outside airspeed increases with building height.

In addition to flow patterns described previously, the turbulence or gustiness of approaching wind and the unsteady character of separated flows cause surface pressures to fluctuate. Pressures discussed here are time-averaged values, with a full-scale averaging period of about 600 s. This is approximately the shortest time period considered to be a steady-state condition when considering atmospheric winds; the longest is typically 3600 s. Instantaneous pressures may vary significantly above and below these averages, and peak pressures two or three times the mean values are possible. Peak pressures are important with regard to structural loads and mean values are more appropriate for computing infiltration and ventilation rates. Time-averaged surface pressures are proportional to wind velocity pressure P_v given by Bernoulli's equation (ASHRAE 2017a):

$$P_v = \frac{\rho_a U_H^2}{2}/2.152 \qquad\qquad (4.6a)$$

$$P_v = \frac{\rho_a U_H^2}{2}/2 \qquad\qquad (4.6b)$$

where

P_v = wind velocity pressure at roof level, lb/ft^2 (Pa)

U_H = approach wind speed at upwind wall height H, mph (m/s) (see Equation 4.8)

ρ_a = ambient (outdoor) air density, lb/ft^3 (kg/m^3)

The proportional relationship is shown in the following equation, in which the difference P_s between the pressure on the building surface and the local outdoor atmospheric pressure at the same level in an undisturbed wind approaching the building is

$$P_s = C_p\, p_v \qquad\qquad (4.7)$$

where

C_p =   local wind pressure coefficient at a point on the building surface

Approach Wind Speed

The local wind speed U_H at the top of the wall required for Equation 4.6 is estimated by applying terrain and height corrections to the hourly wind speed U_{met} from a nearby meteorological station.

U_{met} is generally measured in flat, open terrain (see Category 3 in Table 4.3). The anemometer that records U_{met} is located at height H_{met}, usually 33 ft (10 m) above ground level. The hourly average wind speed U_H in the undisturbed wind approaching a building in its local terrain can be calculated from U_{met} as follows (Faure 2018):

$$U_H = U_{met}\left(\frac{\delta_{met}}{H_{met}}\right)^{a_{met}}\left(\frac{H}{\delta}\right)^{a} \qquad\qquad (4.8)$$

The atmospheric boundary layer thickness δ and exponent a for the local building terrain and a_{met} and δ_{met} for the meteorological station are determined from Table 4.3. Typical values for meteorological stations (Category 3 in Table 4.3) are $a_{met} = 0.14$ and $\delta_{met} = 890$ ft (270 m). The values and terrain categories in Table 4.3 are consistent with those adopted in other engineering applications (e.g., ASCE Standard 7 [ASCE 2010]). Equation 4.8 gives the wind speed that occurs at a certain height H above the average height of local obstacles, such as buildings

Table 4.3 Atmospheric Boundary Layer Parameters

Terrain Category	Description	Exponent a	Layer Thickness δ ft (δ m)
1	Large city centers, in which at least 50% of buildings are higher than 82 ft (25 m), over a distance of at least 0.5 mi (0.8 km) or 10 times the height of the structure upwind, whichever is greater	0.33	1500 (460)
2	Urban and suburban areas, wooded areas, or another terrain with numerous closely spaced obstructions having the size of single-family dwellings or larger, over a distance of at least 1509 ft (460 m) or 10 times the height of the structure upwind, whichever is greater	0.22	1200 (370)
3	Open terrain with scattered obstructions having heights generally less than 30 ft (9 m), including flat open country typical of meteorological station surroundings	0.14	900 (270)
4	Flat, unobstructed areas exposed to wind flowing over water for at least 1 mi (1.6 km), over a distance of 1509 ft (460 m) or 10 times the height of the structure inland, whichever is greater	0.1	700 (210)

and vegetation, weighted by the plan area. At heights at or below this average obstacle height (e.g., at roof height in densely built-up suburbs), speed depends on the geometrical arrangement of the buildings, and Equation 4.8 is less reliable (ASHRAE 2017a).

An alternative mathematical description of the atmospheric boundary layer, which uses a logarithmic function, is given by Deaves and Harris (1978). Although their model is more complicated than the power law used in Equation 4.8, it more closely models the real physics of the atmosphere and has been adopted by several codes around the world (e.g., SA/SNZ 2002).

Example 1. Assuming a 23 mph (10 m/s) anemometer wind speed for a height H_{met} of 33 ft (10 m) at a nearby airport, determine the wind speed U_H at roof level $H = 50$ ft (15 m) above grade for a building located in a city suburb.

Solution. From Table 4.3, the atmospheric boundary layer properties for the anemometer are $a_{met} = 0.14$ and $\delta_{met} = 270$ m (890 ft). The atmospheric boundary layer properties at the building site are $a = 0.22$ and $\delta = 1200$ ft (370 m). Using Equation 4.8, wind speed U_H at 50 ft (15 m) is

$$U_H = 23(890/33)^{0.14} (50/1200)^{0.22} = 18.2 \text{ mph} \tag{4.9a}$$

$$U_H = 10(270/10)^{0.14} (15/370)^{0.22} = 7.8 \text{ m/s} \tag{4.9b}$$

Figure 4.12 shows the local wind speed for different heights for different meteorological weather wind speeds data at 33 ft (10 m).

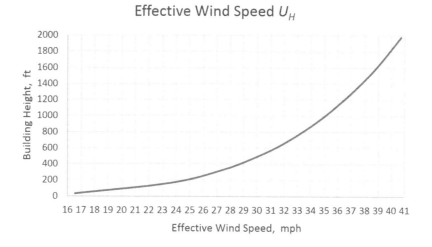

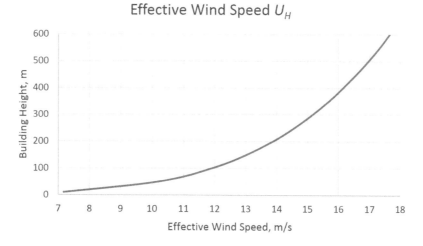

Figure 4.12 Local wind speed (in mph [m/s]) at different heights for different meteorological weather wind speed data at 33 ft (10 m).

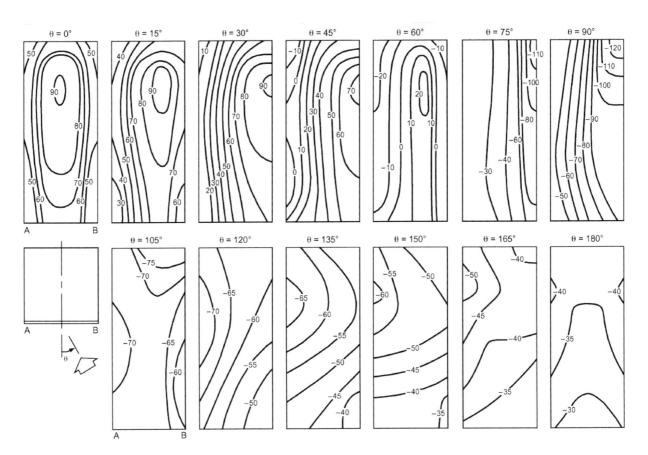

Figure 4.13 Local pressure coefficients ($Cp*100$) for high-rise buildings with varying wind direction. (Davenport and Hui 1982)

WIND PRESSURE

Wind pressure is derived from wind speed. First, one must determine the wind speed to calculate the wind pressure:

$$P_w = 0.5\ \rho\ C_p\ V_z^2 \tag{4.10}$$

where

P_w = surface pressure due to wind, lb/ft^2 (Pa)

ρ = density of air, lb$_m$/ft^3 (kg/m^3)

C_p = wind pressure coefficient at a given position on the building surface

V_z = mean wind velocity at height z, ft (m)

Figure 4.13 shows local pressure coefficients (Davenport and Hui 1982). Figure 4.14 shows surface-averaged roof pressure coefficients. Figure 4.15 shows surfaced-averaged wall pressure coefficients.

The wind pressure coefficient C_p is derived from the wind direction and the building's surface. It is difficult to derive this wind pressure coefficient and is typically reliant upon a wind tunnel test using a scale model of the building and its habitat.

The wind pressure coefficient is typically expressed as a mean value for each building surface. The data produced does not usually take surrounding obstacles that could protect the building from the wind into account. Please consult *A Guide to Energy Efficient Ventilation* (AIVC 1996) for mean surface values relative to various degrees of protection and wind direction.

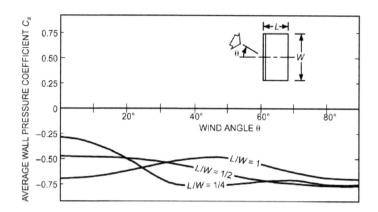

Figure 4.14 Surface-averaged roof pressure coefficients for tall buildings.
(ASHRAE 2017a)

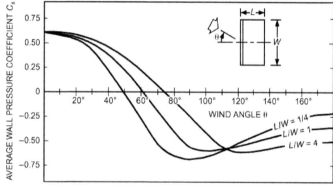

Figure 4.15 Surfaced-averaged wall pressure coefficients.
(Akins et al. 1979)

This reliability of this mean data for tall, supertall and megatall buildings is reduced because the pressure distribution can vary relative to the height of the building. Some test data for high-rise buildings have been published by Bowen (1976). For a single-sided pressure analysis, average data should not be used because of the relationship between wind pressure and the height of the façade, which can vary dramatically. It is recommended that accurate wind tunnel testing of the building and its habitat be carried out (CIBSE 2015).

The wind speed V_z is always expressed as a value for a given building height z. Since this term is raised to the power two in the pressure calculation, it is imperative that remote weather station data are corrected for terrain and building height as described by Equation 4.4. The use of unadjusted weather data may result in considerable overestimation of air infiltration or natural ventilation rates.

The procedure for calculating wind pressure at any location on the building surface may be accomplished as follows:

• Determine building height

• Determine nature of surrounding terrain

• Correct meteorological wind speed data according to building height and terrain classification (Equation 4.10)

• Determine the approximate wind pressure coefficient (Figure 4.13) for each face or for each opening in the building envelope or undertake wind tunnel studies if more accurate values of wind pressure coefficient are required.

Turbulent Fluctuations

Atmospheric wind is turbulent, which results in variations in wind pressures and their distribution. These variations cover a wide range, with the most prominent variations coming from local terrain roughness and the directions of an eddy shedding upwind. Transient variations of pressure distribution cannot be represented by steady-state pressure coefficients and are not considered in computational mathematical studies. It has been shown in some experimental instances that pressure variations provide an added component to the infiltration rate. This occurrence is can occur when there is a small mean pressure difference over an opening relative to the size of the varying component. Fluctuating air can then move freely through a building envelope and mix with the internal air volume. Openings can be located on opposite sides of a building. Should the wind pressure be parallel to the openings, the average wind pressure on both sides will be virtually equal, producing a steady-state flow of zero infiltration, but air mixture may occur in practice.

For tall, supertall, and megatall buildings, the distribution of wind pressure against a façade can vary considerably as the pressure is a function of the wind speed. This problem can be overcome using local pressure coefficients to define the wind pressure at any specific location on the building face. Unfortunately, alternative definitions of this parameter exist, none of which are interchangeable.

The first possibility is to retain the concept of a reference wind speed height but to specify individual coefficients on each face of the building according to an array or network of points. This is the method chosen by Bowen (1976), who has published a complete data set of local wind pressure coefficients for a 2:1 rectangular shaped wind tunnel building surrounded by obstructions of varying size.

An alternative approach is suggested by Akin et al. (1979) who attempted to express the vertical pressure distribution by a single "local" pressure coefficient. It is defined by the equation (CIBSE 2015)

$$(P_w)_z = \frac{\rho}{2} * C_{pi} * V_x^2 \qquad (4.11)$$

where

P_w =   surface pressure at height z due to wind, lb/ft^2 (Pa)

C_p =   pressure coefficient

V =   mean wind velocity, fpm (m/s)

In other words, the pressure is based on the wind speed in the approach flow at the height of the location of interest and not building height. Clearly, the resultant pressure coefficient is very much different to that used by Bowen (1976) or as used in several wind pressure codes.

When the wind blows, the external pressure around the opening is changed by the pressure due to the wind, P_{wi}, adding to the hydrostatic pressure, and the pressure drop equation becomes:

$$\Delta_{pi} = P_{E0} - P_{I0} - \Delta\rho_0 \, g \, z_i + P_{wi} \qquad (4.12)$$

P_{wi} =   pressure of the wind at the point on the envelope at which opening i lies, lb/ft^2 (Pa)

P_{E0} =   external pressure at ground level

P_{I0} =   internal pressure at ground level

$\Delta\rho_0$ =   the density difference at ground level

g =   gravitational force

z_i =   height of the opening i above ground

The density difference is defined by

$$\Delta\rho_0 = \rho_E - \rho_I \qquad (4.13)$$

where ρ_E and ρ_I are the densities of the external and internal air, respectively.

If the density of the internal air varies with height, then

$$\Delta p_i = P_E - P_I - \rho_E g z_i + g \int_0^{z_i} \rho_I dz \qquad (4.14)$$

Equation 4.14 allows non-uniform density distributions (as can occur with atria, for example) to be dealt with.

It is common practice to obtain P_{wi} from wind tunnel tests where wind pressures are quoted in the form of the pressure coefficient:

$$C_{pi} = \frac{P_{wi} - P_{ref}}{0.5 \rho U^2} \qquad (4.15)$$

where P_{ref} is a reference pressure (Pa) and U is the wind speed (mph [m·s–1]).

Thus, the pressure difference across an opening whose inlet or outlet is situated in the external flow can be written as:

$$\Delta P_i = P_{EO} - P_{IO} - p_{ref} - \Delta \rho_0 \, g z_i + 0.5 \rho U^2 \, C_{pi} \qquad (4.16)$$

The treatment of wind effect involves several assumptions. For example, the size of the opening is assumed to be small enough for the value of P_{wi} obtained from a point measurement on a wind tunnel model to be appropriate.

$$\Delta P_i = \Delta p_0 - \Delta p_0 \, g z_i + 0.5 p_0 \, U^2 \, C_{pi} \qquad (4.17)$$

Equation 4.17 is the same as Equation 4.16 except that $(P - P - p)$ has been denoted by Δp for brevity.

Although the bracket encloses three terms, it is only the internal pressure P_{I0} that is a variable; P_{EO} and P_{ref} are constant for a given analysis.

For the general case of N openings there are two $N + 1$ equations. The unknowns are qi, Δpi and Δpo. The equations can be solved by determining the value of Δpo at which the continuity equation is satisfied. In physical terms, when the ventilation pattern of a building is changed from one steady state to another (e.g., by opening a window), the internal pressure adjusts until the flows through the openings are such that the continuity equation is again satisfied. Mathematically this adjustment is done by an iterative procedure. When the equations are solved in this way it is referred to as an implicit method. The equations can be solved directly (i.e., without the need for iteration) by specifying the value of Δpi and the values of qi (magnitude and direction) to find the values of Ai that give that flow pattern. When solved in this way, the model is referred to as an *explicit method*. This method is particularly useful in the initial design stages for sizing openings, such that the openings give the required flow rates under a specified design condition. Using these areas, the implicit procedure can then be used for off-design calculation of flow rates (CIBSE 2005).

The explicit procedure is easy to use for openings with a constant discharge coefficient, i.e., one that does not vary with flow rate (Reynolds number). Most purpose-provided openings fall into this category and manual calculations are not difficult. The explicit procedure is not appropriate for adventitious openings because such openings cannot be sized in the same way as air vents and windows. Implicit methods are more appropriate for dealing with adventitious openings because the effect of assumptions about the size and distribution of the adventitious leakage can be quickly assessed. Although envelope flow models can account for adventitious openings, this is not feasible with physical models, because of the very small dimensions of the openings at model scale. Nor is it practically feasible with computational fluid dynamics (CFD), because of the need to specify the detailed geometry of many small openings. Most CFD packages will allow special inlet and outlet flows to be specified as boundary conditions and adventitious openings could be dealt with in this way. Envelope flow models are best suited for dealing with openings with unidirectional flow.

External Wind Pressures

Wind pressures are usually expressed in the form of a pressure coefficient, Cpi, defined by Equation 4.18.

$$C_{pi} = \frac{P_{wi} - P_{ref}}{0.5\rho U^2} \qquad (4.18)$$

where P_{ref} is a reference pressure (Pa) and U is the wind speed (mph [m·s–1]).

The reason for this is that, unlike p_{wi}, C_{pi} does not vary greatly with wind speed. This is primarily because sharp edges on the building fix the positions of flow separation. Thus, for a given building shape and surrounding environment (which determines the characteristics of the approaching wind) the C_{pi} distribution depends only on wind direction and the position of the point where wind speed (U) is measured. Surface pressure coefficients for different generic building forms are available. Pressure coefficients for specific buildings can be estimated from these generalized data sets or they can be generated from wind tunnel studies or, possibly, by CFD.

In general terms, the pressure coefficient of an unobstructed building surface is positive on façades facing the wind and negative on other surfaces. The negative pressures are often associated with flow separation. This means that roofs with slopes less than 30° are usually in a low-pressure region, irrespective of wind direction. Positive pressures may be experienced on roofs of greater pitch, or on deep, flat-roofed buildings where flow reattachment may occur.

The data on wind pressure coefficients are extensive and reference must be made elsewhere for further information.

It is important that the correct value of wind speed (U) is used when evaluating pwi, because it is proportional to U^2, and, in the absence of buoyancy, flow rates are proportional to U. The C_{pi} data set should specify the height at which the reference wind speed was measured and the nature of the terrain surrounding the building. The designer will probably not have wind speed records reference position and it is then necessary to estimate the values of U from the data available, e.g., from ASHRAE Weather Data records for a site that could be far away from the building.

The uncertainty associated with determining wind pressures is another reason why the treatment of ventilation due to wind is less precise than for buoyancy alone. It may be worthwhile to assess how important the effects of wind are to the design compared to buoyancy. In this connection it can be noted that, for a summer design condition, the wind is likely to be less important than buoyancy because the main problem is to achieve adequate ventilation under no-wind conditions. For a winter design condition, when the temperature difference is large, buoyancy can be the dominant driving force at relatively high wind speeds.

Specification of Densities

Buoyancy is much easier to treat than wind because temperatures are subject to much less uncertainty. Accurate records of external temperature are widely available, and the appropriate values will have been defined by the weather data used for the design. The internal temperatures can be taken as the design temperature specified for each of the internal spaces (CIBSE 2005).

It is important to remember that all calculations of density should be based on air temperature rather than, say, dry resultant temperature. When carrying out sizing calculations it is important to use a relatively accurate value for $\Delta\rho$ but the value used for ρ is less important.

For the worked examples given in sections 2 and 1 of CIBSE AM10-2005 (CIBSE 2005), the following approximations have been used (in I-P and SI units):

$$\frac{\Delta\rho}{\rho_0} = \frac{T_i - T_E}{T_e - 459.67} \qquad (4.19a)$$

$$\frac{\Delta\rho}{\rho_0} = \frac{T_i - T_E}{T_e - 273} \qquad (4.19b)$$

$$\frac{\Delta\rho_c}{\rho_0} = \frac{T_c - T_i}{T_i + 459.67} \qquad (4.20a)$$

$$\frac{\Delta\rho_c}{\rho_0} = \frac{T_c - T_i}{T_i + 273} \qquad (4.20b)$$

The reference density ρ_0 has been taken as 0.075 lb_m/ft^3 (1.20 kg·m–3). The reference density could equally well have been taken as the average of the internal and external values, in which case the calculated values of A_i would have differed by a few percent (CIBSE 2005).

These approximations are usually adequate. If the absolute pressure and relative humidity are specified as well as the air temperature, a precise value of $\Delta\rho$ can be obtained by subtracting the densities evaluated in the manner described in CIBSE Guide C. In general, the sizing of openings does not warrant such precision, partly because the sizes of commercially available air vents etc. are unlikely to match precisely the calculated values. Moreover, the uncertainties associated with the calculation procedure, particularly when the wind is present, will generally exceed those in the evaluation of $\Delta\rho$ (CIBSE 2005).

CASE STUDY
Guangzhou Chow Thai Fook (CTF) Finance Center

Guangzhou

Name: Guangzhou Chow Thai Fook (CTF) Finance Centre

Location: Guangzhou, China.

Description: China's third-tallest tower, the CTF Finance Centre aligns the design requirements of supertall construction with cultural, environmental, and contextual sensitivity.

Guangzhou, located on the Pearl River Delta in southern China, is a megalopolis that leads the country in economic power. Completed in 2016, the 1739 ft (530 m) tall CTF Finance Centre is the city's tallest building and represents the region's recent prosperity and urban growth.

The tower is linked to public transportation through basement-level connections and to adjacent buildings via pedestrian-level bridges. A mix of space use types is defined by four main transition points: the program rises upward from office, to residential, to hotel, to the record-breaking top. The building also contains ballroom, retail, restaurant and cinema spaces, with a nearby central park and underground retail concourse that further enhance its urban connectivity.

The tower's multiple uses contribute to its unique form while maintaining dialogue with the city's architectural identity. Vertical massing steps accommodate the changing floor plate size requirements of its varied program types and highlight the tower's relationship with neighboring supertall landmarks, the Guangzhou West Tower and the Canton Tower. The chiseled setbacks also provide a crescendo to the city skyline.

The Centre features a terracotta façade attuned to the material's history. Its shining glazed finish evokes the bright white lines of its nearby companion buildings, maintaining visual regularity while pushing its boundaries.

The façade also has environmental advantages. Terracotta is self-cleaning, corrosion-resistant, and is easily produced and shipped. Ceramic-clad piers preserve floor-to-ceiling views and offer generous shading to the exterior, providing natural ventilation in Guangzhou's tropical climate. The building employs additional sustainability measures, like high-efficiency chillers and heat recovery. Together, the features of CTF Finance Centre symbolize a future where sustainability and international commerce are interdependent—for the client, for the city of Guangzhou, and for China.

Building Function: Hotel/Residential/Office/Retail

Building Height: 1739 ft (530 m)

Building Floor Area: 4,284,036 ft^2 (398,000 m^2) (tower), 5,464,633 (507,681 m^2) (development)

Architects: Kohn Pedersen Fox Associates (Design), Guangzhou Design Institute (Architect of Record)

Executive Architect: Leigh and Orange

Structural Engineers: Arup (Design), Leslie E. Robertson Associates (Peer Review)

MEP Engineers: WSP (Design)

Adapted from a report originally published at Archello.com—
https://archello.com/project/ctf-finance-centre

CHAPTER 5
Stack Effect

INTRODUCTION

Stack pressure is the hydrostatic pressure caused by the weight of a column of air located inside or outside a building. It can also occur within a flow element, such as a duct or chimney that has vertical separation between its inlet and outlet. The hydrostatic pressure in the air depends on density and the height of interest above a reference point.

DRIVING MECHANISMS FOR VENTILATION AND INFILTRATION

Natural ventilation and infiltration are driven by pressure differences across the building envelope caused by wind and air density differences. Mechanical air-moving systems also induce pressure differences across the envelope through operation of appliances such as combustion devices, leaky forced-air thermal distribution systems, and mechanical ventilation systems. The indoor/outdoor pressure difference at a location depends on the magnitude of these driving mechanisms as well as on the characteristics of the openings in the building envelope (ASHRAE 2017a, 2019).

CLIMATE AND THE ATMOSPHERE

As buildings have become taller, the need for elevation-specific meteorological data is becoming more important. The climate at 330 ft (100 m) above grade is not the same as 2000 ft (600 m). However, rarely does the design of upper levels of the building capitalize on that difference. Further, wind conditions at the top of a tall building are different than at ground level; if enough data is known about this difference, it can be incorporated into the design. See Chapter 4 for more information.

INDOOR AIR TEMPERATURE AND PRESSURE

The indoor air temperature is assumed to be a constant 293.1 K (20°C).
The next step is to determine the internal pressure vertically with the building height.

$$P = 14.696(1 - 6.8754 \times 10^{-5} \times Z)^{5.2559} \tag{5.1a}$$

Constant pressure, in. water =   14.696

$$P = 101,325 (1 - 2.25577 \ 10^{-5} \times H)^{5.25588} \tag{5.1b}$$

Constant pressure, Pa   =   101,325

$$\rho = 2.7 \times [P_{abs}/(T + 459.7)] \qquad (5.2a)$$

$$P = \rho[286.9(T + 273.1)] \qquad (5.2b)$$

The internal pressure is assumed to be 401.7 in. water (99,961 Pa).

where

T =   temperature, °F (°C)

T_G =   ground temperature, °F (°C)

P_{abs} =   absolute pressure, psi (kPa)

P =   pressure, psi (kPa)

INTERNAL AIR DENSITY

Now the internal pressure is known it is possible to determine the density of the air vertically with the height of the building. For this we use the following formula:

$$\rho = P_{abs}/[286.9(T + 273.1)] \qquad (5.3)$$

where

P_{abs} =   absolute pressure, in. of water (Pa)

The internal air density is assumed to be 0.075 lb/ft^3 (1.19 kg/m^3).

Air density is a function of local barometric pressure, temperature, and humidity ratio. As a result, standard conditions should not be used to calculate the density. For example, a building site at 5000 ft (1500 m) has air density that is about 20% less than if the building were at sea level. Air temperature increases from –20°F to 70°F (–30°C to 20°C) causes a similar air density difference. Combined, these elevation and temperature effects can reduce air density by about 45%. Moisture effects on density are generally much less but can be significant if the change in elevation is great (e.g., in a natural draft cooling tower). Saturated air at 105°F(40°C) has a density of about 5% less than that of dry air at the same pressure.

Assuming the air temperature and humidity ratio are constant over the height of interest, the stack pressure decreases linearly as the distance above the reference point increases (Figures 5.1 and 5.2). For a single column of air, the stack pressure can be calculated as

$$P_s = P_r - \rho g H \qquad (5.4a)$$

$$P_s = P_r - 0.00598 \rho g H \qquad (5.4b)$$

where

P_s =   stack pressure, in. of water (Pa)

P_r =   stack pressure at reference height, in. of water (Pa)

g =   gravitational acceleration, 32.2 ft/s^2 (9.81 m/s^2)

ρ =   indoor or outdoor air density, lb$_m$/ft^3 (kg/m^3)

H =   height above reference plane, ft (m)

0.00598 =   unit conversion factor, in. of water·ft·s^2·lb$_m$

For tall buildings or when significant temperature stratification occurs indoors, the equation is modified to include the density gradient over the height of the building.

Temperature, and thus air density differences between indoors and outdoors cause stack pressure differences that drive airflows across the building envelope; the stack effect is this buoyancy phenomenon (Figures 5.1 and 5.2). The building is then characterized by an effective stack height and neutral pressure level (NPL) or leakage distribution, as described in the section on Neutral Pressure Level. Once calculated, these parameters can be used in physical, single-zone models to estimate infiltration (ASHRAE 2017a).

Neglecting vertical density gradients, the stack pressure differences any vertical location is

$$\Delta p_s = (\rho_o - \rho_i)g(H_{NPL} - H) \qquad (5.5a)$$

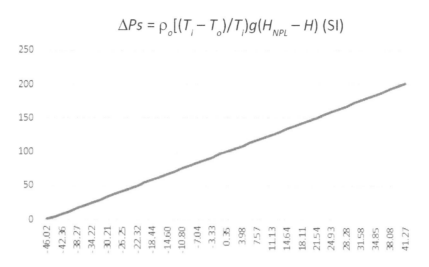

Figure 5.1 Stack effect difference at 32°C outdoor temperature and assuming H_{NPL} = 44 (0.5).

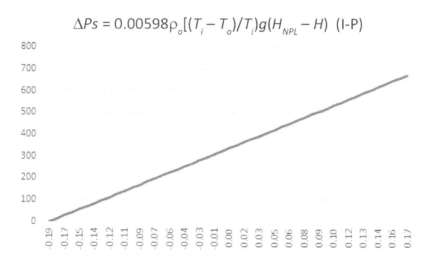

Figure 5.2 Stack effect difference at 89.6°F outdoor temperature and assuming H_{NPL} = 336 (0.5).

$$\Delta p_s = \rho_o((T_i - T_o)/T_i)g(H_{NPL} - H) \qquad (5.5b)$$

where

T_o =   absolute outdoor temperature, K (°R)

T_i =   absolute indoor temperature, K (°R)

ρ_o =   outdoor air density, lb/ft³ (kg/m³)

ρ_i =   indoor air density, lb/ft³ (kg/m³)

H_{NPL} =   height of neutral pressure level above the reference plane without any other driving forces, ft (m)

and

$$\Delta p_s = 0.00598(\rho_o - \rho_i)g(H_{NPL} - H) \qquad (5.6a)$$

or

$$\Delta p_S = 0.00598 \rho_o g (H_{NPL} - H) \tag{5.6b}$$

where

T_o =   absolute outdoor temperature, K (°R)

T_i =   absolute indoor temperature, K (°R)

ρ_o =   outdoor air density, lb/ft^3 (kg/m^3)

ρ_i =   indoor air density, lb/ft^3 (kg/m^3)

H_{NPL} =   height of neutral pressure level above the reference plane without any other driving forces, ft (m)

Chastain and Colliver (1989) showed that, when there is stratification, the average of the vertical distribution of temperature differences is more appropriate to use in Equations 5.5 and 5.6 than the localized temperature difference near the opening of interest.

By convention, stack pressure differences are positive when the building is pressurized relative to outdoors, which causes flow out of the building. Therefore, absent other driving forces and assuming no stack effect within the flow elements themselves, when indoor air is warmer than outdoors, the base of the building is depressurized and the top is pressurized relative to outdoors; when indoor air is cooler than outdoors, the reverse is true. At some elevation in the building, with such conditions, the pressure indoors is equal to the outdoors: this height is the neutral pressure level.

Absent other driving forces, the location of the NPL is influenced by leakage distribution over the building exterior and by interior compartmentation. As a result, the NPL is not necessarily at the mid-height of the building; with effective horizontal barriers in tall buildings, it is also possible to have more than one NPL. NPL location and leakage distribution are described in the Combining Driving Forces and Neutral Pressure Level sections.

For a penetration through the building envelope for which (1) there is vertical separation between its inlet and outlet and (2) air indoor the flow element is not at the indoor or outdoor temperature (e.g., in a chimney), more complex analyses than Equations 5.6 and 5.7 are required to determine the stack effect at any location on the building envelope.

WIND PRESSURE

When wind impinges on and flows around and over a building, it creates a distribution of static pressures on the building's exterior surfaces that depends on the wind direction, wind speed, air density, surface orientation, and surrounding conditions. Wind pressures are generally positive with respect to the static pressure in the undisturbed airstream on the windward side of a building and negative on the leeward sides and roof. However, these pressures depend highly on wind speed, angle, turbulence, the surroundings, and building shape. Static pressures over building surfaces are almost proportional to the velocity pressure of the undisturbed airstream. The wind pressure or velocity pressure is given by the Bernoulli equation, assuming no height change or pressure losses:

$$0.0129 P_w = C_p \rho \frac{U}{2} \tag{5.7a}$$

$$P_w = C_p \rho \frac{U^2}{2} \tag{5.7b}$$

where

P_w =   wind surface pressure relative to outdoor static pressure in undisturbed flow, in. of water (Pa) (Figures 5.3 and 5.4)

ρ =   outdoor air density, lb/ft^3 (kg/m^3) (about 0.075 (1.2) at or near sea level)

U =   wind speed, mph (m/s)

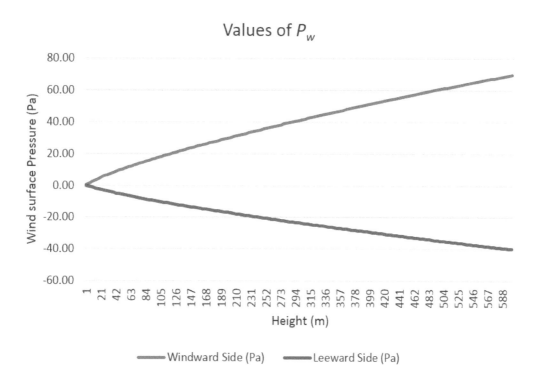

Figure 5.3 Values for P_w at 42.8°F outdoor temperature.

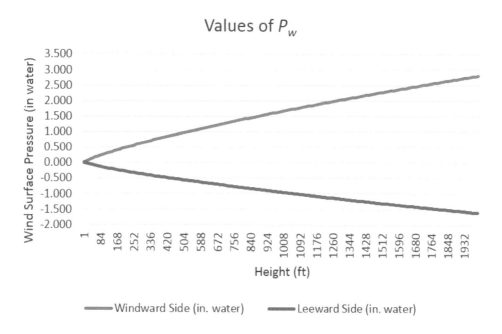

Figure 5.4 Values for P_w at 6°C outdoor temperature.

C_p =   wind surface pressure coefficient

0.0129=   unit conversion factor, in. of water·ft^3/lb$_m$·mph^2

    C_p is a function of location on the building envelope and wind direction. Chapter 4 provides additional information on values of C_p.

Most pressure coefficient data are for winds approaching perpendicularly to upwind building surfaces.

The measured data used to develop the harmonic function from Akins et al. (1979) and Wiren (1985) show that typical values for the pressure coefficients are $C_p(1) = 0.6$, $C_p(2) = -0.3$, and $C_p(3) = C_p(4) = -0.65$. Because of geometry effects on the flow around a building, application of this interpolation function is limited to low-rise buildings of the rectangular plan on flat, featureless sites, with the longest wall less than three times the length of the shortest wall. For less regular buildings or sites, simple correlations are inadequate and building-specific pressure coefficients are required; computational fluid dynamic models are often used. Chapter 4 discusses wind pressures for complex building shapes and for high-rise buildings in more detail.

The wind speed most commonly available for infiltration calculations is that measured at the local weather station, typically the nearest airport. This wind speed needs to be corrected for reductions caused by the difference between the height where the wind speed is measured and the height of the building, and reductions caused by shelter effects.

The reference wind speed used to determine pressure coefficients is usually the wind speed at the building height for a high-rise building. However, meteorological wind speed measurements are made at a different height, typically 33 ft (10 m) for official weather stations, and at a different location than for the buildings of interest. The difference in terrain between the measurement station and the building under study must also be addressed. Chapter 4 shows how to calculate the effective wind speed U_H from the reference wind speed U_{met} using boundary layer theory and estimates of terrain effects.

MECHANICAL SYSTEMS

Operation of mechanical equipment, such as supply or exhaust systems and vented combustion devices, affects pressure differences across the building envelope and thus air change rates. Interior static pressure adjusts such that the sum of all airflows through openings in the building envelope plus equipment-induced air flows balances to zero. To predict these changes in pressure differences and airflow rates caused by mechanical equipment, the location of each opening in the envelope and the relationship between pressure difference and airflow rate for each opening must be known. The interaction between mechanical ventilation system operation and envelope airtightness has been discussed for low-rise buildings and for office buildings (Persily and Grot 1985; Tamura and Wilson 1967a, 1967b; Wilson and Tamura 1970).

Air exhausted from a building by a whole-building exhaust system must be balanced by increasing airflow into the building through other openings or the air-handling systems. As pressures vary, air leakage at some location's changes from outflow to inflow. When using makeup air and no dedicated exhaust, the situation is reversed, and envelope inflows may become outflows. Thus, the effects of a mechanical system on a building must be considered. Depressurization caused by an improperly designed exhaust system can increase the rate of radon entry into a building and can interfere with the proper operation of combustion device venting or other exhaust systems. Pollutant entry can be increased from garages and other attached storage spaces. Depressurization can also force moist outdoor air through the building envelope; for example, during the cooling season in hot, humid climates, moisture may condense in the building envelope and cause rust, rot, or mold. A similar phenomenon, but in reverse, can occur during the heating, and potentially humidifying, the season in cold climates if the building is pressurized. Active pressure control is often recommended, as is a proper use of moisture retarders, drainage, and drying of in situ building materials.

The interaction between mechanical systems and the building envelope also pertains to systems serving zones of buildings. Performance of zone-specific exhaust or pressurization systems is affected by leakage in partitions between zones as well as through exterior walls.

Mechanical systems can also create infiltration-driving forces in single-zone buildings. Specifically, some single-family houses with central forced-air duct systems have many distributed supply registers, yet only one central return grille. When insufficiently undercut internal doors are closed in these houses, large positive indoor-to-outdoor pressure differentials are

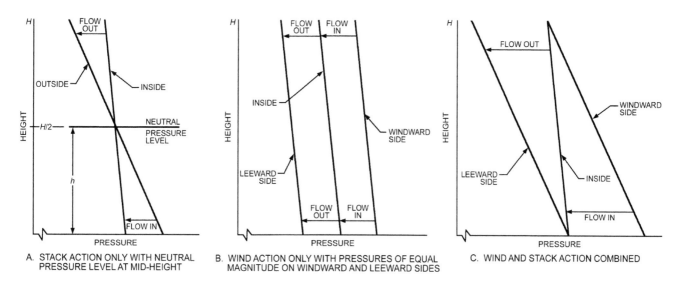

A. STACK ACTION ONLY WITH NEUTRAL PRESSURE LEVEL AT MID-HEIGHT

B. WIND ACTION ONLY WITH PRESSURES OF EQUAL MAGNITUDE ON WINDWARD AND LEEWARD SIDES

C. WIND AND STACK ACTION COMBINED

Figure 5.5 Distribution of indoor and outdoor pressures over height of building.

created for rooms with only supply registers, whereas the room or hallway with the return grille tends to depressurize relative to the outdoors. This is caused by the resistance of the internal door undercuts, often partially blocked by carpeting, to flow from the supply register to the return; the magnitudes of the indoor/outdoor pressure differentials created average 0.0120559 to 0.0241119 in. of water (3 to 6 Pa) (Modera and Wilson 1990). Balanced airflow systems with ducted air return and distributed grilles or adequately sized transfer grilles (where still allowed by fire code) reduce this effect significantly.

Building envelope airtightness and interzonal airflow resistance can also affect the performance of mechanical systems. The actual air flow rate delivered by these systems, particularly ventilation systems, depends on the pressure differences they work against.

LOCATION OF NEUTRAL PLANE

In this section, methods of determining the location of the neutral plane are described for a single shaft connected to the outdoors only. The methods of effective area can be used to extend this analysis to buildings. Using these neutral plane locations, the flow rates and pressures throughout the building can be evaluated (Kote 1989).

NEUTRAL PRESSURE LEVEL

The neutral pressure level (NPL) varies and is that height or heights in the building envelope where, at that instant, there is no indoor-to-outdoor pressure difference. Internal partitions, stairwells, elevator shafts, utility ducts, chimneys, vents, operable windows, and mechanical supply and exhaust systems complicate the prediction of NPL location. An opening with a large area relative to the total building leakage causes the NPL to shift toward the opening. Exhaust systems increase the height of the NPL; outdoor air supply systems lower it.

Figure 5.5 qualitatively shows the addition of driving forces for a building with uniform openings above and below mid-height and without significant internal resistance to airflow. The slopes of the pressure lines are a function of the densities of the indoor and outdoor air. In Figure 5.6a, with indoor air warmer than outdoor and pressure differences caused solely by thermal forces, the NPL is at mid-height, with inflow through lower openings and outflow through higher openings. For the low air velocities typical in and around buildings, the direction of flow is always from the higher to the lower-pressure region.

Figure 5.6b presents qualitative uniform pressure differences caused by wind alone, with opposing effects on the windward and leeward sides. When temperature difference and wind effects both exist, the pressures caused by each are added together to determine the total pressure difference across the building envelope. In Figure 5.6b, there is no NPL because no locations on the building envelope have zero pressure difference. Figure 5.6c shows the combination, where the wind force of Figure 5.6b has just balanced the thermal force of Figure 5.6a, causing no pressure difference at the top windward or bottom leeward side.

The relative importance of wind and stack pressures in a building depends on building height, internal resistance to vertical airflow, location and flow resistance characteristics of envelope openings, local terrain, and the immediate shielding of the building. The taller the building and the smaller its internal resistances to airflow, the stronger the stack effect. The stack effect can be reduced by effectively sealing the building internally between floors, typically by gasketing elevator and stairway doors, and sealing pipe, duct, and electrical penetrations; these measures, when done by code-approved means, also typically reduce undesired smoke migration during fire events. Gasketing interior doors, especially those from exterior spaces or to elevator lobbies, in tall buildings can also help restrict air leakage paths.

The effect of mechanical ventilation on envelope pressure differences is more complex and depends on both the direction of ventilation flow (exhaust or supply) and the differences in these ventilation flows among the zones of the building. If mechanically supplied outdoor air is provided uniformly to each story, the change in the exterior wall pressure difference pattern is uniform. With a nonuniform supply of outdoor air (e.g., to one story only), the extent of pressurization varies from story to story and depends on internal airflow resistance. Pressurizing all levels uniformly has little effect on pressure differences across floors and vertical shaft enclosures, but pressurizing individual stories increases the pressure drop across these internal separations. Pressurizing the ground level is often used in tall buildings in winter to reduce negative air pressures across entries; vestibules and revolving doors are also used to limit air leakage. Vestibules may also be used for elevator lobbies and stair towers to reduce air and smoke movement vertically through tall buildings.

Available data on the NPL in various kinds of buildings are limited. In tall buildings studied by Tamura and Wilson (1967a, 1967b), the NPL varied from 0.3 to 0.7 of total building height.

LOCATIONS OF THE NPL

While leakage openings in the exterior walls of a building are not always distributed uniformly from the bottom to the top, the in-•ow always equals the out-flow. If the openings at the lower part of a building were larger than those at the higher part, and therefore a smaller resistance to flow is imposed, the pressure difference across the bottom would be less than that across the top. This would be equivalent to a shift of the indoor pressure line to the right and a lowering of the NPL (Wilson and Tamura 1970). Because of the non-uniform leakage area of a building, however, the location of the NPL can be estimated by equating the flows through the two parts of the leakage areas. The location of the NPL (h) can be expressed by

$$h = \frac{H}{1 + (A_1/A_2)^2 T_1/T_o} \tag{5.8}$$

where A_1 and A_2 are the lower and higher leakage areas, T_o and T_i are the outdoor and indoor absolute temperatures, and H is building height (.

Another method developed by Phillips[2] uses the following formula:

NPL estimate = sum (exterior crack + opening areas * h from ground) /
            sum (interior crack+ opening areas) (5.9)

where the crack opening areas are

- Entrance doors
- Exterior wall leakage cracks
- Stair shaft wall

---

2. Personal communication with Duncan Philips, Principal/Senior Consultant at RWDI, 2019.

- Stair shaft doors
- Elevator shaft wall
- Elevator doors

The basic stack effect theory is expressed as:

$$\Delta Ps = C_2 r_i g \, (h - h_{neutral})(T_i - T_o)/T_o \qquad (5.10)$$

where

ΔPs = stack pressure difference (indoor – outdoor), in. of water (Pa)

$C_2 r_i g$ = air density and gravity constant

h = building height, ft (m)

$h_{neutral}$ = height of neutral pressure level, ft (m)

i = indoor

T = absolute temperature, R

Figures 5.7 and 5.8 show the stack pressure relationship through the height of the building. The building has been divided into three sections and the neutral plane has been calculated for each section.

The building is typically split into suitable sections as determined by the design engineer; this is dependent upon the number of elevators, transfer floors, refuge floors and other such transformations[3].

ρ_o = air density at 273K (459.67 R), lb/ft^3 (kg/m^3)

T = absolute temperature of air mass, K

Thus, the pressure gradient is inversely proportional to the absolute temperature of the air mass.

Pressure gradients and the absolute pressure distribution for a building in which two openings, h_1 and h_2, are vertically separated a distance h apart. The level of alignment of the internal and external pressures (neutral pressure plane) is a function of the overall distribution and flow

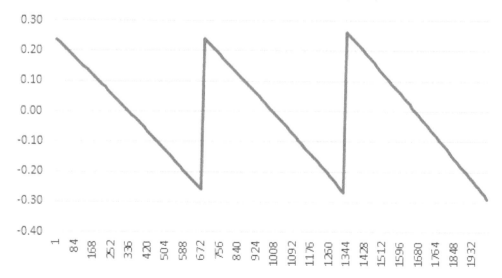

$$\Delta Ps = C_2 r_i g \, (h - h_{neutral})(T_i - T_o)/T_o \; \text{(I-P)}$$

Figure 5.6 Stack pressure relationship, I-P.

---

3. Originally published at https://mycourses.aalto.fi/pluginfile.php/430671/mod_resource/content/1/Ene-58_5181_stack%20effect.pdf.

characteristics of openings and is fixed such that a mass flow balance is maintained. Knowledge of this level is not a   prerequisite of air infiltration modeling. The stack-induced pressure at h_2, with respect to the pressure at h_1, is represented in Figures 5.7 and 5.8 by the net horizontal displacement of the pressure curves at these locations $(A + B)$ and is given by

$$P_s = -\rho_o g 273(h_1 - h_2)\left[\frac{1}{T_{ext}} - \frac{1}{T_{int}}\right] \qquad (5.11)$$

where

T_{ext} = absolute external temperature, K

T_{int} = absolute internal temperature, K

VERTICAL SHAFTS

The vertical airflow routes in a high-rise building are elevator shafts, stairwells, and various mechanical shafts. The main vertical airflow routes with the most significant effect on the pressure distribution of each floor are the passenger elevator shafts, which are connected to each serving floor. The emergency elevator shaft or stairwells, which are inevitably included in high-rise buildings, are also highly vulnerable to stack pressure difference problems, and the building code usually requires that they are connected to all floors and that vertical airflow routes are thereby created. However, additional partitions and vestibules can be installed to increase the airtightness of these shafts, in order to reduce excessive pressure differences. Also, these shafts are rarely used in daily routines, and therefore do not have a significant impact on the airflow of the entire building (Jo et al. 2009).

THERMAL DRAFT COEFFICIENT

Stack-induced pressure differences are proportioned over building elements according to the structure of the building and the leakage area of each building element. An effective means

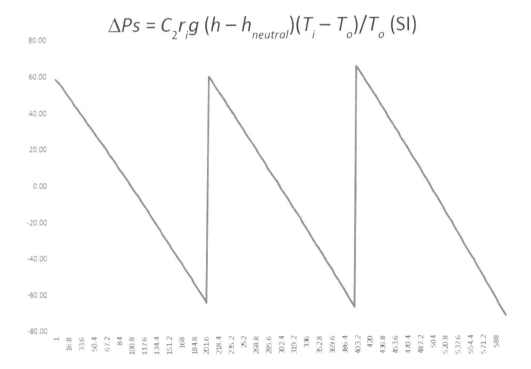

$$\Delta Ps = C_2 r_i g\ (h - h_{neutral})(T_i - T_o)/T_o\ \text{(SI)}$$

Figure 5.7 Stack pressure relationship, SI.

of reflecting this proportion is the thermal draft coefficient (TDC), which is defined by ASHRAE (2017) as the sum of the top and bottom pressure differences across the exterior walls divided by the total theoretical pressure differences, and which has been discussed in detail by Tamura and Shaw (1976, Tamura 1994). Hayakawa and Togari (1989) indicated that the proportions of pressure differences will be similar if the typical • oor plans are similar and interpreted the TDC as the proportion of pressure difference supported by the exterior walls. Examining the typical floor plans of high-rise buildings, each • oor can be simplified so that it is separated by a • rst partition formed by the exterior walls, a second partition formed by the entrance and the wall between the residential unit and the corridor, and a third partition formed by the elevator door and the wall of the elevator shaft. In this study, the equivalent leakage area of the exterior walls and the equivalent leakage area of interior separations were used to determine the pressure difference across the exterior walls of each floor (Jo et al. 2009).

DATA GATHERING FOR STACK PRESSURE PREDICTION

The prediction of the pressure distribution in high-rise buildings requires an analysis of the key parameters influencing the pressure distribution and to define the precise values for these parameters, which is the main source of the stack effect. Based on the pressure profile derived from calculations the required key information consists of the indoor and outdoor temperature differences, the height of the building, the location of the NPL, the height of the vertical compartment, and the ratio of the airtightness of the exterior walls and interior partitions which is derived by TDC.

HEIGHTS OF VERTICAL COMPARTMENTS

There are many components of high-rise buildings that play a main role as a vertical airflow path such as elevator shafts, stairwells, and shafts that accommodate mechanical equipment. Because shafts for passenger elevators occupy most of the area allocated to vertical shafts and they are the most frequently used shafts, they are generally the most influential components contributing to pressure distribution in high-rise buildings. Moreover, if elevator shafts are vertically compartmentalized, i.e. by low-rise and high-rise elevators, there is a discontinuous point in the pressure profile at the top and bottom of each shaft; thus, it is essential to know the height of the shafts in order to predict pressure distribution in buildings. In this research, we have defined this parameter as the height of the vertical compartment (S) and it is included in the key factors, which is used when vertical pressure distribution is predicted.

In buildings with two-zone type, for example, height of the low-rise elevator shaft (S_{low}) and high-rise elevator shaft (S_{high}) are the key factors.

AIRTIGHTNESS OF EXTERIOR WALLS AND INTERIOR SEPARATIONS

Since most of the stories in high-rise buildings have identical floor plans, with the exception of basement floors and the ground floor, the overall pressure difference between vertical shafts and the exterior is distributed to elements on the airflow path based on the airtightness of each element. Therefore, the pressure pro• le of each • oor can be derived if TDC(γ) or ITDC (Internal Thermal Draft Coefficient, the expression of the ratio of the airtightness of internal compartments and exterior walls), is known. Pressure differences acting on interior compartments are drawn from ITDC and the overall pressure difference on each floor. The sum of the pressure difference on the interior compartments on the ith • oor can be derived by ΔP_s (stack pressure difference on ith floor) multiplied by ITDC. The stack pressure difference on the ith • oor ΔP_s can be drawn from the theoretical equation. TDC, which is a proportion of the pressure difference covered by the overall exterior walls, can be calculated by using equivalent leakage areas. TDC and ITDC provide the total pressure difference operated on interior partitions, and this is defined as the as the internal stack pressure difference on the ith • oor $\Delta P_{T, i}$, which is calculated for each floor.

PREDICTION OF STACK-INDUCED PRESSURE DISTRIBUTION

The prediction strategy is composed of the following two procedures, and the key parameters are as follows in each step:

1. Predicting the vertical stack pressure distribution: the height of each elevator shaft (h_{low}, h_{high}), the location of the neutral pressure level for each shaft, ($h_{NPL, low}$, $h_{NPL, high}$), and the outdoor and interior temperatures of each shaft (t_o, t_s).
2. Predicting the horizontal stack pressure distribution: the equivalent leakage areas in exterior walls (A_w) and interior partitions including the vertical shafts (A_e).

Predicting the vertical stack pressure distribution. To predict stack-induced pressure distribution over a building, the magnitude of maximum pressure difference must be calculated for each floor by first assuming the position of the neutral pressure level. The main parameters affecting the stack-induced pressure difference are the building height, the indoor-outdoor temperature difference, and the height of the neutral pressure level, which may differ depending on the proportion of openings on the upper and lower parts of a building. The building height is closely related to the height of the vertical shafts within the building and because the main airflow within a building depends on the heights of the passenger elevator shafts, the heights of the vertical zoning of such shafts must be considered. The vertical distance from the neutral pressure level of each passenger elevator shaft, along with the indoor-outdoor temperature difference, is used to complete the basic calculation equation, and consequently, the vertical stack pressure distribution may be predicted by determining the magnitude of the stack-induced pressure difference for each floor.

PRACTICAL EXAMPLES

A 2000 ft (600 m) megatall building has been divided into three sections. Because of the building's use. each section has been calculated separately. The neutral plane for each section has been calculated as previously shown. The neutral plane can be seen at different positions for each section. The stack effect calculations have been made using both temperature and density differentials.

Pressure Relationships, Summer

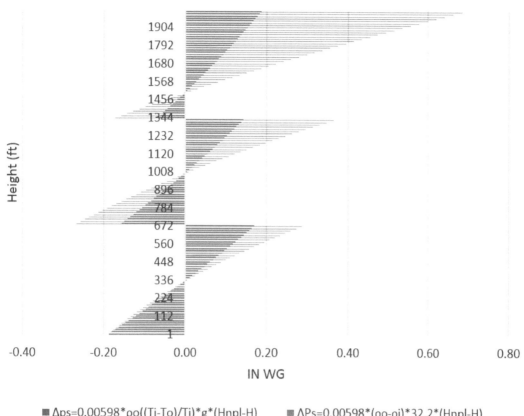

■ Δps=0.00598*ρo((Ti-To)/Ti)*g*(Hnpl-H)   ■ ΔPs=0.00598*(ρo-ρi)*32.2*(Hnpl-H)

Pressure Relationships, Summer

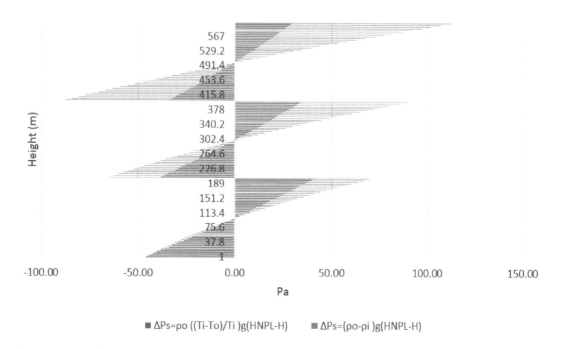

■ ΔPs=ρo ((Ti-To)/Ti)g(HNPL-H)   ■ ΔPs=(ρo-ρi)g(HNPL-H)

Figure 5.8 Pressure relationships over the three building sections during the summer, I-P and SI.

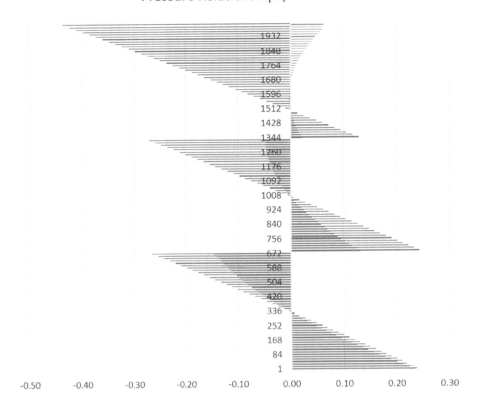

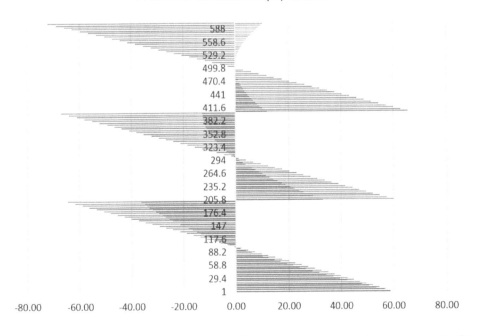

Figure 5.9 Pressure relationships over the three building sections during the winter (I-P, SI).

CHAPTER 6
Heating and Cooling Loads

INTRODUCTION

This chapter identifies the base case energy consumption of a 2000 ft (600 m) megatall building against a proposed design having a façade with 65% glazing. Climates at different heights will be used for this analysis and energy numbers show how a building's energy consumption can be kept at a minimum.

From Chapter 4 we have seen how the external load to a space can be calculated. The calculations in Chapter 4 assume a constant outside temperature over the height of the building. From Chapter 3 we have seen how air temperature, density, and pressure vary over the height of a building

For this exercise, we use the same hypothetical building and location presented in Chapter 4. To simplify the calculations, we divide the building up into sections as opposed to calculating every floor, as we would for a real project. We have therefore split the building up into six 330 ft (100 m) sections and have calculated the heating and cooling loads for each section. The variable outside temperature method will be compared to a traditional method where the outdoor air temperature, density, and pressure are constant over the height of the building.

Not only does this chapter evaluate constant outdoor temperature against variable outdoor temperature, but it also investigates the difference of 40% WWR against 65% WWR. The base case for ANSI/ASHRAE/IES Standard 90.1 compliance is 40% WWR (see Chapter 4).

Table 6.1 shows the steady-state heat gain to a typical floor of a megatall building with 40% code compliant glazing at 0 to 2000 ft (0 to 600 m). The traditional steady-state heat gain calculations shown in Table 6.1 consist of a transmission heat gain of 25,957 Btu/h (6.697 W) and a solar gain of 86,722 Btu/h (24,970 W) for a total exterior heat gain per floor of 112,689 Btu/h (31,666 W).

The total steady-state heat gain for the whole building (140 floors) is calculated at 4,433,291 W (15,117,522 Btu/h).

Table 6.2 shows the outdoor temperatures used for a constant outdoor temperature and a variable outdoor temperature. As shown in Table 6.2, the outdoor temperature is varied as calculated using the formula shown in Chapter 4. For design calculations, it is recommended to use the variable outdoor temperature for each floor. As mentioned previously, this example divides one 2000 ft (600 m) building into six 330 ft (100 m) sections.

As previously explained, the building has been divided up into six sections. The external load for each floor having a 40% WWR is shown as well as the total external load to the building. The external load as a function of the floor area is also shown.

The total steady state heat gain for the whole building is calculated as shown in Table 6.3, with the resulting total external loads for each of the alternatives.

- Using 65% WWR and a constant outdoor temperature increases the total building external load from 15,117,522 to 23,650,699 Btu/h (4,433,291 W to 6,935,689 W), an increase of 8,533,177 Btu/h (2,502,398 W), or 56%.

- When using a variable outdoor temperature during the summer, the total building load for a building with 40% WWR is 14,154,869 Btu/h (4,150,988 W), compared to a constant outdoor temperature for 40% WWR where the total building load is 15,117,522 Btu/h (4,433,291 W). The building's external load is reduced by 962,653 Btu/h (282,203 W) or 6%.

- When using a variable outdoor temperature during the summer compared to a constant outdoor temperature for 65% WWR, the building's external load is reduced from 23,650,699 Btu/h (6,935,689 W) to 18,288,290 Btu/h (5,363,135 W)—a reduction of 5,362,409 Btu/h (1,572,554 W), or 23%.

Table 6.1 Constant Outdoor Temperature

Summer	Energy Code 40% Glass SHGC= 0.4					
Height, (0 to 1980 ft) 0 to 600 m	Area, ft^2 (m^2)	U-Factor, Btu/ft^2·°F (W/m^2·K)	Outdoor Temperature, °F (°C)	Indoor Temperature, °C (°F)	ΔT, K (°F)	Energy, Btu (W)
North—Wall	2243 (204)	0.104 (0.592)	85.6 (29.8)	74 (24)	5.8 (11.6)	2706 (700)
South—Wall	2243 (204)	0.104 (0.592)	85.6 (29.8)	74 (24)	5.8 (11.6)	2706 (700)
East—Wall	672 (61)	0.104 (0.592)	85.6 (29.8)	74 (24)	5.8 (11.6)	811 (210)
West—Wall	672 (61)	0.104 (0.592)	85.6 (29.8)	74 (24)	5.8 (11.6)	811 (210)
North—Glass	1495 (136)	0.42 (2.38)	85.6 (29.8)	74 (24)	5.8 (11.6)	7285 (1876)
South—Glass	1495 (136)	0.42 (2.38)	85.6 (29.8)	74 (24)	5.8 (11.6)	7285 (1876)
East—Glass	448 (41)	0.42 (2.38)	85.6 (29.8)	74 (24)	5.8 (11.6)	2183 (562)
West—Glass	448 (41)	0.42 (2.38)	85.6 (29.8)	74 (24)	5.8 (11.6)	2183 (562)
						25,967 (6697)

Table 6.2 Variable Outdoor Temperature

Section, ft (m)	Constant Outdoor Temperature, °F (°C)	Variable Outdoor Temperature, °F (°C)
0 to 330 (0 to 100)	85.6 (29.8)	85.64 (29.8)
330 to 660 (100 to 200)	85.6 (29.8)	84.2 (29.0)
660 to 990 (200 to 300)	85.6 (29.8)	83.12 (28.4)
990 to 1320 (300 to 400)	85.6 (29.8)	81.86 (27.7)
1320 to 1650 (400 to 500)	85.6 (29.8)	80.78 (27.1)
1650 to 1980 (500 to 600)	85.6 (29.8)	79.52 (26.4)

Table 6.3 Total Steady-State Heat Gain

Whole Building	Energy Code 40% Glass SHGC = 0.4 Btu/h (W)	Energy Code 65% Glass SHGC = 0.04 Btu/h (W)
Constant temperature—Summer	15,117,522 (4,433,291)	23,650,699 (6,935,689)
Variable temperature—Summer	14,154,869 (4,150,988)	18,288,290 (5,36,135)
Constant temperature—Winter	−18,355,386 (−5,382,811)	24,632,050 (−7,223,475)
Variable Temperature—Winter	−19,272,369 (−5,651,721)	25,866,296 (−7,585,424)

- When using a variable outdoor temperature during the winter compared to a constant outdoor temperature for 40% WWR, the building's external load is increased from –18,355,386 to –19,272,369 Btu/h (–5,382,811 to –5,651,721 W), a 916,983 Btu/h (268,910 W) increase, or 5%.

- When using a variable outdoor temperature during the winter compared to a constant outdoor temperature for 65% WWR, the building's external load increases from –24,632,050 to –25,866,296 Btu/h (–7,223,475 W to –7,585,424 W), a 1,234,246 Btu/h (361,948 W) increase, or 5%.

Table 6.4 shows the calculated external loads for a typical floor in the 0 to 330 ft (0 to 100 m) section.

- Using 65% WWR and a variable outdoor temperature increases the typical low-level floor external load from 107,981 Btu/h to 168,934 Btu/h (31,666 W to 49,541 W), a 60,954 Btu/h (14,322 W) increase, or 52%, per floor.

- For the low-level floors in summer, for both 40% WWR and 65% WWR, there is no difference in external loads between a load calculated with a constant outdoor temperature and a variable outdoor temperature and one calculated with both temperatures are the same.

- For the low-level floors in winter, for both 40% WWR and 65% WWR, there is no difference in external loads between a load calculated with a constant outdoor temperature and a variable outdoor temperature and one calculated with both temperatures are the same.

Table 6.5 shows the calculated external loads for a typical floor in the 1650 to 1980 ft (500 to 600 m) section.

- Using 65% WWR and a variable outdoor temperature increases the total building external load from 107,981 to 168,934 Btu/h (31,666 W to 49,541 W), a 60,954 Btu/h (14,322 W) increase, or 52%.

- When using a variable outdoor temperature in the summer compared to a constant outside temperature for 40% WWR, the building's external load is reduced from 107,981 Btu/h to 94,597 Btu/h (31,666 to 27,741 W), a 13,384 Btu/h (3926 W) reduction, or 12%, per floor.

- When using a variable outdoor temperature in the summer compared to a constant outside temperature for 65% WWR, the building's external load is reduced from (168,934 to

Table 6.4 Calculated External Loads—Lower Levels

Typical Floor—Low	Energy Code 40% Glass SHGC = 0.4 W (Btu/h)	Energy Code 65% Glass SHGC = 0.04 W (Btu/h)
Constant temperature—Summer	31,666 (107,981)	49,541 (168,934)
Variable temperature—Summer	31,666 (107,981)	49,541 (168,934)
Constant temperature—Winter	–38,449 (–131,111)	–51,596 (–175,942)
Variable Temperature—Winter	–38,449 (–131,111)	–51,596 (–175,942)

Table 6.5 Calculated External Loads—Higher Levels

Typical Floor—High	Energy Code 40% Glass SHGC = 0.4 W (Btu/h)	Energy Code 65% Glass SHGC = 0.04 W (Btu/h)
Constant temperature—Summer	31,666 (107,981)	49,541 (168,934)
Variable temperature—Summer	27,741 (94,597)	42,062 (143, 431)
Constant temperature—Winter	–38,449 (–131,111)	–51,596 (–175,942)
Variable Temperature—Winter	–42, 259 (–144,103)	–56,709 (–193,377)

Table 6.6 External Loads per Floor, Summer

Section Height, ft (m)	No. of Floors	Floor Area, ft² (m²)	Variable Outdoor Temperature, °F (°C)	40% WWR External Load, Btu/h (W)	40% WWR External Load per Floor Area, Btu/h·ft² (W/m²)	65% WWR External Load, Btu/h (W)	65% WWR External Load per Floor Area, Btu/h·ft² (W/m²)
0 to 330 (0 to 100)	24	470,759 (46,656)	85.64 (29.8)	2,591,576 (759,993)	5.51 (16.29)	4,054,405 (1,188,975)	8.61 (25.48)
330 to 660 (100 to 200)	22	431,529 (42,768)	84.2 (29)	2,306,316 (676,339)	5.34 (15.81)	3,623,548 (1,062,624)	8.40 (24.85
660 to 990 (200 to 300)	23	451,144 (44,712)	83.12 (28.4)	2,356,815 (691,148)	5.22 (15.46)	3,715,342 (1,089,543)	8.24 (24.37)
990 to 1320 (300 to 400)	23	451,144 (44,712)	81.86 (27.7)	2,293,423 (672,558	5.08 (15.04)	3,630,276 (1,064,597)	8.05 (23.81)
1320 to 1650 (400 to 500)	24	470,759 (46,656)	80.78 (27.1)	2,336,443 (685,174)	4.96 (14.69)	3,712,031 (1,088,572)	7.89 (23.33)
1650 to 1980 (500 to 600)	24	470,759 (46,656)	79.52 (26.4)	2,268,243 (665,776)	4.82 (14.27)	3,442,388 (1,009,498)	7.31 (21.64)
	140	2,746,094 (272,160)		14,154,869 (4,150,988)	5.15 (15.25)	22,177,989 (6,503,809)	8.08 (23.9)

143,431 Btu/h (49,541 to 42,062 W), a 25,503 Btu/h (7479 W) reduction, or 15%, per floor.

- When using a variable outdoor temperature in the winter compared to a constant outdoor temperature for 40% WWR, the building's external load increases from –131,111 to –144,103 Btu/h (–38,449 to –42,259 W) by 12,992 Btu/h (3810 W), or 10% per floor.
- When using a variable outdoor temperature in the winter compared to a constant outdoor temperature for 65% WWR, the building's external load increases from –175,942 to –193,377 Btu/h (–51,596 W to –56,709 W), a 17,435 Btu/h (5113 W) increase, or 10% per floor.

Table 6.6 shows the external loads expressed as a function of floor area for each section of the building during the summer. By using these external loads per floor area, the designer can take advantage of the decrease in outside temperature over the building's height.

Table 6.7 shows the external loads expressed as a function of floor area for each section of the building for the winter. Using these external loads per floor area, the designer can take into consideration the decrease in outdoor temperature over the building's height. The required heating load is considerably higher than if it were calculated in a traditional manner and problems when heating the building after night operation and shutdown will occur if the correct outdoor air temperature is not used.

TOWARD A NET ZERO DESIGN

Many architects and building designers pursue a carbon-neutral or net zero energy design. For the remainder of this example, we introduce a net zero alternative. To reduce the overall energy consumption to facilitate a net zero design, the lighting power densities are reduced from 1.2 to 0.4 W/ft² (20 to 6 W/m²). The plug loads are reduced from 2 to 0.6 W/ft² (12 to 4 W/m²). All other assumptions remain identical.

DISCUSSION

The calculation procedure presented in this chapter shows how cooling load calculations can take advantage of variable outdoor temperatures which would decrease annual energy consumption and equipment sizes. However, when using variable outdoor temperatures for heat

Table 6.7 External Loads per Floor, Winter

Section Height, ft (m)	No. of Floors	Floor Area, ft² (m²)	Variable Outdoor Temperature, °F (°C)	40% WWR External Load, Btu/h (W)	40% WWR External Load per Floor Area, Btu/h·ft² (W/m²)	65% WWR External Load, Btu/h (W)	65% WWR External Load per Floor Area, Btu/h·ft² (W/m²)
0 to 330 (0 to 100)	24	470,759 (46,656)	8.06 (−13.3)	3,146,741 (−922,768)	6.68 (19.78)	4,046,695 (−1,186,714)	8.60 (25.44)
330 to 660 (100 to 200)	22	431,529 (42,768)	6.8 (−14.00)	2,945,050 (−863,651)	6.82 (20.19)	4,131,761 (−1,211,660)	9.57 (28.33)
660 to 990 (200 to 300)	23	451,144 (44,712)	5.72 (−14.6)	3,133,251 (−918,842)	6.95 (20.55)	4,204,673 (−1,233,042)	9.32) (27.58)
990 to 1320 (300 to 400)	23	451,144 (44,712)	4.46 (−15.30)	3,196,640 (−937,431)	7.09 (20.97)	4,289,739 (−1,257,988)	9.51 (28.14)
1320 to 1650 (400 to 500)	24	470,759 (46,656)	3.38 (−15.90)	3,392,323 (−994,816)	7.21 (21.32)	4,552,333 (−1,334,995)	9.67 (28.61)
1650 to 1980 (500 to 600)	24	470,759 (46,656)	2.12 (−16.60)	3,458,466 (−1,014,213)	7.35 (21.74)	4,641,095 (−1,361,025)	9.86 (29.17)
	140	2,746,094 (272,160)		19,272,369 (−5,651,721)	7.02 (20.77)	25,866,296 (−7,585,424)	9.42 (27.87)

loss calculations. The heat loss rate increases with the height of the building. This would require an increase in heating energy consumption and equipment sizes.

CASE STUDY
International Commerce Center (ICC)

Hong Kong

Name: International Commerce Centre/The Ritz-Carlton, Hong Kong

Location: Hong Kong

Description: The International Commerce Centre (ICC) represents a shift in the tall building paradigm to include not only achievements in height, design, and engineering, but also the most forward-thinking moves towards connectivity for smart growth in a highly dense region.

The 118-story tower accommodates offices, a 360-degree observation deck, and the world's highest hotel, The Ritz-Carlton Hong Kong. The tower is the centerpiece of the Union Square reclamation project, establishing a new urban center with office, retail, hotel, and recreation spaces, as well as a new transportation hub, Kowloon Station, which connects to Central

District, Hong Kong, the International Airport, and mainland China via a network of high-speed rail, subway, buses, and ferry terminals.

The tower's subtly tapered reentrant corners and the gently sloped curves at its base are designed to optimize its structural performance. These curves splay out at the base of the tower, rooting the tower in its surroundings, while creating sheltering canopies on three sides, and a dramatic atrium on the north side. The atrium gestures towards the rest of the development and serves as a public connection space for retail and rail station functions. KPF's scheme succeeds in wedding the high-rise building model with a highly efficient structural and operational agenda.

Energy. The energy use index (EUI) of ICC's energy performance in 2013 was 14.6 kWh/ft^2(157.3 kWh/m^2), placing it among the top 10 percent of energy-efficient commercial buildings. A computerized building management system manages and controls the energy use in the building. The total energy consumption of the project was reduced from 56.3 million kWh in 2012 to 49.9 million kWh in 2013, a reduction of 6.4 million kWh, or 11%.

The air-conditioning system is a high-voltage water-cooled chiller system with a centrifugal separator enhancing the chiller's coefficient of performance (COP), resulting in an 8^2 reduction in energy consumption. The system's original corrugated aluminum separator box filter was replaced with a more advanced mini-pleat filter, reducing system pressure by 25^2 and consequently reducing energy consumption as well. Management has carried out a life cycle testing program with Hong Kong Polytechnic University, resulting in energy optimization and significant savings of 7 million kWh from 2011 through 2013. ICC has saved an estimated HK $7 million (US$900,000) annually through this program.

Other energy-saving features include a low-emission curtain wall, natural lighting of the atrium, the wide adoption of energy-efficient lighting fixtures such as LEDs and T5 fittings, and double-decker elevators with destination control and power regeneration functions. Simple actions such as deactivating elevators during low-use periods are equally important. Through these investments, the building reduced CO_2 emissions by 4630 tons (4.2 million kg) in 2013.

Building Function: Hotel/office

Building Height: 1588 ft (484 m)

Building Floor Area: 2,950,000 ft^2 (274,064 m^2)

Architects: Kohn Pedersen Fox Associates (Design), Wong and Ouyang (Architect of Record)

Engineers: Arup (Design), Beijing Institute of Architectural Design (Engineer of Record)

MEP Engineer: J Roger Preston Limited (Design), Beijing Institute of Architectural Design (Engineer of Record)

Adapted from reports originally published at Architizer.com and SkyscrapterCenter.com—
https://architizer.com/projects/international-commerce-centre/ and
http://legacy.skyscrapercenter.com/hong-kong/international-commerce-centre/137/

CHAPTER 7
Indoor Air Quality and Thermal Comfort

PROVIDE APPROPRIATE AIR AND QUANTITIES FOR EACH ROOM OR ZONE

Outdoor air[2] has been provided to indoor spaces for centuries, but the nature of building ventilation changed with the advent of electricity and the ability to provide ventilation to buildings mechanically, without relying on natural drafts. Ventilation with outdoor air is required for all occupied spaces. Inadequate outdoor air ventilation rates can result in poor IAQ and the potential for adverse health effects and reduced productivity for occupants, along with increased occupant complaints.

The ventilation rate procedure in ASHRAE Standard 62.1-2019, *Ventilation for Acceptable Indoor Air Quality* (ASHRAE 2019b), specifies minimum ventilation rates for the United States. Local building codes usually reference or include these rates but may differ in various ways from the standard. If local codes require more ventilation than specified in the standard, the local code requirements must be met. After the designer determines the outdoor air required for each zone, the quantity of air for the ventilation system must be adjusted to account for air distribution effectiveness and air-handling system ventilation efficiency.

ASHRAE Standard 62.1-2019 specifies two distinct ventilation rate requirements. The first is a per-person requirement to dilute pollutant sources associated with human activity that are proportional to the number of occupants. The second is a per-unit-area requirement designed to dilute pollutants generated by building materials, furnishings, and other sources not associated with the number of occupants.

The ventilation rates are specific to the type of occupant activity. For example, the outdoor air ventilation rates for different parts of an office building may vary depending on the occupant activity in the zones.

During short-term episodes of poor outdoor air quality, ventilation can be temporarily decreased using a short-term conditions procedure from ASHRAE Standard 62.1-2019. Similarly, consideration may be given to increasing outdoor air ventilation rates beyond those required in the standard where the quality of the outdoor air is high and the energy consumed in conditioning it is not excessive.[3]

---

2. This chapter provides partial text from *Indoor Air Quality Guide: Best Practices for Design, Construction, and Commissioning* (ASHRAE 2009) from the section titled "Provide Appropriate Air and Quantities for Each Room or Zone" to the section "Why Natural Ventilation?". For this information to integrate smoothly into this book, the figure and table numbering have been modified from the original and minor grammatical changes have been made; otherwise the content remains as originally published.

Continuously Monitor and Control Outdoor Air Delivery

Accurate monitoring and control of outdoor air intake at the air handler is important for providing the correct amount of outdoor airflow to a building. It has been a common practice for designers to use fixed minimum outdoor air dampers. However, this approach does not necessarily provide good control of outdoor air intake rates, particularly in variable-air-volume (VAV) systems.

In most systems, it is difficult to accurately measure outdoor airflows at the outdoor air dampers during balancing, commissioning, or operation. As a result, both overventilation and underventilation can commonly occur. Furthermore, in occupied buildings, overventilation is common because occupancy rates per floor area in most buildings are less than design values. It is estimated that the current amount of energy for ventilating U.S. buildings could be reduced by as much as 30% (first order estimate of savings potential) if the average minimum outdoor rate is reduced to meet the current standards (Fisk et al. 2005).

Accurate measurement of airflows in ducts also requires careful design, proper commissioning, and ongoing verification. Under carefully controlled laboratory conditions, commercially available airflow sensors are very accurate. However, in most cases, laboratory conditions and accuracies cannot be replicated in the field; therefore, appropriate correction factors in the programming of the controls may be required.

Continuous monitoring of the outdoor rates at the air handler does not guarantee that the proper amount of ventilation is delivered locally within the building. Poor air mixing both in the ductwork and in the occupied space, especially in larger and more complex air distribution systems, can result in parts of a building receiving less than the design minimum amount of ventilation.

Measuring Outdoor Airflow

Straight Ducts

Accurate airflow measurements require long, straight duct runs. This presents a challenge to the designer because space and architectural constraints often limit achieving sufficient straight duct lengths.

VAV Systems

VAV systems with single outdoor air intakes should be designed with modulating dampers and with airflow sensors appropriate for the expected airflow range. In VAV systems with airside economizers, a separate minimum outdoor air intake duct with airflow sensors and a dedicated outdoor air fan with speed control can help ensure accurate control and measurement of the outdoor airflow.

Placement of Sensors

In general, the best accuracies can be expected when sensors are placed within the manufacturer's guidelines and field-verified for optimum performance. Some research has shown

---

3. Note for residential ventilation in China: For the sake of occupants' health and comfort, the ventilation rate should meet the requirements listed in China's national standard for residential buildings requiring 0.4 to 0.7 air changes per hour (ach). If the living-space area is less than approximately 100 ft² (10 m²/person), the ventilation rate should be not less than 0.7 ach; if living space is 100 to 500 ft²/person (10 to 50 m²/person), the rate should be 0.4 to 0.7 ach; and if living space is greater than 500 ft²/person (50 m²/person), the rate should be not less than 0.4 ach. The ASHRAE Standard 62.1-2013 requirement for outdoor air is calculated as the sum of two parts: 5 cfm (2.5 L) of outdoor air per second per person plus 0.06 cfm (0.3 L) of fresh air per second per square foot (meter) of construction area. CIBSE Guide A: *Environmental Design 2015* requires a rate of 0.4 to 1 ach (CIBSE 2015b). Overall, the required ventilation rate for common residential buildings is 0.4 to 1 ach. To meet the requirements for different situations, 1 ach was used as the criterion to evaluate the optimization design in this study. This means that if the ACH is lower than 1 or the mean age of air is greater than 60 minutes, the natural ventilation performance poor. Ventilation rates of 60 m³/h per person are required by federal law in the Russian Federation.

that accuracies of certain measurement technologies may be improved when installed in the following locations: (1) between the fixed louver blades where the air speeds are more uniform compared to air speeds downstream of the louvers or (2) at the outlet face of the louvers (Fisk 2008). Limited research has shown that in some applications, installation of airflow or pressure sensors downstream of the louvers and upstream of the dampers in combination with an airflow straightening device between the louvers and the airflow or pressure sensors may result in inaccurate airflow measurements (Fisk 2008). Regardless of whether airflow sensors are factory or field installed, accuracies of these sensors should be verified with appropriately calibrated equipment at start-up and during occupancy on regular time intervals.

Indirect Measurement Methods

Direct measurement methods for measuring outdoor airflow rates are considered to be substantially more accurate than indirect methods. Indirect methods for measuring outdoor airflow rates include plenum pressure control, CO_2 concentration balance, CO_2 mass balance, supply/return differential calculation, variable-frequency-drive-controlled fan slaving, adiabatic proration formulae, and fixed minimum position intake dampers.

Design Issues for Commissioning and O&M

The designer should make provisions for measurement and verification of the minimum outdoor airflows during the initial commissioning as well during the ongoing commissioning of a building. Such provisions include easy access to the airflow sensors, hardware and software that can detect sensor (e.g., airflow) and equipment (damper motor) malfunctions. In addition, the design criteria and occupancy assumptions should be listed in a clear format in the O&M manual so that one can evaluate the continued relevance of design outdoor airflow rates. The building maintenance staff should be informed of the need to adjust the minimum amount of outdoor air as space use and occupancy change.

EFFECTIVELY DISTRIBUTE VENTILATION AIR TO THE BREATHING ZONE

Ventilation only works when the air is delivered to the breathing zone. Different methods of distribution have different efficiencies. For an inefficient system, the quantity of outdoor air at the air handler must be increased in order to provide the required minimum quantities in the breathing zone that are required by code and by ASHRAE Standard 62.1.

Zone Air Distribution Effectiveness

The airflow rate that needs to be distributed to a zone varies by the effectiveness of the distribution within the room. The ventilation airflow rate provided to the zone must be sufficient to provide the required ventilation air to the breathing zone.

The zone outdoor airflow is given by Equation 6.2 from ASHRAE Standard 62.1, as follows:

$$V_{oz} = V_{bz}/E_z$$

where

V_{oz} = quantity of ventilation air delivered to the occupied zone, cfm (L/s)

V_{bz} = quantity of ventilation air delivered to the breathing zone, cfm (L/s)

E_z = zone air distribution effectiveness

Thus, the less efficient an air distribution system is within a zone, the greater will be the required flow of outdoor air to the zone. Choosing air distribution configurations that improve effectiveness, or at least do not decrease it, is therefore an important design decision.

EFFECTIVELY DISTRIBUTE VENTILATION AIR TO MULTIPLE SPACES

Ventilation only works when the air is delivered to the breathing zone. Different methods of distribution have different efficiencies. For an inefficient system, the outdoor airflow rate at the air handler must be increased to provide the required minimum outdoor airflow rate to the breathing zone. For multiple-zone recirculating systems, the system will have an efficiency E_v that needs to be calculated to determine the outdoor airflow rate required at the air handler. This efficiency is for the system and needs to be used in addition to the corrections for effectiveness of distributing air within the zone E_z. The values for system efficiency can range from 1.0 to 0.3 or lower, with higher values being more efficient (better).

USE DEDICATED OUTDOOR AIR SYSTEMS WHERE APPROPRIATE

The 100% outdoor air approach makes calculating the required outdoor ventilation airflow more straightforward than for multiple-space systems. Having the ventilation system decoupled from the heating and air-conditioning system can provide many advantages for HVAC system design. A disadvantage may be that there is an additional item of equipment, the 100% outdoor air unit itself.

100% outdoor air systems must address latent loads, the largest being the latent load from the outdoor air in some cases. The 100% outdoor air may also be designed to remove the latent load from both the outdoor air and the building (total latent load), in which case there are multiple advantages.

If the exhaust airstream is located close to the ventilation airstream, both sensible and latent energy can be recovered in the 100% outdoor air. This feature makes a 100% outdoor air system much more energy efficient. It is not necessary that the exhaust and supply airflows be exactly the same rate, but if they differ, the difference must be accounted for in the equipment sizing calculations.

100% Outdoor Air Component Combinations

Integration of energy recovery technology can reduce the load on the heating and cooling coils. Energy recovery components can be either total (enthalpy) energy recovery or sensible energy recovery. Because of the latent load of outdoor air, in many areas use of an active desiccant wheel or a passive dehumidification component may be cost effective. These devices assist in managing humidity within the building.

USE DEMAND-CONTROLLED VENTILATION WHERE APPROPRIATE

Demand-controlled ventilation (DCV) is a control strategy that varies the amount of ventilation by resetting the outdoor air intake flow set points to an occupied space based on the changing number of occupants. The goal is to avoid underventilation (which would increase the potential for poor IAQ) as well as overventilation (which wastes energy).

The simplest approach to DCV is control of the outdoor air rate in an on/off manner based on signals from a room occupancy sensor, time clock, or light switch. A more sophisticated approach uses a signal that is proportional to the number of persons in a space to automatically modulate the amount of outdoor air.

Appropriate Application of DCV

DCV is most appropriate in densely occupied spaces with intermittent or variable population. For these spaces, DCV offers the potential for both energy savings and improved IAQ. The benefit of DCV increases with the level of density, transiency, and cost of energy.

Occupancy categories most appropriate for DCV include theaters, auditoriums/public assembly spaces, gyms, some classrooms, restaurants, and office conference rooms. Densely occupied spaces with people-related pollutants other than normal bioeffluents (such as waiting areas of health-care facilities) are less appropriate for DCV despite their intermittent or variable population. Densely and continuously occupied office spaces (such as call centers) are less likely to see the benefits of DCV given the lack of variability in occupancy.

Although the energy-conserving benefits of DCV may be small in general office buildings, making DCV a not very cost-effective energy-saving strategy in such applications, certain aspects of DCV controls may be beneficial to such a building in ensuring that the design ventilation rates are supplied under all operating conditions. For example, continuous measurement of outdoor airflow rates and indoor CO_2 levels can help building personnel find ventilation system faults or make adjustments to the HVAC system set points, thus avoiding overventilation or underventilation relative to the design or code requirements.

DCV in Multiple-Zone Systems

Application of DCV in single-zone systems is fairly straightforward. However, neither ASHRAE Standard 62.1-2019 nor its associated user's manual address the design and operation of DCV for systems that serve multiple spaces. There is currently no published guidance for DCV in multiple-zone systems.

CO_2-Based DCV

Measurement and control of indoor CO_2 concentrations has been the most popular DCV method because CO_2 sensors and associated controllers are relatively inexpensive and, in controlled environments, have been shown to correlate well with people-related contaminant levels (Persily 1997). Several packaged HVAC equipment manufacturers now offer CO_2 sensors and controllers as an option for their equipment. This method is based on the fact that the rate of CO_2 generation indoors by occupants is proportional to the number of occupants and their activity levels. Other indoor sources of CO_2 and removal mechanisms may exist in some buildings, and in some cases they may be significant enough to compromise the viability of a CO_2-based DCV.

Design Considerations for CO_2-Based DCV. CO_2-based DCV is required by some building codes. However, despite its relatively low cost and short payback, the CO_2-based DCV market has grown slowly since 1990 and has not necessarily reached its peak potential. This is partially due to the limited data on the long-term performance of these sensors. Limited studies have indicated that there are numerous issues that need to be addressed by further research. Some of the reported issues with the CO_2 sensors relate to the accuracy of the sensors while others relate to maintenance/calibration and to the sensor lag times (Shrestha and Maxwell 2009a, 2009b, 2010; Emmerich and Persily 2001; Fisk et al. 2013). Also, the CO_2 generation rates measured and reported for sedentary adults (1.2 met units) need to be adjusted for other situations, such as for children in classrooms.

The following considerations should be made during the design of a CO_2-based DCV system:

- In HVAC systems with open plenum returns, CO_2 sensors should be located in the room so that the average concentrations at breathing level can be obtained. Enough sensors should be placed within a space in order to increase the certainty of the sensed average space CO_2 concentration. Sensors placed in return air plenums will not necessarily yield a reliable value representative of the average breathing concentration for the space.

- In HVAC systems with ducted returns, CO_2 sensors may be placed in the return air duct from a zone if the designer can relate the CO_2 measurement in the return duct to breathing-level average measurements provided that same occupancy types and space usage are serviced by the return duct in that zone.

- In all rooms with CO_2 sensors, DCV controls should maintain CO_2 concentrations (with respect to the outdoor air CO_2 concentration) between the maximum level expected at design population and the minimum level expected at minimum population.

- Outdoor air CO_2 concentration should be measured continuously using a CO_2 sensor located near the outdoor air intake. Alternatively, outdoor air CO_2 concentration can be assumed to be constant, provided the constant level is conservatively high and based on recent historical data for the area where the building is located. If an assumed value is used, consideration should be given in the controls to offsetting potential errors such as the tendency to overventilate at higher densities and underventilate at lower densities.

- CO_2 sensors should be specified by the manufacturer to have an uncertainty no greater than ±50 ppm for concentration ranges typically found in HVAC applications (e.g., 400 to 2000 ppm), be factory and field calibrated, and require calibration no more frequently than once every five years while operating under typical field conditions per manufacturer specifications (limited research indicates that field-based calibration should be performed once every one to two years [Fisk 2008]).
- Provisions (such as physical access and verification that the sensor is operating correctly) should be provided for periodic maintenance and calibration. This will assist in (a) properly maintaining the DCV system and components and (b) validating that the proper amount of ventilation is supplied under all variable occupancy levels and load conditions. Data logging of CO_2 concentrations can be considered; it allows review of CO_2 trend data in part to ensure that the CO_2 sensors and controls are operating as intended.

Alternatives to CO_2-Based DCV

In certain limited applications, such as classrooms, where occupancy is either zero or nearly 100%, the control of outdoor air rates in an on/off manner based on signals from a room occupancy sensor, time clock, or light switch is a practical and energy-saving solution. Other forms of DCV are based on technologies that can count the number of persons entering and exiting a space and adjust ventilation accordingly. In its simplest form, this is done by estimating the number of persons during certain time periods and programming the ventilation supply accordingly. However, new advances in sensing and microcomputing technologies may automate this task. Dynamic infrared imaging hardware and software are now used for marketing and security purposes, and research proposals have been submitted to evaluate these technologies with DCV. New technologies have reduced signal delays and calibration drifts when compared to chemical-sensor-based DCV.

USE NATURAL OR MIXED-MODE VENTILATION WHERE APPROPRIATE

Natural ventilation is typically used to describe nonmechanical means to provide ventilation air and cooling. As a result, naturally ventilated buildings achieve a wider range of indoor environmental conditions by dynamically adapting to ambient conditions that can provide conditions that may be comfortable for the occupants in accordance with ASHRAE Standard 55-2013, *Thermal Environmental Conditions for Human Occupancy*.

Clearly, there are locations that are not suitable for natural ventilation/natural cooling, especially where tight temperature and humidity control is required or in locations that experience prolonged periods of high outdoor temperature, high humidity, chronic outdoor air pollution, or other severe weather conditions. On the other hand, there are many locations that can take advantage of natural ventilation strategies for the whole of the year or a significant portion of the year.

When considering the use of natural ventilation, early consideration and analysis of the appropriateness of the prevailing climate must be evaluated in some detail. Climatic issues such as the ambient air temperatures, humidity, cleanliness of the outdoor air, wind speeds, nearby outdoor noise levels, and wind airflow patterns need to be considered.

Natural ventilation generally works well with other sustainable strategies; for instance, energy-efficient design typically requires the reduction/control of thermal gains and losses, which in turn is an essential design component for natural ventilation. Daylit buildings with narrow floor plates and high floor-to-ceiling areas work well for natural ventilation. Also, naturally ventilated buildings often take advantage of thermally massive elements such as concrete/masonry structures to provide a more stable mean radiant temperature by absorbing and releasing heat slowly. Mass can also be used to temper incoming air, especially when using night flushing, and can moderate mean radiant temperature, which improves comfort. Mass provides a thermal damper, so the building requires less overall energy to heat and cool (Willmert 2001). Displacement ventilation and decoupled 100% outdoor air strategies can work well with natural ventilation, as well.

Natural ventilation and mixed-mode ventilation systems are now more common in buildings, especially in the Pacific North West, Japan, and Europe. With mixed-mode systems, natural ventilation is commonly used for ventilating and cooling for most of the year, and

Figure 7.1 Natural ventilation concept for a supertall building.

mechanical ventilation and cooling systems are used for peak cooling and when natural ventilation is not available.

Also, pressure sensors and motor-driven dampers are being used to control pressures in various parts of buildings and to take advantage of stack effect or wind pressure to deliver ventilation where and when it is needed. These sophisticated ventilation control systems need considerable care in design and operation as well as end-user education.

Key issues for consideration in selecting and designing natural ventilation systems include the following:

- Delivering enough outdoor air to dilute indoor pollutants and maintain the required thermal comfort (in accordance with ASHRAE Standard 62.1 [ASHRAE 2016b] and ASHRAE Standard 55 [ASHRAE 2017b])

- Reducing the entry of undesirable constituents in polluted outdoor air

- Good solar control and modest internal gains, plus an acceptance that the internal temperature will exceed 77°F (25°C) for some period of time (CIBSE 2005)

- Controlling airflow through passive or active means, which requires well-designed systems with thorough consideration of airflows under the wide range of outdoor weather conditions to which the building will be subjected

- A satisfactory acoustic environment (natural ventilation openings provide a noise transmission path from outside to inside, which may be a determining factor in some building locations; in addition, naturally ventilated buildings often include large areas of exposed concrete in order to increase the thermal capacity of the space, and such large areas of hard surface require careful attention to achieve a satisfactory acoustic environment for the occupants)

- Smoke control (because smoke can follow natural ventilation paths, the integration of the fire safety strategy must be integrated with the natural ventilation design)

- Health and safety (many natural ventilation openings will be at significant heights above floor level, so safe/easy access to these openings/control devices is required to be considered in the design)

WHY NATURAL VENTILATION?

Natural ventilation, however, may not be good for every location. Previous studies have indicated that at least 30% of the day must be able to be use natural ventilation for it to "break even" in terms of cost effectiveness and practicality reasons. Most areas within the United States would better be suited with mixed-mode conditioning systems where natural ventilation is used seasonally, when it is at least usable for 30% or more of the day, with the rest of the year using a mechanical system. Operable openings however can be used if exterior conditions allow when the "mechanical system part" of the year is in effect. Within the United States, the southern states are typically too hot and humid, whereas the northern states are typically too cold for most of the year. An ideal location for using natural ventilation would be the San Francisco region, where more than 30% (closer to 40%) of the time natural ventilation can be utilized.

Another large concern with natural ventilation is air quality. In some areas, the quality of air can deter designers from risking using natural ventilation. Locations such as China have high air pollution and will therefore pose a health hazard by relying on natural ventilation. Governing agencies define contaminants within certain regions that must be disclosed to clients before natural ventilation models are incorporated into buildings.

In moderate climates, enthalpy or temperature controls can be used with forced ventilation fans to cool the building with outdoor air, when the outdoor temperature is low enough and airflow rate is high enough to meet the cooling load. Historically, though, enthalpy controls are high-maintenance types of controls.

Natural ventilation to supplant mechanical air conditioning may be acceptable in some buildings and some climatic regions. In most tall buildings with high cooling loads, this is not a viable option. Using windows or other openings in the building to increase ventilation air to a high enough level to even partially supplant conditioned air is not practical in most commercial tall buildings.

Table 7.1 Natural Ventilation Top 10 Feasibility Questions[1]

Data to Review	Question to be Asked (If Answer is Yes, Move to Next Question)
Building envelope	Is the building envelope performance optimized to minimize solar gain into the building? Target a maximum total solar load of 1.26 Btu/h/ft^2 (4 W/m^2) of sun patch floor area in a cooling condition.
Internal heat loads	Is the total internal heat load minimized to less than 0.63 Btu/h/ft^2 (2 W/m^2) for naturally conditioned space or within the cooling capacity of auxiliary systems?
Weather normals: mean maximum/ mean minimum	In looking at the climate data's monthly mean minimum and mean maximum, are there at least six months where the monthly maximum is less than 80°F (26.7°C) but mean minimum is higher than 32°F (0°C)?
Frequency of occurrence psychrometric chart	In further looking at climate data, does the frequency of occurrence psychrometric chart for occupied hours have more than 30% of the time between 60°F to 80°F (15.6°C to 26.7°C) and less than 70% relative humidity?
Ambient environment, possible locations of openings	Is the surrounding environment suitable for direct intake of air from outside (i.e., there are no security concerns; the ambient environment is sufficiently quiet; air quality meets standard; openings are not near street level, highways, or industrial plants, or at elevation of a neighbor's discharge)?
Window locations and sizes, accessibility	Can the equivalent of 4% to 5% of the floor area as window opening area be found with direct access to the window by everyone within 20 ft (6 m)?
Wind rose, feasible flow paths: inlet to outlet under all wind conditions	Can one rely on wind-driven effects for cooling? Is there a direct low-pressure airflow path from a low-level opening to a high-level opening within the space, and will it be preserved once furniture/ tenant improvement work is complete?
High afternoon temperatures	Does the climate have regular outdoor air temperatures over 80°F (26.7°C)? If yes, review whether exposed thermal mass is possible.
Diurnal range on hot days	Does the climate have a diurnal range that has nighttime temperatures below 65°F (18.3°C) for at least 8 hours a night on the worst-case days? If yes, move to multizone modeling of thermal mass and consider night purge.
Dew-point temperatures throughout year	Throughout the year, do you have consistent outdoor air dew points throughout the year of less than 64°F (17.8°C)? If yes, move to multizone modeling and consider a radiant cooling system.

1.   Table courtesy of Erin McConahey.

Stack effect could be used as the driving force to ventilate restrooms, stairwells, and equipment rooms if the flows can be controlled. However, most building codes do not allow credit for infiltration flows toward the minimum required ventilation rates.

Increased ventilation to supplant mechanical cooling is only appropriate when the outdoor air conditions can meet the cooling load. In addition, occupant thermal comfort has been linked directly to productivity. Most occupants will not tolerate unacceptable comfort conditions and, if known, poor IAQ. As such, the use of natural ventilation may not appropriate to commercial tall buildings in most climates. However, the rising cost of energy is propelling the desire for cheaper indoor air ventilation, forcing the industries to move into an adaptive comfort model (discussed later in this chapter) for naturally ventilated spaces.

VENTILATION PER ASHRAE STANDARD 62.1-2019

ASHRAE Standard 62.1-2019, *Ventilation for Acceptable Indoor Air Quality*, defines the requirements for minimum ventilation rates (ASHRAE 2019b). The ventilation rate procedure given in the standard prescribes the rate at which ventilation air must be delivered to a given space. The discussion in this guide is based on the use of the ventilation rate procedure. This method is the most common method used to determine ventilation rates for a system under design.

An alternative method, the indoor air quality procedure (IAQP), provides guidelines for the specification of acceptable concentration of certain contaminants in indoor air but does not prescribe ventilation rates or air treatment methods. This method may be used in situations where the ventilation rate procedure does not provide appropriate results. For example, the IAQP may be used under the following conditions:

- If the ventilation rate determined by the ventilation rate procedure is not adequate to control a specific contaminant
- If contaminant concentrations can be maintained at acceptable levels with lower ventilation rates than called for by the ventilation rate procedure

The ventilation requirements for commercial and institutional buildings are given in ASHRAE Standard 62.1-2019. These ventilation rates were chosen to achieve an acceptable level of IAQ by control of CO_2, particulates, odors, and other contaminants common to those spaces. If cleaned, recirculated air is used to reduce the indoor air below the recommended values, the IAQP must be used. The requirements are given in terms of airflow of ventilation air per person, or per unit of floor area. If the actual number of occupants in a space is not known, the table in ASHRAE Standard 62.1 provides typical occupancies in terms of people per 1000 ft^2 (people per 93 m^2).

Office spaces and conference rooms require 20 cfm (9.4 L/s) of outdoor air per person. Office spaces have an estimated maximum occupancy density of 70 people per 1000 ft^2 (70 people per 93 m^2), and conference rooms have an estimated maximum occupancy density of 50 people per 1000 ft^2 (50 people per 93 m^2), respectively.

The IAQP provides designers with an important option or adjunct to the prescriptive ventilation rate procedure (VRP) in ASHRAE Standard 62.1, thereby increasing the potential for good IAQ control.

In general,[4] the attainment of good IAQ can be achieved through the removal or control of irritating, harmful, and unpleasant constituents in the indoor environment. The established methods for contaminant control are source control, ventilation, and filtration and air cleaning. Source control approaches should always be explored and applied first because they are usually more cost effective than either ventilation (dilution) or fresh air conditioning (FAC)

---

4. This chapter provides partial text from *Indoor Air Quality Guide: Best Practices for Design, Construction, and Commissioning* (ASHRAE 2009) from the section below through to the section "Provide Comfort Conditions that Enhance Occupant Satisfaction. For this information to integrate smoothly into this book, the figure and table numbering have been modified from the original; otherwise the content remains as originally published.

(extraction). Other strategies in this guide discuss various aspects of ventilation for attainment of acceptable IAQ as presented by ASHRAE Standard 62.1-2016. However, the main focus of ASHRAE Standard 62.1 is the VRP, which specifies minimum outdoor air ventilation rates to dilute indoor contaminants.

This discussion focuses on an alternative compliance pathway to the VRP that is referred to in ASHRAE Standard 62.1-2016 as the *IAQ procedure*. The application of the IAQP typically uses a combination of source control and enhanced extraction through filtration and/or gas-phase chemical air cleaning, in some cases resulting in a reduction in the minimum outdoor air intake flow required, compared to the more commonly used prescriptive VRP.

The IAQP generally uses all three basic control methods:

- Source control
- Ventilation
- FAC, which combines the strengths of each to yield the following potential benefits:
  o A methodology for documenting and predicting the outcome of source control approaches and rewarding source reduction tactics by potentially lowering ventilation requirements is used.
  o It can lower the heat, moisture, and pollutant burden of outdoor air by reducing the outdoor airflow rate to the conditioned space.
  o The use of enhanced FAC lowers the constituent concentrations of contaminants of concern (COC) contained in the outdoor air.
  o The use of enhanced FAC can lower the constituent concentration of COCs created and recirculated within the conditioned space.
  o Enhanced FAC can result in cleaner heat exchange surfaces and more energy-efficient HVAC system operation.
  o Lower outdoor air intake rates can lower system capacity and operating costs.

The IAQP was first introduced in the original ASHRAE Standard 62 in 1973, discussed in ASHRAE Standard 62-1981, and formalized in ASHRAE Standard 62-2013 as an alternate path of compliance to attain acceptable IAQ. However, the IAQP was not widely accepted by model code bodies, so approval by the authority having jurisdiction typically requires a code variance. For this reason, the procedure has not been widely used by designers, who are also reluctant to use it because of its complexity, the potential liability involved, and the additional engineering rigor required, including more calculations, analyses, and/or testing. The occasional use of the procedure has been predominately in areas with high outdoor humidity and heat loads, in buildings having high internal contaminant generation, and in buildings having high density and diversity, such as arenas, schools, auditoriums, theaters, convention centers, and hotels.

Related Strategies

There is considerable interaction of the application of the IAQP to other areas of the design process. These include the following:

- The evaluation of sources, components, and concentrations of COC in the outdoor air
- The selection and evaluation of the building component materials for their outgassing and contaminant source contributions
- The determination of filtration needs and the selection of the appropriate FAC efficacy and equipment type
- The evaluation and selection of the ventilation system
- The selection of HVAC systems and equipment so that enhanced filtration can be installed with adequate access, space, and fan horsepower

Applying the IAQP

ASHRAE Standard 62.1-2019 allows several alternative approaches of applying the IAQP. The alternatives include a mass balance approach using steady-state calculations of COCs, a comparison with similar buildings approach to document successful usage elsewhere, and a contaminant monitoring approach where actual contaminant levels are monitored. By following a set of predefined steps, it is possible to both enhance the IAQ and substantially reduce the outdoor airflow requirements in some buildings. The steps include evaluation of COCs, target levels of acceptability, methods for determining acceptability, examination of ventilation requirements, material selection, FAC options, and implementation and documentation.

PROVIDE COMFORT CONDITIONS THAT ENHANCE OCCUPANT SATISFACTION

Thermal conditions indoors, combined with occupant activity and clothing, determine occupant thermal comfort, which in turn impacts occupant productivity and perceptions of air quality. Dry-bulb temperature is only one physical parameter out of many that interact in a complex manner to produce occupant satisfaction.

Thermal conditions affect chemical and biological contaminant levels and/or the intensity of occupants' reactions to these contaminants, but our knowledge of these effects and their mechanisms is very limited. Despite this limited knowledge, achieving high performance in thermal comfort is likely to result in lower contaminant levels and better occupant perceptions of IAQ.

Tools exist for calculating the proportion of people likely to be satisfied by the combination of comfort factors that include dry-bulb temperature, humidity, air velocity, and radiant temperature. The most commonly known tool in the U.S. is the Center for the Built Environment (CBE) Thermal Comfort Tool (Hoyt et al. 2019). To use this tool, the amount of clothing worn by occupants and their levels of metabolic (or physical) activity must be provided in units of clo (clothing level) and met (metabolic rate), respectively.

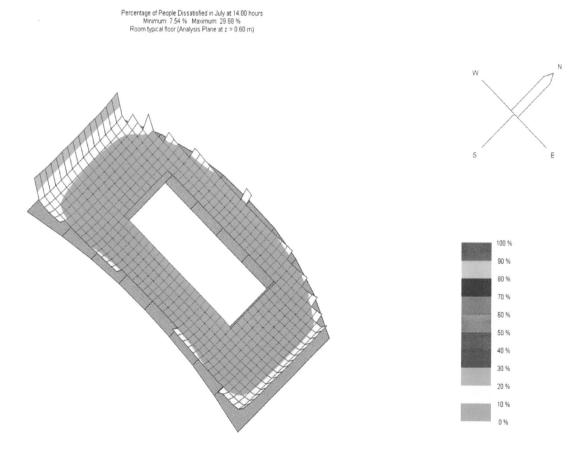

Figure 7.2 Thermal comfort analysis of a typical floor of the Pearl River Tower.

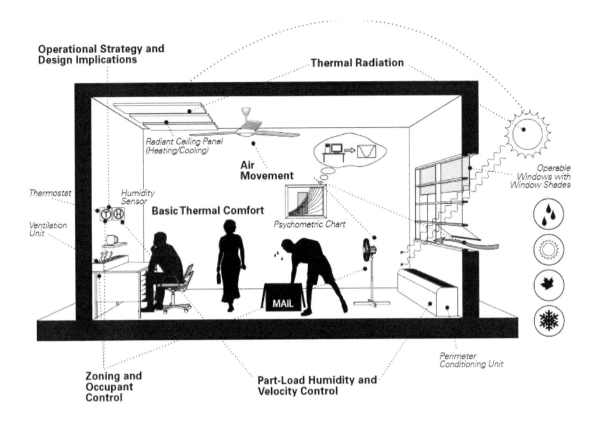

Figure 7.3 The typical interactions determining occupant comfort.

In traditional designs, the HVAC designer's role in achieving comfort conditions often begins and ends at the selection of an indoor design condition and the sizing of the HVAC system to provide these conditions at peak load. The selection of a design dry-bulb condition involves both comfort and cost or energy considerations and can dictate critical design features of the system. For example, some designers may pick a relatively high design cooling condition such as 78°F (26°C) to conserve energy, while others may select one such as 72°F (22°C) to maximize the number of satisfied occupants. Selecting systems and controls that perform efficiently at part load can mitigate the energy downside of the latter.

Each person having control over his or her own environment, referred to as *personalized ventilation and conditioning* (as provided in many automobiles and airplanes, for example) is the ideal situation but is not easily attained in buildings. It is wise, therefore, to select zones carefully and consider using as many as is needed to create sufficient homogeneity within each zone to improve the ability to satisfy comfort needs of occupants in the zones. Rooms and areas having loads that vary over time in patterns that are significantly different from areas that surround them benefit from having their own conditioning control loops and thermostats.

It is expected that individual occupants in the same temperature control zone will have different thermal comfort needs. They can be encouraged, therefore, to adjust their clothing to fit their own needs. However, if the occupants have an adjustable thermostat in the space, then so-called "thermostat wars" may occur, where occupants frequently readjust the thermostat that others have set. This situation can reduce both the efficiency and effectiveness of the comfort system. The solution in some cases may be either giving control to a neutral party, such as the building operator or office manager, or using thermostats for which the temperature adjustment range is limited.

The control of humidity at part load is a comfort goal that needs to be considered in the design of systems and their control sequences. Controlling moisture is also important to limit condensation and mold.

Air diffusion devices should be selected so that the required air velocity conditions in occupied zones are maintained at low airflow, as would occur in a VAV system. It is also important to choose thermostat locations that best represent the conditions that occupants will experience and that are not affected by solar radiation or other heat sources.

ADAPTIVE COMFORT

Humphreys and Nicol created the original papers on the adaptive model in the 1970s. Their statistical analyses of comfort questionnaire data from building occupants are can be classified today as adaptive models. "Comfort temperature" (also called *neutrality*) inside a building, was described as well as its relationship with the mean temperatures prevailing inside the building at the time of the survey. Humphreys and Nicol noted that naturally ventilated buildings and buildings operating in free-running mode had indoor comfort temperatures strongly correlated with the mean monthly temperature outdoors at the time of the survey, suggesting that people can adjust to a broader range of temperatures than was previously considered. In addition, ASHRAE 55-2017 adapts mean monthly outdoor air temperature to evaluate the indoor comfortable operative temperature (ASHRAE 2017b).

In the latest ASHRAE Standard 55 (2017b), the standard replaces the mean monthly temperature with prevailing mean air temperature. On the other hand, for the EN 15251 Standard, *Indoor Environmental Input Parameters for Design and Assessment of Energy Performance of Buildings—Addressing Indoor Air Quality, Thermal Environment, Lighting and Acoustics,* it adapts the running mean outdoor air temperature to predict indoor comfortable operative temperature (CEN 2007).

The acceptable comfort zone is prescribed by ASHRAE Standard 55, (ASHRAE 2017b). Comfort is defined as the conditions under which 80% or more of the building occupants find an area thermally acceptable in still air and shade conditions.

When natural ventilation and natural conditioning are pursued, it is important to ensure that the minimum outside air requirements are achievable under all conditions, inclusive of those hours when the backup mechanical ventilation system is operational. This is a requirement of ASHRAE Standard 62.1 (ASHRAE 2019b). Complying with the natural ventilation requirements does not imply any likelihood of compliance with the comfort standard. At high outdoor air temperatures, the amount of air necessary to provide a heat-absorption function is far higher than the amount of air required to meet the minimum ventilation requirements. The design team should never assume that complying with ASHRAE 62.1 will result in a comfortable space.

Confirming the Requirement to Meet a Comfort Standard

Neither the International Mechanical Code (ICC 2018) nor the California Mechanical Code (CMC 2015) reference ASHRAE Standard 55 as a requirement for human comfort. Thus it would be the local jurisdiction to require compliance with the ASHRAE Standard 55 (ASHRAE 2017a) as a comfort standard.

California Title 24 Part 6 (CEC 2015a) does not explicitly address the permissibility of natural conditioning as a space conditioning option. The code does allow the design team to demonstrate that a backup heating and cooling system does not have to be modeled if the indoor condition model of the natural ventilation system can show that the space can be controlled to remain within a prescribed set of temperatures, namely the space thermostat throttling range of 2°F (1°C). By the very nature of naturally conditioned spaces, the indoor temperatures will likely fluctuate far more than this. Thus, if natural conditioning is pursued in California, it is likely that a modification will need to be negotiated with the authority having jurisdiction to redefine the comfort range. It is recommended that the comfort control range be widened to at least ASHRAE Standard 55 (ASHRAE 2017a) as an alternate compliance path by showing the authority having jurisdiction the comfort control parallels between a natural conditioning system and the code-required design of space conditioning systems. This relies on the pre-existing code explicitly referencing the need to size space conditioning equipment "as a rule" to meet ASHRAE Standard 55 under Section 140.4, as excerpted below:

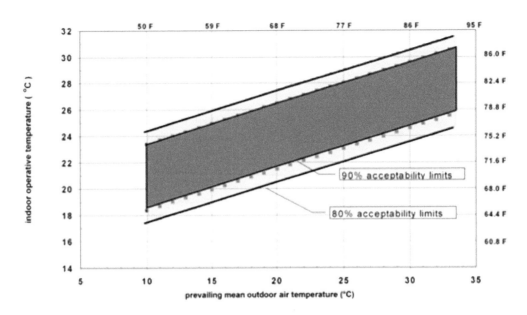

Figure 7.4 The acceptable operative temperature (t_o) ranges for naturally conditioned spaces.

"(b) Calculations. In making equipment sizing calculations under Subsection (a), all of the following rules shall apply: ....

3. Indoor design conditions. Indoor design temperature and humidity conditions for general comfort applications shall be determined in accordance with ASHRAE Standard 55 or *ASHRAE Handbook–Fundamentals*, Chapter 8, except that winter humidification and summer dehumidification shall not be required."

Methodology

To determine the applicability for acceptable indoor operative temperature in occupant-controlled naturally conditioned spaces in ASHRAE Standard 55, the standard defines acceptable thermal environments only for occupant-controlled naturally conditioned spaces that meet all of the following criteria:

a. There is no mechanical cooling system.
b. Representative occupants have metabolic rates ranging from 1.0 to 1.3 met
c. Representative occupants are free to adapt their clothing to the indoor and/or outdoor thermal conditions within a range at least as wide as 0.5 to 1.0 clo.
d. The prevailing mean outdoor temperature is greater than 50°F (10°C) and less than 92.3°F (33.5°C).

The allowable indoor operative temperatures t_o is determined from Figure 7.4, which uses prevailing mean outdoor air temperature based on the arithmetic average of the mean daily outdoor temperature over the period based on no fewer than 7 days and no more than 30 sequential days prior to the day in question. The following equations correspond to the acceptable operative temperature ranges in Figure 7.4:

$$\text{Upper 80\% acceptability limit (°C)} = 0.31t + 21.3$$

$$\text{Upper 80\% acceptability limit (°F)} = 0.31t + 60.5$$

$$\text{Lower 80\% acceptability limit (°C)} = 0.31t + 14.3$$

$$\text{Lower 80\% acceptability limit (°F)} = 0.31t + 47.9$$

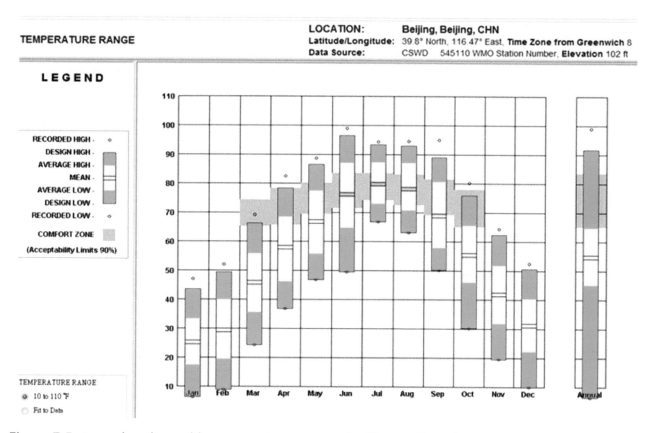

Figure 7.5 Annual and monthly average temperature in Climate Consultant.

In EN 15251, the running mean outdoor air temperature defines indoor operative temperature. The exponentially weighted running mean of the daily mean external air temperature Θ_{ed} is such a series and is calculated from the formula:

$$\Theta_{rm} = (1 - \alpha) \cdot \{\Theta_{ed-1} + \alpha \cdot \Theta_{ed-2} + \alpha 2 \cdot \Theta_{ed-3}\} \qquad (7.1)$$

This equation can be simplified to the following:

$$\Theta_{rm} = (1 - \alpha)\Theta_{ed-1} + \alpha \cdot \Theta_{rm-1} \qquad (7.2)$$

where

Θ_{rm} =   running mean temperature for today

Θ_{rm-1} =   running mean temperature for previous day

Θ_{ed-1} =   the daily mean external temperature for the previous day

Θ_{ed-2} =   is the daily mean external temperature for the day before and so on.

α =   a constant between 0 and 1. Recommended to use 0.8

Evaluation of Adaptive Comfort in Buildings

A theoretical building in Beijing is used to investigate the adaptive comfort model in a naturally ventilated building. The climate in Beijing is of the continental monsoon type with cold and dry winters and hot and humid summers. The range of temperature is wide and the adaptive comfort hours are 1393 hours in Climate Consultant Software (Energy Design Tools 2015) from Figure 7.5 and Figure 7.6.

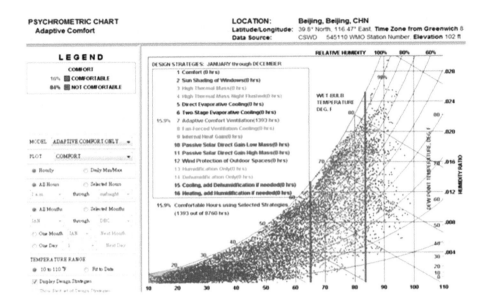

Figure 7.6 Weather data distribution and adaptive comfort zone in Climate Consultant.

The contrast between the ASHRAE 55-2013 adaptive comfort model and EN 15251 is apparent when EN 15251 is applied to the same theoretical building. As shown in Figure 7.4, all of the predicted operative temperatures fall outside the 80% acceptability limit.

Figure 7.7 shows the adaptive comfort results for several months of the year. Nearly all the hourly results are within the prescribed limits. Using the ASHRAE 55-2013 method analyzing naturally ventilated spaces for adaptive comfort compliance is a good method of assessing the potential of natural ventilation during the design stage.

The results shown in Figure 7.7 for a weekly running mean assessment of natural ventilation shows that many of the results are outside of the compliance zone. The debate when using this method is what weekly ambient conditions should be used for the analysis.

Taking the data, the results show the comparison between the flat mean and prevailing running mean methods for a month's worth of data. As noted in Figure 7.8, it is clear that the prevailing mean fluctuates in response to the outdoor air temperatures and runs sometimes lower and sometimes higher than the flat mean.

Demonstrating Compliance with the ASHRAE Standard 55 Adaptive Comfort Method

A further post-processing bins the flat and prevailing mean results to show how many hours in the month meet the comfort standard, with and without elevated air speed, for the model's current configuration of openings. The primary observation shown in Figures 7.9 and 7.10 is that there is less than a 5% difference in the estimate of the hours falling into the compliance zone, with or without elevated speed. The greatest percent differential is in the too hot category, but as the total number of noncompliant hours is so low, this represents a total of 17 hours difference in the variability of using the flat mean instead of the prevailing mean.

There remain several hours in the too hot category that fall into the definition of exceedance hours. Per the definitions in Section 3 of ASHRAE Standard 55 (ASHRAE 2017a), these are "the number of occupied hours within a defined time period in which the environmental conditions in an occupied space are outside of the comfort zone." The designer can either perform iterations to increase opening sizes to comply with the Adaptive Comfort Method for 100% of occupied hours.

Alternatively, one could discuss with the owner and the authority having jurisdiction what the acceptable number of exceedance hours can be. If one looks for parallels with mechanical comfort conditioning systems, ASHRAE Standard 90.1 (ASHRAE 2016a) clauses 11.5.2.i and G3.1.2.3 require that unmet load hours not exceed 300 in terms of equipment sizing and perfor-

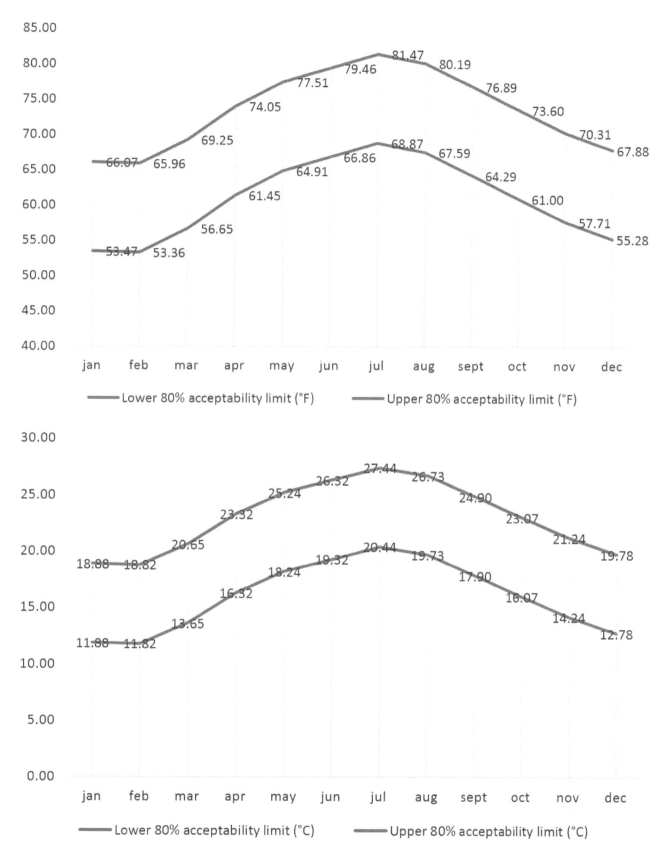

Figure 7.7 Monthly 80% upper and lower temperature limits for natural ventilation compliance in New York, I-P and SI.

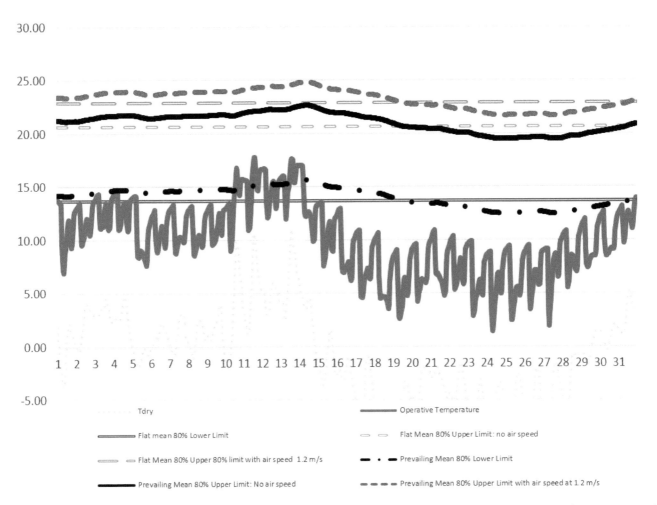

Figure 7.8 ASHRAE 55 adaptive comfort comparison of indoor operative temperature to flat mean and prevailing mean criteria: Buoyancy driven for Moscow in the month of March. Alpha = 0.7 for prevailing mean.

Table 7.2 ASHRAE Standard 55 Adaptive Comfort Compliance Status

ASHRAE 55 Adaptive Comfort Compliance Status	March
Flat mean too cold	183
Flat mean no speed good	15
Flt mean with speed good	15
Flat mean too hot	0
Prevailing mean too cold	190
Prevailing mean no speed good	8
Prevailing mean with speed good	8
Prevailing mean too hot	0

mance within the energy model showing compliance for energy efficiency. In a similar manner, the Nonresidential Alternative Calculation Method Reference Manual for the 2016 Building Efficiency Standards (CEC 2015a) defines that the heating system and cooling system must each individually have less than 150 unmet load hours (UMLH) each to comply with the energy code modeling protocol.

From Figure 7.9 we can see that the months March, October, and November have a majority of hours which are "too cold" and therefore natural ventilation should not be considered

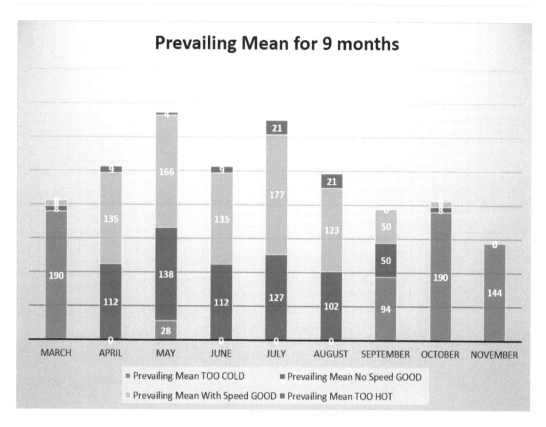

Prevailing Mean for 9 months

Figure 7.9 ASHRAE 55 prevailing mean natural conditioning compliance hours project due to buoyancy driven ventilation for a typical floor of the Moscow for nine months of the year.

during these months (as well as in December, January, and February). September has more than 90 hours when it is "too cold," so it is not recommended to use natural ventilation during this month.

Checking Simultaneous ASHRAE Standard 62.1 Compliance

The ROOM tool (White and Holmes 2009) has an output of ventilation caused by outdoor air entering the space. This hourly data can be plotted and evaluated for the number of total hours that natural ventilation complies with both ASHRAE Standards 55 and 62.1 or with both ASHRAE Standard 55 and the Russian Energy Code. Figure 7.10 demonstrates the visualization on this type of analysis. The zero hours are hours of nonoccupancy and can thus be disregarded. There are, however, a handful of hours that are noncompliant. An iteration to increase opening sizes would have to be completed to comply.

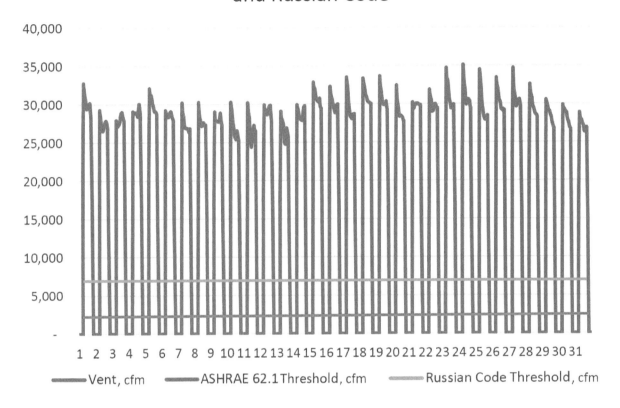

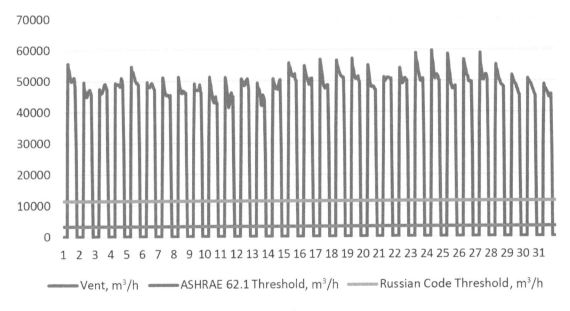

Figure 7.10 Natural-ventilation-created cfm (m³/h) versus ASHRAE 62.1 (1945 cfm [3320 m³/h]) and Russian Code (6745 cfm [11,460 m³/h]), in March as a result of buoyancy-driven ventilation. Location: Moscow.

CHAPTER 8
HVAC Systems

INTRODUCTION

The systems applied in tall commercial office buildings have evolved over the past decades in response to the changes in the perceived goals of the entity that is constructing the building, the expanding needs of the potential occupants (be they a corporate end user or a leasing party), and the concerns of the owner with the availability and cost of energy to operate the building. More recently, environmental concerns, including IAQ and the growing challenge to provide safer buildings, have further influenced the approach taken in the system selected for a modern tall commercial building.

To meet the challenge of providing systems that address these major issues, commercially available equipment deployment has also gone through a period of modification in some design details recently. This process of evolution will undoubtedly continue, but the basic general system categories available today and discussed in this chapter will also undoubtedly continue to find wide usage in tall commercial buildings. It is the technical details of the system design that have been and will be subjected to ongoing modification.

ASHRAE Handbook—HVAC Systems and Equipment (2016b) provides guidelines to allow a quantitative evaluation of alternative systems that should be considered in the system selection process. *ASHRAE Handbook—Fundamentals* (2017a) provides means for estimating annual energy costs. *ASHRAE Handbook—HVAC Applications* (2019a) discusses mechanical maintenance and life cycle costing which may be useful in the evaluation process with regard to alternative systems.

This chapter discusses the air-conditioning systems that currently find application in tall commercial buildings. Pertinent details of the installation of these systems are covered in subsequent chapters of this design guide or in *ASHRAE Handbook* references.

CONSIDERATIONS IN SYSTEM SELECTION

There are alternative means of providing air conditioning for the modern high-rise office building. This statement applies to both the system selected, details of the equipment installed, and the location of the installed equipment that is required to provide the operational basis for the selected system. The determination of the appropriate HVAC system and supporting equipment for a project must, as a minimum, be responsive to the following considerations:

- Capital cost
- Initial and future occupancy requirements
- Architectural and structural restraints and objectives

- Internal and external environmental requirements
- Acceptable acoustical levels desired in occupied spaces
- Seismic requirements (when applicable)
- Energy consumption and energy source depletion
- Annual operating and maintenance cost
- Smoke and fire management

This list of points of concern and analysis does not differ in any way from the same type of list that would be prepared for a low-rise building. The alternative systems that could find application will also come from a very similar list of alternative choices but, as noted in the following sections, the choices for the high-rise office building are probably more limited than those for a low-rise project.

Typical air-conditioning systems include VAV or fan-coil units. Newer systems that can provide more flexibility in comfort and air quality and reduction in the main plant size are hybrid systems using radiant ceilings, active beams, and displacement ventilation systems, both sidewall and underfloor.

ALL-AIR VARIABLE-AIR-VOLUME SYSTEM

All-air VAV systems in various configurations are the most commonly used solution in tall commercial buildings. The conditioned air for the VAV system can be provided from a central fan room or from a local floor-by-floor air-conditioning system. These alternative means of obtaining the conditioned air are discussed in Chapter 7. This chapter is primarily concerned with the functioning of the system, the configurations finding application, and variations possible in the system design.

The VAV system controls space temperature by directly varying the quantity of cold supply air with the cooling load. Previous all-air systems in tall commercial buildings used a constant quantity of air and varied the temperature of the supply air by reheat or, in the case of dual-duct systems, by mixing air from a cold duct with that from a warm duct. Because of their inherently higher use of energy, these alternatives are infrequently used now in tall commercial buildings.

VAV terminals or boxes are available in many configurations. All of the configurations control the space temperature by varying the quantity of cold supply air as the cooling load changes in the space. For most projects, pressure-independent terminal units are recommended. The VAV terminals used can vary as a function of the details of the design being used and the nature of the space being supplied with conditioned air.

Interior spaces that have a cooling load at all times of the year regardless of the outdoor air temperature can use any one of three types of VAV boxes:

- A pinch-off box that simply reduces the supply air volume directly with a reduction of the cooling load. This type of terminal is very commonly used in commercial projects. It has the advantage of the lowest vertical dimension of any terminal used in an office building. It has the disadvantage that at low cooling loads, the airflow may be reduced to the point where poor air circulation may result in the space. This disadvantage can be overcome by putting a stop or minimum flow of air below which the terminal will not reduce the airflow. However, the setting of a minimal air flow from the terminal can result in an inability, when light loads are present, to maintain a thermostatic setting for the space.
- A series flow fan-powered VAV terminal that maintains a constant airflow into a space by mixing the required amount of cold supply air with return air from the space. The VAV terminal contains a small fan to deliver the constant airflow to the space. The fan mounted in the unit always operates. This can result in a reduction in the air-conditioning supply fan energy because of the VAV box losses being overcome by the unit-mounted fan. However, because the unit-mounted fan has a very low efficiency, the overall usage of energy by the system will usually be slightly larger than would be the case with a pinch-off box. The slight increase in energy usage is so insignificant, however, that it is rarely a consideration

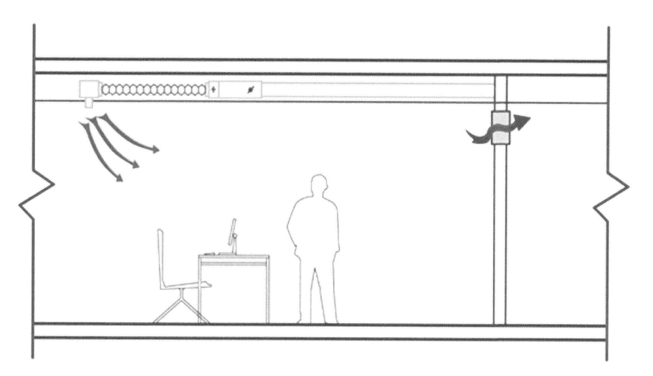

Figure 8.1 A typical overhead VAV system.

in the terminal selected for a project. The primary advantage of the fan-powered box is that the airflow in the space it supplies is constant at all conditions of load and the constant airflow provides excellent, consistent air distribution at all conditions of load. This is of importance if low-temperature air, discussed later, is used to reduce the distributed air quantity and the energy necessary to distribute the system air.

• An induction box that will reduce the supply air volume while simultaneously inducing room air to mix with the supply air, thus maintaining a constant supply airflow to the space. These units require a higher inlet static pressure to achieve the velocities necessary to effect the induction with a concomitant increase in the supply fan energy required for the system. Operational problems have been experienced with units of this type, which has limited their extensive use in large projects. While undoubtedly finding application on commercial projects, this type of terminal is not frequently the choice of many design engineers.

The exterior zone can use any of these three VAV box types, but in geographic locations requiring heat, the system must be designed with an auxiliary means of providing the necessary heat. This can be done external to the VAV terminal by either of two alternatives. In the first, a hot-water baseboard is installed. The flow of the hot water in the convector can be thermostatically controlled, but, more frequently, the temperature of the hot water is scheduled inversely with the outdoor air temperature to increase the amount of heat as the outdoor air temperature decreases. The second alternative is to use electric baseboard on the exterior wall, which is thermostatically controlled separately from the VAV terminal.

An approach that does not utilize baseboard hot water or electric heat is to include, in either the pinch-off or the fan-powered VAV terminal, a hot water or electric coil that is energized as the space temperature continues to drop after the supply airflow has been reduced to a preset minimal flow condition established in the VAV box.

The air system provides base level cooling, dehumidification, and ventilation with sufficient air provided to ensure acceptable air movement for comfort control.

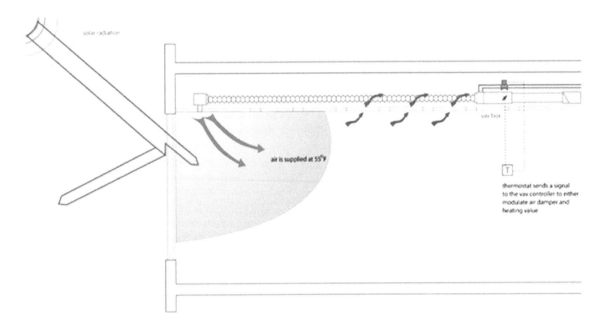

Figure 8.2 The principle of a traditional overhead VAV system.

The terminal VAV units can be installed in a pressure-independent configuration to maintain airflow under fluctuating upstream duct pressures as system flow changes. Therefore, the modulation of a damper in one area, resulting in a change in system volume, will not affect another zone.

The system airflow is varied dependent on the duct static pressure; thus, as less air is required by the zones, the dampers close, increasing the pressure in the duct. The pressure sensor signals the supply fan to slow in order to reduce supply air volume. The system therefore only supplies and conditions air necessary to satisfy demand, thus saving energy. System static pressure will be reset based on the polled damper position to further reduce fan energy.

Each modulating damper can be controlled via the set point of a zone thermostat. Each modulating damper is provided with a minimum turndown, usually 20% of airflow for cooling and 50% airflow for heating, to ensure that outdoor air is provided during periods that the building is occupied. The perimeter can be zoned separately from the interior.

Carbon dioxide sensors located in the space can allow for reduction in minimum outdoor air volume whenever levels are below a preset limit, and energy savings can result. Carbon dioxide sensors do not override the economizer cycle.

LOW-TEMPERATURE-AIR VAV SYSTEMS

All the preceding variations can be designed using conventional temperature differentials between the supply air temperature and the room temperature. These temperature differentials are between 16°F (8.8°C) and 18°F (10°C). Several buildings recently designed are using low-temperature supply air between 48°F (8.9°C) and 50°F (10°C). This increases the temperature supply differential to approximately 28°F (16°C).

This lower-temperature air can be obtained by operating the refrigeration machines with the leaving chilled water at 40°F (4.4°C). If ice storage has been included in the project as a means of reducing the electric demand load in the project, the 40°F (4.4°C) water can be provided as part of the ice storage design. The use of low-temperature air is not in and of itself an argument for ice storage, in that low-temperature air can be obtained using refrigeration equipment providing lower temperature water to obtain the cold air. If the chiller supplies 40°F (4.4°C) chilled water, the operating cost of the refrigeration plant will be increased, and the

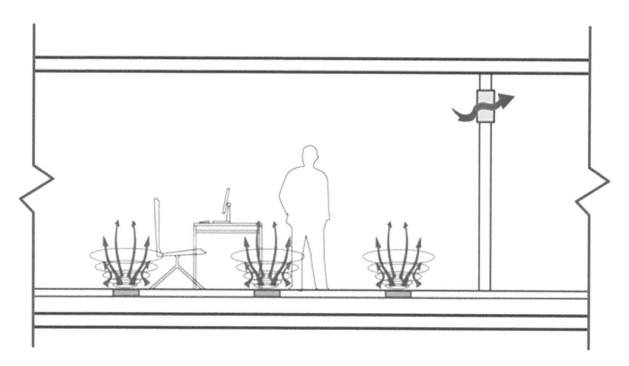

Figure 8.3 A diagram of a typical underfloor conditioning/ventilation system.

chiller will have to operate for a longer period of time before the economizer cycle can be used. Moreover, the use of absorption refrigeration machines and some centrifugal machines may not be possible, in that they usually are not capable of providing 40°F (4.4°C) chilled water.

Of greater importance is that with a solution using low-temperature supply air, there is a dramatic reduction in the quantity of air delivered in the building. This reduction in the distributed air and the reduction in fan power results in a saving in fan power that more than offsets the additional energy used by the chiller. The application of this lower-temperature air mandates the use of fan-powered VAV terminals to avert the problem of reduced airflow at less than design loads, particularly in the interior zone of the project.

UNDERFLOOR AIR SYSTEMS

Of more recent impact has been the consideration of underfloor air-conditioning systems where the space beneath the raised floor is used as a distribution plenum or where terminal units are installed beneath the raised floor. This is contrasted with more traditional systems where the terminal units are installed above the ceiling. Either system, with ceiling-mounted terminals or one distributing air through the raised floor, when properly designed, will meet the comfort requirements of the occupants. The underfloor air-conditioning system typically has higher first cost than comparable overhead distribution systems because of the cost of the raised floor. The cost premium can vary as a function of design details for the project. The cost premiums can be substantially offset if the decision has been made by the owner to incorporate a raised floor for power wiring and information technology cable distribution. Without this fundamental decision, the increase in the cost of the floor itself and a possible increase in the floor-to-floor height (with the resultant premium that must be paid for the exterior wall and the extended internal shafts, piping, and stairs) may well be too great to justify the inclusion of the underfloor distribution system.

The underfloor air-conditioning system design in and of itself contains multiple variations. One such variation uses the principle of *displacement*. Designs typically are implemented with all-air systems in which air is distributed beneath the floor with the void between the slab and the raised floor serving as a supply air plenum. The conditioned air is provided at relatively elevated temperatures of approximately 60°F to 64°F (16°C to 18°C) by blending cold supply air with warm return air. This air then passes from the air-conditioned floor through floor outlets at low velocities and rises vertically to the ceiling through its own buoyancy, removing the heat of people and office equipment as it rises. The ceiling and the space above it function as a return air plenum where the distributed air is collected and returns to the air-conditioning supply system, which can be either a central air-conditioning system or a floor-by-floor type system. The plenum above the ceiling, because of the absence of supply ductwork, can be reduced in its depth when compared to that required for an overhead distribution system.

Another variation of the underfloor air-conditioning system uses all-air terminals or fan-coil units beneath the floor in the exterior zone. The use of a thermostatically controlled terminal can be advantageous in altering the unit capacity in the exterior zone with its widely varying loads. In addition, the use of a fan-coil unit, with both its ability to modify its capacity output as the load varies and with its inherently greater capacity on a percent basis when compared to an all-air terminal, may well provide a more cost-effective solution for tall commercial buildings, particularly those with larger glass elements in the exterior wall. The design using fan-coil units is the same as with all-air terminal designs, in that the air is distributed through floor grilles, with the ceiling acting as a return air plenum.

The fact that projects in Europe nearly always include a raised floor for power wiring and information technology cabling has led to the wide acceptance of underfloor distribution systems throughout the continent. While finding application in the United States, such systems usually have more limited application. This limited application is probably due to the infrequent use of raised floors in the United States and the requirement under the National Electrical Code® (NFPA 2020) in the United States, as also discussed in Chapter 15, that all cabling distributed in an air plenum must be installed in conduit or carry a plenum rating. Where a raised floor is used for cable distribution only, this need for conduit or plenum-rated cabling is not a requirement, but once the raised floor is used for the free discharge of supply air, conduit or plenum-rated cabling becomes mandatory. This can increase the cost of cabling by a substantial percent and can therefore be a significant consideration in the decision process.

There is a wider application of underfloor distribution systems using VAV or fan-coil terminals because of the potential advantage with these systems resulting from the lower cost of reconfiguring a space as the occupancy changes. This is because all that is required is a relocation of a floor diffuser to meet the altered space needs. This is not dissimilar to the relocation of an electrical outlet to meet a new occupant layout. The increase in the interior design layout modifications at lower cost resulting from an underfloor distribution system is a matter worthy of full consideration by the owner and his design team.

Floor supply systems that mix with the total air mass in the occupied zone are not displacement systems. Displacement systems result in temperature gradients in the occupied space, whereas fully mixed systems minimize the room temperature gradients. The displacement system effectively delivers supply air to those parts of the space where heat gain occurs and not to the whole occupied volume; thus, less supply air should be needed. (*Fully mixed* floor supply systems are capable of handling spaces with high heat gains [31.69 Btu/h/ft^2 (>100 W/m^2)], a considerably greater capacity than can be handled by displacement systems alone [12.6 Btu/h/ft^2 (~40 W/m^2)]).

The floor supply system creates zones of discomfort near the outlet that can be between 3 and 4.5 ft (1 and 1.5 m) radius, which should not be near sedentary occupants. The air volume per outlet is relatively low when compared with high-level diffuser systems, which require the use of more supply outlets.

Performance of the system improves with ceiling height. Because the air supply stream is delivered directly into the occupied zone, supply velocity and temperature are restricted, limiting maximum sensible cooling load to 12.6 Btu/h/ft^2 (40 W/m^2) for a 10 ft (3 m) high floor-to-ceiling height; higher loads can be handled where the floor-to-ceiling height is greater. Floor-to-ceiling heights less than 10 ft (3 m) must be considered with great caution, because the higher temperatures developed at the ceiling may cause uncomfortable radiant effects if t_{max} = 86°F (30°C).

Exhaust air heat recovery should be considered. Recirculation of room air should be minimized, because this will be hot, vitiated air, with generally a higher specific enthalpy than outdoor air.

If air patterns in the space are subject to considerable disruption through occupant movement, high infiltration rates, etc., the effectiveness of the system will be reduced.

Displacement ventilation systems should not be used for heating, because the low-velocity heated air will make effective air distribution very difficult. A separate perimeter heating system should be provided.

The selection of supply outlets should be based on minimizing the zone of discomfort around the supply outlet; this will entail using smaller outlets, rather than fewer large ones. The geometry of the supply outlet is not as critical as that for diffusers and registers used in conventional mixing systems. The supply volume flow will be matched to the volume flow rate of the plumes set up by internal heat sources at the given boundary height. The boundary plane that is established will be higher if excessive supply air is introduced and lower if insufficient air is delivered.

Displacement Ventilation

Displacement ventilation is based on the concept of an ideal airflow pattern. Instead of total mixing achieved by other air distribution systems, the flow is unidirectional with the minimum possible spreading of contaminants.

Supply air enters the occupied space at a low velocity and a relatively high temperature when compared with conventional systems. This creates a "pool" of fresh air, which is distributed evenly across the floor. At local heat sources, such as people or machinery, the air temperature is raised. The natural buoyancy of the heated air gives rise to air currents.

Cool, clean air rises in the plume created by the heat source and replaces the warmed/contaminated air. The air plume generated from the heat source carries with it odors and gaseous and particulate contaminants emitted in the occupied space. These warm, contaminated plumes spread out below the ceiling, and an upper contaminated layer is formed. The art of designing a displacement ventilation system is to ensure this hot, contaminated region is outside the occupied zone.

The supply and exhaust are balanced to produce a boundary layer above which the air is contaminated and below which the air is clean, conditioned air in the occupied zone.

Ventilation effectiveness is improved with displacement systems, compared to conventional mixed systems, which depend upon dilution to reduce contaminants. However, the success of the system relies upon reasonable ceiling heights and maintaining relatively 'fragile' air movement patterns.

The system works better with high temperature difference between the supply and exhaust air and is not suitable for applications that require tight temperature and humidity control.

In this respect, the system will function better where a large floor-to-ceiling height exists and therefore favors applications such as industrial spaces or large auditoriums, atria, concourses, some offices, and industrial spaces where higher ceiling heights mean that higher extract temperatures can be tolerated.

Displacement ventilation has the potential for improving energy efficiency and IAQ control for the following reasons:

- Improved air quality because there is little mixing between contaminants and the bulk air
- Lower fan energy because ventilation effectiveness is better
- Higher supply temperature means greater use can be made of free cooling of outdoor air

There are, however, several potential pitfalls that may reduce the benefits:

- Performance on heating
- Disruption of the air patterns within the space through infiltration, occupancy traffic, or other cooling sources (e.g., chilled beams)
- Dehumidification control

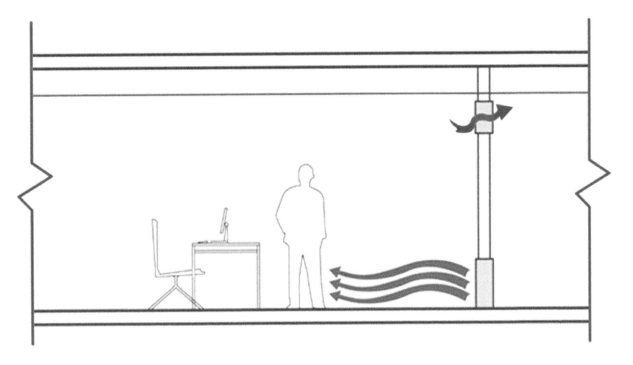

Figure 8.4 The principle of a typical displacement ventilation system.

AIR/WATER SYSTEMS

The air/water systems historically have included induction systems, but today usually use fan-coil units. When this solution is employed, the fan-coil units are installed at the exterior of the building, the interior spaces are usually supplied by an all-air VAV system, and the exterior is provided with a constant volume of air. The fan-coil units in a tall building that requires winter heat are usually designed with a four-pipe secondary water system. Air from the same duct system that supplies the interior can also supply the exterior space to provide the necessary outdoor ventilation air. However, the terminals for the exterior are usually constant-volume boxes to ensure air movement and the delivery of ventilation air to these spaces at all times.

An advantage of the air/water system is a reduction in the required capacity of the supply air and return air systems and in the size of the distribution air ducts from those required with an all-air system (including a low temperature all-air solution). This provides a concomitant reduction in space needed for air-conditioning supply systems in the mechanical equipment room and that required for the distribution ductwork in the ceiling cavity. The air/water system will, however, require space for heat exchangers and pumps to obtain the hot and cold secondary water for the fan-coil units. As discussed in Chapter 2, a reduction in the depth of the ceiling cavity can offer savings in the cost of the exterior wall as well as other vertical elements in the building.

RADIANT CEILINGS

There is a tremendous potential for the application of radiant ceilings as part of buildings' HVAC systems. Some of the many potential applications are classrooms, offices, and museum spaces. With the introduction of radiant ceilings, there are always questions regarding condensation. To obtain the maximum performance of ceiling panels, especially in cooling mode, the surface temperature of cooling panels must be carefully controlled to ensure that the panel surface temperature does not drop below the dew-point temperature of the space operating temperature. The control of space humidity levels and panel surface temperature can be controlled by traditional HVAC methodologies. The supply air temperature and volumetric flow can be selected to balance space air moisture content. The largest problem encountered when design-

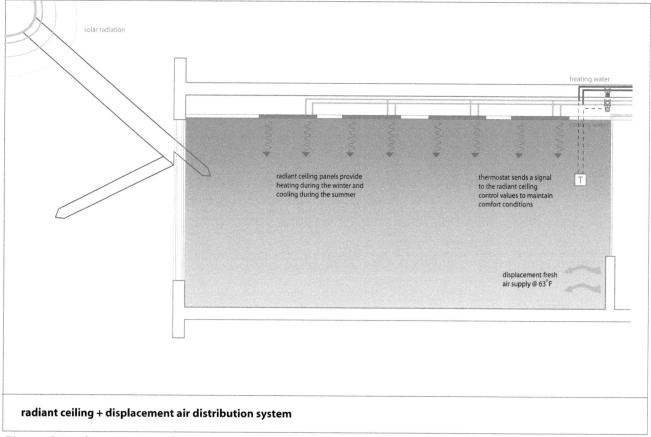

radiant ceiling + displacement air distribution system

Figure 8.5 The principle of a radiant ceiling system.

ing radiant ceilings is their performance in naturally ventilated or partially naturally ventilated spaces. This section will illustrate the performance of spaces conditioned with radiant ceilings for cooling with a mechanical ventilation system and a natural ventilation option.

PASSIVE BEAMS

Passive beams[5] are characterized by heat transfer from natural convection of room air across the hydronic coil. This natural convection occurs because of buoyancy forces. When the cooler surface of the heat exchanger comes in contact with warmer room air, the air cools and its density increases, and the heavier air is moved downward into the space.

ACTIVE BEAMS

An active chilled beam is an air diffusion device that introduces conditioned air to the space for the purposes of temperature and latent control. Primary air is delivered through a series of nozzles, creating induction of room air through a unit-mounted chilled-water coil, which conditions the air prior to its reintroduction to the space. Depending on the nozzle size and configuration, active beams typically induce two to five parts of room air for every part of primary air they deliver to the space. Sensible heat removal by the beam's integral cooling coil complements the cooling effect of the primary air supply.

5. This section provides partial text from *Active and Passive Beam Application Design Guide* (ASHRAE 2015) from the section titled "Passive Beams" to the section "Application Considerations." For this information to integrate smoothly into this book, the figure and table numbering have been modified from the original; otherwise the content remains as originally published.

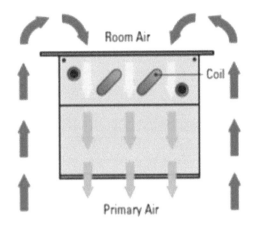

Figure 8.6 The function of a passive beam.

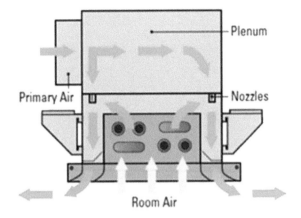

Figure 8.7 The function of an active beam.

Application Considerations

Active-beam systems must be designed to treat sensible and latent space heat gains, provide adequate space ventilation and maintain occupant comfort in conformance with ANSI/ASHRAE Standard 55-2017, *Thermal Environmental Conditions for Human Occupancy* and/or other applicable codes.

In general, active beams offer the opportunity to capitalize on the benefits of decoupled ventilation systems. Active-beam systems offer the designer the opportunity to manage the sensible loads in the space separate from the ventilation and latent needs. Active beams work well with dedicated outdoor air and demand-controlled ventilation systems.

Benefits of Active-Beam Systems

Heat extraction or addition by the coil allows for significant reduction in primary airflow requirements over all-air ducted systems. Energy to transport cooling and/or heating media is reduced because of the high specific heat and density of water. As a result, chilled-beam systems require less space for the mechanical services because of smaller duct work and air-handling unit sizes. Because of the reduction in mechanical service space requirements, it is possible to reduce the floor-to-floor height of a multistory building.

Free-cooling opportunities may be extended as a result of the lower secondary chilled-water temperatures and provide an improved selection of available system options including, but not limited to, geothermal, dry coolers, and closed-circuit fluid coolers. Active-beam systems offer opportunities to enhance chiller efficiencies and provide broader evaporator ranges because of higher chilled-water temperatures and cascaded evaporator flows between primary and secondary chilled-water loops. Higher inlet water temperatures also make chilled-beam systems an excellent choice for geothermal applications where suitable electrical costs permit this as an option.

Active-beam systems are typically operated with a constant (minimal) volume supply air flow to the space. Constant-volume systems offer the benefit of enhanced thermal comfort from consistent room air movement and an improved acoustic environment.

Maintenance of chilled beams is virtually nonexistent. Vacuuming the coils is occasionally required and is typically guided by the needs of the space. Often, it is expected that service intervals could extend between three and five years. An absence of moving parts within chilled beams inherently produces a highly reliable system, and because most beams contain no filters, servicing costs are minimal.

Limitations of Active-Beam Systems

Active-chilled-beam supply water temperatures should be maintained at or above the room dew-point temperature to prevent condensation on the coil and its supply water piping. Passive-chilled-beam supply water temperatures should be maintained slightly (34°F [1°C]) above the room dew-point temperature. In both cases, the chilled-water supply piping must be adequately insulated to prevent condensation on the pipework itself. In cases where adequate control of space humidity levels cannot be ensured, higher supply water temperatures and/or condensation controls should be considered.

Cooling

The objective of active-beam design is to minimize primary airflow rates, ideally reducing them to the space minimum ventilation requirement. However, where zone cooling requirements cannot be achieved with the minimum primary airflow rate, chilled beams may be used with air-handling units that mix return and outdoor air volumes.

Active and passive chilled beams rely on the primary air supply for dew-point control. As such, the design conditions must be evaluated to confirm that the primary air is appropriately treated to manage the latent space loads. Chilled beams are intended to operate without condensation. Consequently, supply water temperatures to the coil must be maintained at or above the space dew-point temperature.

Terminal filtration and condensate pans are not required with a properly designed primary air system and chilled-water temperatures maintained above the room dew point. Heating coils provide sensible heat only, and filtration and condensate capture devices are not necessary. Active-beam systems designed with noncondensing (dry) coils should be treated similarly.

Heating

The hot water servicing the coil within the active beam must be chosen to limit the discharge air temperature to less than 44.6°F (7°C) above the room design set point. Additionally, to ensure proper room air distribution, the discharge velocity should be selected in accordance with ANSI/ASHRAE Standard 55-2017 requirements.

Thermal Comfort

Active-beam systems are designed to optimize the delivery of cooling to the space, but the paramount consideration in sizing and located the beams within the room should focus on occupant thermal comfort. ANSI/ASHRAE Standard 55-2017 defines limits on local air temperatures and velocities that will maintain acceptable levels of occupant thermal comfort. The standard defines the *occupied zone* as one in which stationary occupants reside. The height of this zone is generally considered 5.5 ft (1.7 m) for standing occupants or 3.6 ft (1.1 m) for predominantly seated occupants. The standard prescribes that velocities within the occupied zone should not exceed 50 fpm (0.25 m/s), while occupied zone vertical temperature gradients should be maintained at 37°F (3°C) or less.

Active beams directly supply a mixture of primary and secondary air to the space and should therefore be treated like the other air distribution devices used in fully mixed air distribution systems. Since the temperature of the chilled water supplying the coil within the beam must be at (or above) the space dew-point temperature, it is typically 60°F to 64°F (16°C to 18°C). Thus, the reconditioned air leaving the coil is several degrees warmer than that of the primary air with which it is subsequently mixed. This results in beam design discharge air temperatures ranging from 57°F to 60°F (14°C to 16°C), which is warmer than those normally used by conventional all-air systems. Because the required supply airflow rate is inversely proportional to the room to supply air differential, active beams must discharge 15% to 25% more air to the space to satisfy its sensible heat gains.

Space Control and Zoning

An active-beam systems' primary airflow rates are much closer to the space ventilation rates than all-air systems. Primary control of the space temperature is normally accomplished by throttling the chilled-water flow. Proportional valves are recommended for passive beams and active beams in applications where more precise space temperature control is required.

In applications where primary air is supplied at conventional temperatures (55°F to 59°F [13°C to 15°C]) to spaces with significant sensible load variations, it may also be necessary to reset the primary airflow rate or temperature during low-load conditions. One method of doing so is to vary the primary airflow rate in reaction to thermal demands and/or occupancy of the space.

Supply of primary air at or close to room temperature overcomes the potential for over-cooling. This, however, will result in reduced beam cooling capacities and will necessitate the use of more or larger beams. It will likely also necessitate the use of desiccant technologies to provide adequate dehumidification of the primary air. Spaces with high ventilation requirements and significant cooling turndown rates, such as large conference rooms, may be better served by a VAV solution.

Thermal zoning of chilled-beam systems should be performed in a manner generally consistent with other HVAC systems. Each thermal zone consists of a space thermostat, a chilled-water (and where applicable hot-water) control valve and multiple chilled beams.

Operational Considerations

Water supply service to active and passive beams should not be activated until space dew-point temperatures are at or below the chilled water's supply temperature.

In cases where the maintenance of adequate space dew-point temperatures cannot be ensured, some type of condensation detection and mitigation strategy should be used. Designers are afforded various methods of accomplishing this, including the following:

- Sensors attached to the supply water pipe can sense the formation of surface moisture and discontinue the chilled-water flow until the moisture has evaporated. This method is relatively inexpensive but also reactive and results in termination of secondary air cooling during the period that condensation exists.

- Dew-point calculation and reset of the chilled-water supply temperature is a proactive strategy that does not involve full suspension of secondary cooling. This method can be applied on a room-by-room basis, but calculation on a floor-by-floor basis will usually be sufficient and less costly.

- For applications in spaces with operable windows or doors, occupants and staff should be educated on the effect this has on their thermal environment.

- In certain applications, condensate trays may be used to collect temporary and infrequent condensation. Where applied, adequate condensate removal means must be ensured. Evaporation of the condensate should not be assumed. This may involve the use of condensate pumps when gravity drainage cannot be accomplished.

VARIABLE-FREQUENCY-DRIVE FAN-COIL UNITS

Multiple fan-coil units with electronically commutated motor (ECM) (variable-speed) fans, filters, and hot-water heating and chilled-water cooling coils will be provided on each floor to meet the space heating and cooling demands on the perimeter zone, typically the exterior 20 ft (6 m) wide zone in each building. The interior zones will be served by two-pipe units. The cooling coil in the fan-coil unit (FCU) will have 60°F to 64°F (16°C to 18°C) as the chilled-water supply and return temperatures and 180°F and 149°F (82°C and 65°C) for the heating coil water supply and return temperatures.

VARIABLE-REFRIGERANT-FLOW (VRF) FAN-COILS WITH 100% OUTDOOR AIR VENTILATION

Variable-refrigerant-flow (VRF) comes in two system formats. The first is heat pumps (HP), a two-pipe system that has heating and cooling modes just like a standard HP. Because a VRF system will generally have two or more indoor units (IDU), the HP IDUs will all be in cooling or in heating together. The second style system is heat recovery (HR), a three pipe system that has a special box that controls the flow of suction gas and hot gas through the evaporator. By switching from suction gas in the coil to hot gas, the indoor unit can be switched from cool to heat while other IDUs remain in cooling mode. While this adds to the first cost, it allows for zone-by-zone selection of cooling or heating as desired by the occupant. The heating mode also allows for an increase in overall efficiency when used simultaneously with cooling on a single system. This increase is accomplished because the heating units function as a condenser, providing subcooled liquid back into the liquid line that is used by cooling IDUs.

VRF uses refrigerant as the cooling and heating medium and allows one outdoor condensing unit to be connected to multiple indoor FCUs, each individually controllable by its user, while modulating the amount of refrigerant being sent to each evaporator. VRF operates a flow of refrigerant that is required for conditioning. During part-load operation operating, energy can be reduced. There are certain heat recovery units that can provide heating and cooling to different spaces when required. Internal heat recovery is used to improve compressor efficiency. It is often possible to reduce energy costs by 55% by installing VRF units, compared to unitary systems. VRF is typically implemented with the use of an air-conditioner inverter, which adds a DC inverter to the compressor to support variable motor speed and, thus, variable refrigerant flow, rather than on/off operation.

The condensing units can be installed on the refuge floors.

AIR-CONDITIONING SUPPLY SYSTEMS—CONCLUSIONS

For tall commercial office buildings, the air-handling systems that find application fall into two major categories with regard to their distribution ductwork. The first is a central air-conditioning supply system, located in a mechanical equipment room within the building, that serves multiple floors above and/or below the mechanical equipment room. The second category is a local floor air-conditioning system that usually serves the floor within which the equipment is located. The local floor air-conditioning systems come in two alternative configurations. The first uses air-handling units that contain chilled-water coils. The second uses self-contained direct-expansion air-conditioning units. These differing approaches are discussed in detail in Chapter 7.

The combination of system components and the resultant system configuration for a specific building are limited only by the imagination of the designer. As stressed earlier, the chosen alternative is of interest and concern to the owner, architect, and other engineering consultants and therefore should be subjected to the scrutiny and review of the entire design team before the selection is included for a given project.

Technical Comparison

Space Requirements

- **Primary Air-Handling Unit (PAU) + FCU**
  Common open space office needs 14 to 16 in. (350 to 400 mm) of space for installation (including condensed water slope). AC doesn't occupy any area on working level in the office, only the PAU will be placed on equipment level. Typically, the PAU would be placed on each floor.
- **AHU (Variable Frequency) + VAV Box**
  Ducts require at least 22 to 24 in. (550 to 600 mm) of space for installation in common open space office. One to two AHU rooms are needed each floor, which occupies some

area on working level. It should be noted that the AHU for the VAV system requires 10 times more air than a primary AHU for FCU, radiant ceiling, or active beam systems

- **Underfloor System: AHU (Variable Frequency) + VAV Box**
  Return ducts require 12 to 14 in. (300 to 350 mm) above the ceiling. No return ducts are required, as the ceiling plenum can be used. Supply ducts and VAV boxes need 20 to 22 in. (500 to 550 mm). The TROX TFTU used in Cheung Kong Center[6] is 12 in. (300 mm) high underfloor, so total occupied space is larger than VAV. One to two AHU rooms are needed each floor, which occupies some area on the working level. There only needs to be a single dedicated outdoor air system on each floor.

- **Underfloor System: AHU (Variable Frequency) + FTU**
  Return ducts require 12 to 14 in. (300 to 350 mm) above the ceiling. Supply ducts and FTU need 20 to 22 in. (500 to 550 mm) underfloor, so total occupied space is larger than for VAV.

- **Active Beam: PAU + ACB**
  Common open space office needs 12 to 14 in. (300 to 350 mm) of space for installation (no space for condensed water slope). Active beams do not require condensate drain. AC doesn't occupy any area on the working level in the office, only the PAU will be placed on the equipment level.

- **Radiant Cooling Ceiling: PAU + CRCP**
  Common open space office needs 12 to 14 in. (300 to 350 mm) space for installation (no space for condensed water slope). Radiant ceilings do not require condensate drain. AC doesn't occupy any area on working level in the office, only PAU will be placed on the equipment level.

IAQ and Noise Problems

- **PAU + FCU**
  Common open space office needs 14 to 16 in. (350 to 400 mm) space for installation (including condensed water slope). AC doesn't occupy any area on working level in the office, only PAU will be placed on the equipment level. This solution provides 100% outdoor air to each space

- **AHU (Variable Frequency) + VAV Box**
  These make the most noise, and the system uses recirculated air. Ducts require a large area—22 to 24 in. (550 to 600 mm) is needed for installation in common open space office. One to two AHU rooms are needed for each floor, which occupies some area on working level.

Table 8.1 System Configuration

Type Of System	Air Supply and Returning System	Equipment Locations
A	Both supply and return are located in ceilings	PAU: PAU room FCU: ceiling
B	Both supply and return are located in ceilings	AHU: AHU room VAV-box: ceiling
C	Air supply is underfloor, returning could be underfloor or in the ceiling	AHU: AHU room VAV-box: underfloor
D	Both supply and return are underfloor, partial returning could be on higher level	AHU: AHU room FTU: underfloor
E	Only outside air, located in ceiling	PAU: equipment level ACB: ceiling
F	Only outside air, located in ceiling	PAU: equipment level CRCP: ceiling

6. Cheung Kong Center is a skyscraper in the Central District of Hong Kong. It is 68 stories tall with height of 928 ft (283 m) and a gross floor area of 1,260,000 ft^2 (117,100 m^2). It was the third-tallest building in the city when built in 1999.

- **Underfloor System: AHU (Variable Frequency) + VAV Box**
  Return ducts require 12 to 14 in. (300 to 350 mm) above the ceiling, Return ducts are not required as the air can be returned through the ceiling plenum. Supply ducts and VAV box need 20 to 22 in. (500 to 550 mm) of underfloor space, but present-day designs only require 12 in. (300 mm), so total occupied space is larger than for VAV. One to two AHU rooms are needed for each floor, which occupies some area on the working level.
- **Underfloor System: AHU (Variable Frequency) + FTU**
  Return ducts require 12 to 14 in. (300 to 350 mm) above ceiling, Return ducts are not required, the air can be returned through the ceiling plenum. supply ducts and VAV box need 20 to 22 in. (500 to 550 mm) underfloor, present-day designs only require 12 in. (300 mm) so total occupied space is larger than for VAV. One to two AHU rooms are needed each floor which occupies some area on working level.
- **Active Beam: PAU + ACB**
  Common open space office needs a 12 to 14 in. (300 to 350 mm) high plenum for installation (no space for condensed water slope). Active beams do not require condensate drains. AC doesn't occupy any area on working level in the office, only the PAU will be placed on the equipment level. PAU can be installed at each floor level
- **Radiant Cooling Ceiling: PAU + CRCP**
  Common open space office needs 12 to 14 in. (300 to 350 mm) space for installation (no space for condensed water slope). Radiant ceilings do not require condensate drains. AC doesn't occupy any area on the working level in the office, only PAU will be placed on the equipment level. PAU can be installed at each floor level

Flexibility

- **PAU + FCU**
  When needing adjustment, FCU should be adjusted at the same time as water pipes and ducts. Slope for condensing water should also be guaranteed. Flexibility is relatively slow. Fan coil units, when laid out correctly, do not need to be moved. If they need to be moved, they are fitted with quick release fittings. The fan coil units do not require condensate drains.
- **AHU (Variable Frequency) + VAV Box**
  When needing adjustment, the VAV box could be adjusted according to different independent rooms so as to meet temperature requirements in each room. Flexibility is good.
- **Underfloor System: AHU (Variable Frequency) + VAV Box**
  Locations of supply and return diffusers are related to furniture in the room. There are relatively more opportunities to adjust. Flexibility of adjusting air ducts is lower than that of VAV.
- **Underfloor System: AHU (Variable Frequency) + FTU**
  No air ducts needed. FTU could be moved according to clients' requirements. Flexibility is similar to VAV.
- **Active Beam: PAU + ACB**
  When needing adjustment, active beam and water pipes should be adjusted at the same time. Flexibility is relatively low.
- **Radiant Cooling Ceiling: PAU + CRCP**
  When needing adjustment, radiant cooling ceiling and water pipes should be adjusted at the same time. Flexibility is relatively low. As radiant cooling ceiling and common ceiling are installed in the same construction unit, the system should keep appearance consistent and aesthetically pleasing. When designed correctly radiant ceiling panels are never moved.

Maintenance Requirements

- **PAU + FCU**
  Number of FCU is bid and distributed among office area. Connections between water pipes have high possibility in leaking. Tenants are disturbed a lot by maintenance.

- **AHU (Variable Frequency) + VAV Box**
  Has little disturbance to tenants. Major maintenance is finished in AHU room. There is no risk of leaking in ceilings.
- **Underfloor System: AHU (Variable Frequency) + VAV Box**
  Has little disturbance to tenants. Major maintenance is finished in AHU room. There is no risk of leaking in ceilings.
- **Underfloor System: AHU (Variable Frequency) + FTU**
  Has little disturbance to tenants. Major maintenance is finished in AHU room. There is no risk of leaking in ceilings.
- **Active Beam: PAU + ACB**
  As no maintenance for fan motor is needed, maintenance is less than FCU.
- **Radiant Cooling Ceiling: PAU + CRCP**
  As no maintenance for fan motor is needed, maintenance is less than FCU.

Technology Maturity and Cost

- **PAU + FCU**
  It has been widely used for a long time. Technology is mature, first cost is relatively low.
- **AHU (Variable Frequency) + VAV Box**
  It has been widely used for a long time. Technology is mature, first cost is medium.
- **Underfloor System: AHU (Variable Frequency) + VAV Box**
  This technology is not familiar. As it is not familiar in the society, there are many mistakes happening in system design, construction, and operation. Though more research has been conducted in recent years, technical materials, codes, and design rules are still missing. Fist cost is high.
- **Underfloor System: AHU (Variable Frequency) + FTU**
  This technology is not familiar. As it is not familiar in the society, there are many mistakes happening in system design, construction and operation. Though more researches were conducted in recent years, technical materials, code and design rules are still missing. First cost is high.
- **Active Beam: PAU + ACB**
  Requires strict humidity control in each space
- **Radiant Cooling Ceiling: PAU + CRCP**
  Requires strict humidity control in each space

CASE STUDY
Jeddah Tower

Name: Jeddah Tower

Location: Jeddah, Saudi Arabia

Description: At over 1000 m (3280 ft) tall and with a total construction area of 530,000 m^2 (5.7 million ft^2), Jeddah Tower—formerly known as Kingdom Tower—is slated to be the centerpiece and first construction phase of the $20 billion Kingdom City development in Jeddah, Saudi Arabia, near the Red Sea.

Expected to cost $1.2 billion to construct, Jeddah Tower will be a mixed-use building featuring a luxury hotel, office space, serviced apartments, luxury condominiums and the world's highest observatory. Jeddah Tower's height will be at least 173 m (568 ft) taller than the Burj Khalifa, which was designed by Adrian Smith while at Skidmore, Owings & Merrill.

The design for Jeddah Tower is both highly technological and distinctly organic, combining its staggering height with delicate details. The tower rises powerfully and intelligently – the three-petal footprint is ideal for residential units and the tapering wings produce an aerodynamic shape helps reduce structural loading due to wind vortex shedding—culminating with a slender, slightly asymmetrical tip, evoking the folded fronds of young desert plant growth.

While the design is contextual to Saudi Arabia, it also represents an evolution and a refinement of an architectural continuum of skyscraper design. Jeddah Tower's design embraces its architectural pedigree, taking full advantage of the proven design strategies and technological strategies of its lineage, refining and advancing them to achieve new heights.

The result is an elegant, cost-efficient and highly constructible design that is at once grounded in built tradition and aggressively forward-looking, taking advantage of new and innovative thinking about technology, building materials, life-cycle considerations and energy conservation. For example, the project will feature a high-performance exterior wall system that will minimize energy consumption by reducing thermal loads. In addition, each of Jeddah Tower's three sides features a series of notches that create pockets of shadow that shield areas of the building from the sun and provide outdoor terraces with stunning views of Jeddah and the Red Sea.

The great height of Jeddah Tower necessitates one of the world's most sophisticated elevator systems. The Jeddah Tower complex will contain 59 elevators, including 54 single-deck and five double-deck elevators, along with 12 escalators. Elevators serving the observatory will travel at a rate of 22 mph (10 m/s) in both directions.

Another unique feature of the design is a sky terrace, roughly 30 m (98 ft) in diameter, at level 157. The sky terrace will be open to the public and will be considered the world's highest observatory when opened in 2020.

Building Function: Residential/serviced apartments
Building Height: 1000 m (3280 ft)
Building Floor Area: 2,624,950 ft^2 (243,866 m^2) (tower), 87,478,300 ft^2 (8,127,000 m^2) (development)
Architects: Adrian Smith + Gordon Gill Architecture (Design), Dar al-Handasah Shair and Partners (Architect of Record)
Structural Engineers: Thornton Thomasetti (Design), Magnussen Klemencic Associates (Peer Review)
MEP Engineers: Environmental Systems Design (Design), Cosentini Associates (Peer Review)

Reprinted with permission of Adrian Smith + Gordon Gill Architecture/Jeddah Economic Company.

CHAPTER 9
Central Mechanical Equipment Room and Floor-by-Floor Fan Rooms

A major decision that must be made by the entire project team in a tall commercial office building is whether to meet the project needs for conditioned air through air-conditioning supply systems installed in a central mechanical equipment room serving multiple floors or by systems installed in a separate local floor fan room located on each floor, supplying air only to the floor on which the system is installed. The choice from any of the alternative schemes outlined in this chapter is one of the most fundamental decisions that must be made during the conceptual design phase. It is an issue that concerns the owner, each member of the design team, and the constructing contractors who will erect the building.

It is important to the owner in that it will affect the very basis of the usage and rental of the building as well as both the first cost and the operating costs for the project. It is important to the architect because the choice will modify the building massing and appearance to the degree that the decision will result in a building that is aesthetically different as a function of the alternative chosen. It is important to the structural engineer in that it will modify the structural system and slab construction for the project. It is important to the contractors in that it will influence the construction schedule and methods. Finally, it is important to the mechanical and electrical consulting engineers in that it will modify their designed product in several obvious and important ways discussed in this chapter.

The decision, therefore, is one that requires full consideration and detailed input from the entire project team, including the contractors who will be implementing the project designs. Although frequently the decision is predicated on what is being done on competitive projects in the same real estate market and may reflect the bias of one or more of the deciding members of the project team, it is possible to establish points of comparison that can be discussed with relative objectivity to allow the decision to be made in a proper manner.

THE ALTERNATIVE SYSTEMS

As was outlined in Chapter 2, the central fan room and the local floor-by-floor alternatives fall into the following three, discrete alternatives. Before the development of a comparative analysis can be prepared, the details of each of the alternative possibilities must be discussed.

Alternative 1—Central Fan Rooms

In this alternative, the conditioned air supply for each office floor originates from multiple air-handling systems located in one or more central fan rooms, which are frequently identified as central mechanical equipment rooms (MERs). The air-handling systems can be factory-fabricated air-handling units but usually, because of the multiplicity of floors being conditioned and the resultant air quantities for the systems, they will be field-erected units. Each air-handling system, depending on the annual temperature and humidity and building code requirements, can be provided with an outdoor air economizer with both minimum outdoor air and variable outdoor air and return/relief dampers. The multiple systems in a given fan room can be interconnected by having supply air delivered into a common discharge duct from all of the supply systems in the MER.

Air from the central fan room(s) is distributed to each floor by means of vertical risers located in two-hour fire-rated shafts within the core of the building. At each floor, horizontal duct connections are made into each riser. The horizontal duct connection contains a fire damper or a fire/smoke damper as required by the local building code when air exits the rated shaft and an automatic, remotely controlled two-position damper. The two-position damper, which can be rated as a smoke damper, provides the capability for individual floor overtime operation and for smoke control. Its position will be controlled by the building management system. This control damper, while required by some energy codes, is not necessary with the current generation of digitally controlled VAV dampers

Return air from each floor's lowered ceiling plenum is drawn through a ducted return that contains fire and smoke dampers into vertical return air shafts for return to the central fan rooms.

The return air is not ducted in the shaft, so the air is carried back to the central fan room in the two-hour rated drywall shaft. In each central fan room, there are located multiple return air fans that draw the return air from the return air shafts and deliver it to a headered return air duct system within the central fan room.

Where an outdoor air economizer is included, the return air is either returned to the supply air system or exhausted outside as a function of the relative enthalpy of the return air and the outdoor air. In those warmer and humid geographic areas where the systems operate on minimum outdoor air at all times, the return air is always returned to the supply air system except for morning startup or where the fans are under a smoke control operating condition as is discussed in Chapter 15, Life Safety Systems.

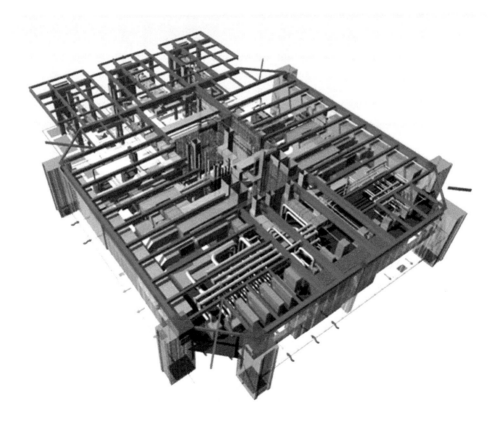

Figure 9.1 A typical central plant layout.

A typical central fan room arrangement and the supply and return air shaft arrangements are shown in Figure 9.2. This figure is for a design that includes four factory-fabricated air-handling supply systems and four return systems, with the ducted supply air being distributed through two shafts. The return air is being brought to the MER in the same shaft within which the supply duct is routed, but it is not ducted in the shaft. The return air is only ducted within the mechanical equipment room. This general arrangement is subject to multiple alternative configurations as a function of the experience, judgment, and analysis of the designing HVAC engineer and, of course, the physical space availability in the building.

Alternative 2—Floor-by-Floor Fan Rooms with Chilled-Water Units

The air supply for each floor in this alternative originates from a local floor fan room, typically located within the building core (see Figure 9.4). This room contains a factory-fabricated chilled-water air-handling unit complete with a cooling coil, filters, and fan. The unit on a given floor usually only supplies the floor on which the unit is installed. Typically, one unit is

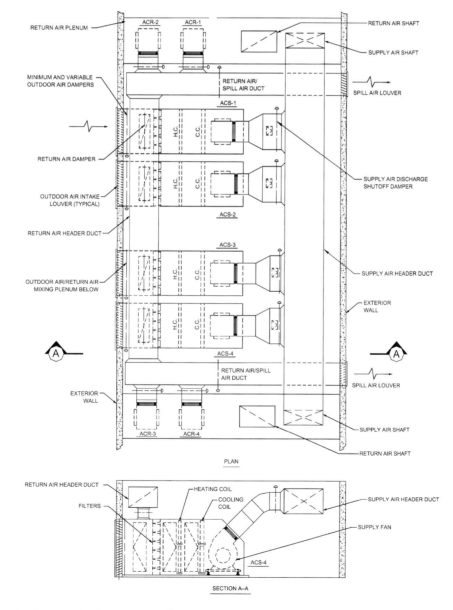

Figure 9.2 A typical central plant room plan.

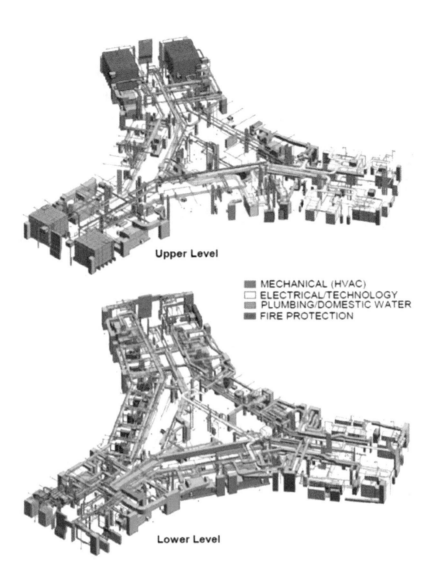

Upper Level

■ MECHANICAL (HVAC)
□ ELECTRICAL/TECHNOLOGY
▨ PLUMBING/DOMESTIC WATER
■ FIRE PROTECTION

Lower Level

Figure 9.3 A two-story mechanical level.
(Courtesy ESD)

installed on each floor except in the case of large floor areas (e.g., those in excess of approximately 25,000 ft^2 [2500 m^2]) where more than one unit may need to be installed. The decision to have multiple units or a single unit per floor is governed by the space available to install ductwork from the fan room around the core of the building. Chilled water for the cooling coil is provided by a central chilled-water plant in the building sized to meet the capacity requirements of the project. The supply air fan in the air-conditioning supply system also serves as a return air fan for returning the air from the conditioned area on the floor back to the air-conditioning supply unit. The return air is ducted to the fan room in the arrangements discussed in this chapter, but the return air is not typically ducted within the fan room. Accordingly, the fan room in most cases acts as a return air plenum.

This system, regardless of geographic location and the outdoor air temperature and humidity variation during the year, usually operates on minimum outdoor air during all periods of occupancy.

Typically, the outdoor air for the system is provided by an air-handling unit located on the roof or in a central mechanical equipment room that provides outdoor air to the unit on each floor by means of a vertical duct riser, in a shaft that is routed to each of the multiple

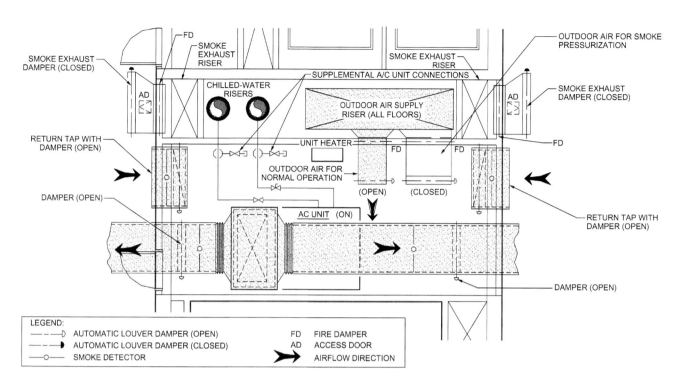

Figure 9.4 A typical floor-by-floor fan room layout.

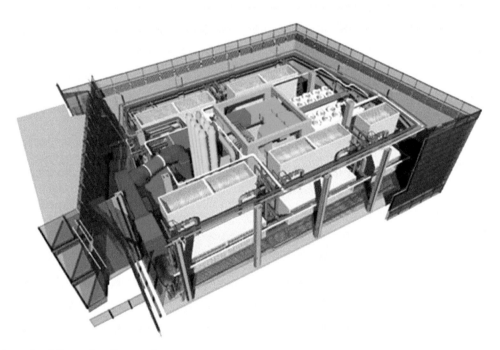

Figure 9.5 A typical floor-by-floor plant room.

air-conditioning local floor-by-floor air-handling units. The unit that provides outdoor air to the local floor-by-floor air-conditioning units can include filters and a preheat coil and cooling coil to treat the outdoor air being introduced into the building. This air can be supplied neutral (i.e., the same dry- and wet-bulb temperature as the space or can be subcooled to remove additional moisture). In many cases, the air to the floor is controlled by a VAV terminal to measure and ensure the required ventilation outdoor air is provided.

Although chilled water for the project will be provided by a central refrigeration plant, the economizer requirements are often provided by cooling the chilled water in mild weather by the condenser water from the cooling tower. The condenser water will cool the chilled water through a flat-plate heat exchanger located at the central chilled-water plant during periods of low wet-bulb temperature. At this time, the condenser water from the tower will have its temperature lowered to 44°F (7°C), which in turn will allow the chilled-water supply to the local floor-by-floor air-handling units to be lowered to below 50°F (10°C).

The ability to use this system as a means of smoke control in the event of a fire is discussed in Chapter 15.

A typical local fan room arrangement showing the supply and return air arrangement and the outdoor air duct provision is shown in Figure 9.4. VAV terminals with heating coils or perimeter radiation are a more common source of warmup and heating. The position of the dampers in a smoke condition in the building is detailed in Chapter 15. The arrangement shown in Figure 9.4 is frequently altered as a function of the location of the local fan room in the core and the prior experience of the designing HVAC engineer, but the equipment should be capable of installation in a space of about 250 to 450 ft^2 (24 to 42 m^2) as a function of the size of the conditioned floor and the precise capacity of the required unit. Figure 9.4 also shows the valved capped connection of the chilled-water piping to allow its extension to a location on the floor that may require the installation of supplemental air-conditioning equipment, such as information technology equipment or a small area with a concentration of data processing equipment. A full-sized data center could probably not be supported by this piped connection because of the limited volume of water that is available in this location. A major data center could only be accommodated if its needs were provided for in the original design of the piping system and the capacity of the piped system.

As shown in Figure 9.4, the walls around the local floor fan room are typically fire rated. The vertical shaft that contains the outdoor air duct from the central fan room, and perhaps the smoke exhaust ducts, constitutes a rated shaft. Accordingly, fire and smoke dampers are only provided at the point where ducts penetrate the shaft wall, not as they leave or enter the local floor fan room itself.

Alternative 3—Floor-by-Floor Fan Rooms with Direct-Expansion Units

A second variation of the floor-by-floor alternative is a floor-by-floor air-conditioning supply system identical in its details to that in Alternative 2, except that the package unit installed on the floor is a self-contained water-cooled direct-expansion (DX) unit complete with one or more refrigeration compressors and water-cooled condensers. The heat of rejection from the compressor is handled by a condenser water system and a cooling tower. If an economizer requirement is needed because of lower local outdoor air temperature and humidity, it is met by a free-cooling coil installed in the package unit that will only operate when the condenser water being delivered to the unit is below a specified temperature of approximately 48°F (9°C). The only central equipment in this alternative is the cooling tower, condenser water pumps, and the central outdoor air supply unit. This unit is functionally the same as the floor-by-floor air-conditioning supply unit in Alternative 2, except that it is a direct-expansion unit, eliminating the need for a chilled-water plant in the building.

The physical arrangement of the unit would not differ from that shown in Figure 9.4 other than that the chilled-water risers would be used for condenser water. It should be noted that, for compliance with present-day energy codes, DX units are at a disadvantage.

Floor-by-Floor Units Located on an Outside Wall

A variation of Alternative 2 and Alternative 3 that should be noted is a package floor-by-floor unit solution where the unit is located on an outside wall. This alternative can still find the unit in a core area where the building core is located on an outside wall. It can also be used where there is a central core with the floor-by-floor unit installed in a location remote from the core. This arrangement is not common, because exterior space, with the usual inclusion of windows, is a preferred location for office space and locating the unit on an outside wall will use valuable space. Where the air-economizer conditions are extremely favorable, some designs integrated with the structure have allowed for air economized with the floor fan room in a traditional, center-core building.

If this alternative location of the floor-by-floor unit on an outside wall is used, it eliminates the need for the separate outdoor air unit located in a central fan room, in that outdoor air can be directly introduced to the floor-by-floor unit through a louver and automatic louver damper for each unit. In locations requiring an economizer, that requirement with this unit location can be satisfied by the inclusion in the design of a minimum and variable air damper behind the outdoor air louver.

Some design precautions are necessary when considering this possibility. First, where an outdoor air economizer is used for either Alternative 2 or Alternative 3, care must be taken in the location of the outdoor air intake and exhaust air to prevent a mixing of the outdoor air and exhaust air. Similar care must be taken if it is determined, in the case of Alternative 3, to use an air-cooled condenser louver to allow the outdoor air to be brought to the air-cooled condenser and to be spilled to the atmosphere with no possibility of mixing the heated discharge air with either the condenser intake air or the outdoor air being brought into the building by the supply air-conditioning unit. This can become a complicated alternative arrangement which may necessitate the air-cooled condenser to be located at a point that is remote from the local fan room.

COMPARISON OF ALTERNATIVE SCHEMES

The comparison of the three alternative systems can be made on a rational basis. The points of evaluation must be part of an overall analysis that is made at a very early stage of the project, because the choice of alternative will impact the architectural core as well as significant portions of the building, including both the location and the configuration of mechanical space in areas other than the typical office floors.

First Cost

The relative cost of the three alternatives outlined in this chapter will vary from project to project and with geographic area. The first cost analysis must include not only the mechanical system cost but also the electrical system and the general construction cost of the different types of spaces provided. There is only one way in which an accurate comparison can be made: a developed set of schematic designs must be provided in sufficient detail to allow a cost estimate to be completed by either the contracting team retained for the project or a professional estimating service. These cost estimates should also reflect the required total space required for each of the three considered alternative schemes. A matrix that details the comparative points of first cost comparison is provided in Table 9.1. The intent of this matrix is merely to outline general points of comparison by discipline; it is only through a complete cost estimate that the true comparative costs can be determined.

The capital costs for the three alternative solutions will be affected by the local construction trades and their abilities and familiarity with the systems. For example, handling more complicated piping, sheet metal, and control systems will be necessary for Alternative 1, with its large central mechanical equipment rooms. Both Alternatives 2 and 3 use package air-handling units in local fan rooms, which are typically repeated on each floor of a high-rise building. The installed simplicity of Alternative 3 is even greater than Alternative 2 in that there is no central chilled-water plant with a need for somewhat complex piping and controls. Further, in Alternative 3, the internal wiring and control of the air-conditioning supply systems is the responsibility of the unit manufacturer, with the temperature control design responsibility of the HVAC engineer limited to the interface between the unit and the building management system.

Project experience with large buildings (i.e., those with 20 or more stories and areas of 400,000 ft^2 [37,000 m^2] to 500,000 ft^2 [46,000 m^2]) in the Northeast United States shows that the mechanical and electrical system costs are approximately equal for all three schemes. When the cost of the additional mechanical equipment room area and volume of Alternative 1, and to a lesser degree Alternative 2, is considered, Alternative 3 may have a lower first cost than either of the other alternatives. The difference, however, is not significant and consideration of other points of comparisons may result in a decision to use either Alternative 1 or Alternative 2.

On smaller buildings with fewer floors, the package DX solution of Alternative 3 will almost always be the least costly. In general, the smaller the building and the fewer the number of floors in the building, the greater the cost advantage of Alternative 3 will become.

At ten floors and fewer, the installation of a central system with roof-mounted packaged equipment will also become cost effective.

It must be apparent that first cost, while always important, is not the only consideration. The nature of the client's specific needs and perception of the market must all be reviewed to allow the owner to select the alternative that best fulfills the owner's understanding of the project requirements.

Corporate headquarters, for example, will usually favor a chilled-water alternative and could well lean toward Alternative 1 with central mechanical equipment rooms, because this will result in simpler maintenance, more flexible operation, and potentially longer equipment life after the building is completed. There is a further advantage in a corporate headquarters with Alternate 1 in that maintenance personnel will not need access to every floor for normal maintenance, which could be a significant advantage from the perspective of office space security. This advantage would also be present in the developer building, eliminating the need to disturb tenants.

Developer buildings, particularly those being constructed with the expectation of single-floor leases, may well favor Alternative 3, which minimizes, if not eliminates, overtime operation by the owner's staff and eliminates the allocation of operating costs that is necessary for Alternative 1 and, to a lesser degree, in Alternative 2. This issue of the allocation of operating costs is discussed in more detail later in this chapter.

Table 9.1 First Cost Considerations of the Alternatives

First Cost Implications		
Alternative 1 **Central Fan Systems** **Central Chilled Water**	**Alternative 2** **Floor-by-Floor Fan Systems** **Central Chilled Water**	**Alternative 3** **Floor-by-Floor DX Systems** **Central Cooling Tower**
Issue—HVAC Impact on Costs		
• Fewer units, field erected	• More units, factory-fabricated and assembled	• More units, factory-fabricated and assembled
• More complex and expensive duct systems	• Simpler ductwork	• Simpler ductwork
• More complex field-installed controls	• Field-installed control system	• Factory-installed control system
• Central chilled water plant	• Central chilled-water plant	• No central chilled water plant; cooling tower and pumps only
Issue—Building Management System Cost		
• Complex controls and interfaces with BMS and smoke control system	• Controls are relatively simple but field installed. Interface with BMS and smoke control system less complex	• Unit controls provided by manufacturer • Interface with BMS and smoke control system simple
Issue—Electrical Impact on Cost		
• Electrical loads concentrated in central location	• Minor cost premium for distributed fan motors	• Additional cost for electrical distribution to local DX units
• Probably lowest electrical cost	• Probably higher electrical cost than Alternative 1	• Highest electrical cost
Issue—General Construction Cost		
• Additional gross space needed • Additional height needed for MER rooms • More exterior louvers required	• Additional cost of sound treatment of local floor-by-floor fan room	• Additional cost of sound treatment of local floor-by-floor fan room
• No separate outdoor air or smoke exhaust shaft	• Need separate outdoor air and smoke exhaust shaft	• Need separate outdoor air and smoke exhaust shaft

CONSTRUCTION SCHEDULE IMPACT

The construction schedule will be affected as a function of which alternative is selected. Issues that will affect the construction schedule are outlined in Table 9.2.

Alternative 1, with field-erected air-conditioning supply units, complex ductwork, and extensive chilled-water and condenser water piping and chiller plant installation (when coupled with the fact that each mechanical equipment room layout in a specific building is unique when compared to the mechanical equipment room from other projects), does not benefit from manufactured product efficiency.

As is discussed further in Chapter 8, the location of the chiller plant will have an impact on the overall project schedule. If located at the top of the building, which is constructed last, the large concentration of labor at that location may lengthen the overall construction schedule for the project. A similar concern will be the case if the central fan room of Alternative 1 is at the penthouse location, because the extensive, complex ductwork will take a disproportionate time frame to be completed, with potential delays in the project schedule.

The opposite end of the scale is Alternative 3. In this alternative, the equipment is factory fabricated and assembled, includes all of the internal control wiring, and is extremely repetitive on a floor-by-floor basis. The duct fabrication, the piping to the units, and both the power wiring and the building management system connections are the same on each floor and are relatively simple. The cost-related advantage of these factors will be reflected in the estimates of the alternative schemes, but the impact on the project schedule can also be a matter of significance.

Alternative 2 is very close in the construction time involved to that of Alternative 3. There can be, however, a nominal increase over Alternative 3 because of the need to provide more complex piping for the chilled-water plant, as well as the necessary power wiring for the plant and building management system connections for the plant and the floor-by-floor units. The increase in time, however, is not significant. Moreover, the repetitive nature of everything involved in this construction is still apparent and can be used to improve the project construction schedule if the comparison is limited to Alternative 1 and Alternative 2. In most high-rise buildings, the cooling towers are on the roof and are one of the last items that can be installed. However, this is equally an issue for the outdoor equipment in all alternatives.

Table 9.2 Construction Schedule Impact

Construction Schedule Impact		
Alternative 1 **Central Fan Systems** **Central Chilled Water**	**Alternative 2** **Floor-by-Floor Fan Systems** **Central Chilled Water**	**Alternative 3** **Floor-by-Floor DX Systems** **Central Cooling Tower**
Issue—General Complexity of Installation		
• Central mechanical equipment room space and complex construction technology for both chiller plant and fan systems locations	• Chiller plant space is required with the need for more complex construction technology	• Areas that contain complex construction technology are limited
• Requires piping of a major chiller plant	• Requires piping of a major chiller plant	• No major chiller plant • Cooling tower only
• Chiller plant location critical to construction schedule	• Chiller plant location critical to construction schedule	• Chiller plant is not required
• Heavier slab construction at central mechanical equipment room and chiller plant	• Heavier slab construction for chiller plant only	• Very limited special slab construction
• Extensive complex ductwork in central mechanical equipment room and shafts	• Limited ductwork, repetitive fan room arrangement on each floor	• Limited ductwork, repetitive fan room arrangement on each floor

OWNER ISSUES

The owner will be concerned with other issues that should be considered in the decision process. The owner will have a strong interest in the first cost and construction schedule just discussed, but an additional list of specific other matters of concern to the owner is provided in Table 9.3. Of special consideration in developer buildings are the discussions under the heading "Issue—Marketing/Electric Metering." An issue in lease negotiations for developer buildings is the allocation of operating costs. In today's market, most multiple-tenant buildings have separate electric meters for each tenant. These separate meters will cover all of the tenants' lighting and small power consumption, but the energy used to provide HVAC is a much more difficult issue to meter, and therefore energy cost is allocated by area served.

For a multiple-tenant building and lease terms of multiple years during which the cost of energy will fluctuate, as will the operating labor for the building, the problem can be quite complex. The difficulty is most apparent in developer buildings using Alternative 1 with central fan rooms and central chilled water. For those projects, the operating energy costs are paid for by the owner, and a means to pass this cost through to the several tenants is required. For example, if all tenants utilized their space from 8 am to 6 pm on weekdays only, the problem would be relatively simple, but many professional service firms in the fields of accounting, law, architecture, and engineering typically operate on extended schedules of overtime which can extend into the evenings as well as weekends. To solve this problem, a relatively complex and, for the tenant, possibly expensive arrangement must be provided to allow the tenant to obtain air conditioning in periods other than the normal occupancy hours of most offices. The arrangement should include the cost of the labor and energy to operate the chilled-water plant

Table 9.3 Typical Owner Issues

Alternative 1 Central Fan Systems Central Chilled Water	Alternative 2 Floor-by-Floor Fan Systems Central Chilled Water	Alternative 3 Floor-by-Floor DX Systems Central Cooling Tower
Issue—Marketing/Electric Metering		
• Tenant lights and small power can be metered directly	• Tenant lights, small power and fan energy can be metered directly for any floor with a single tenant. Multitenant floors will require allocation of fan energy only	• Tenant lights, small power, fan and cooling energy can all be metered for any floor with a single tenant. Multitenant floors will require allocation of fan energy and cooling energy only
• Fan energy and chiller plant energy, as well as heating energy and operating costs are allocated unless heating is by electric resistance heat	• Chiller plant energy, as well as heating energy and operating costs are allocated unless heating is by electric resistance heat	• Heating energy operating cost must be allocated unless heating is by electric resistance heat
• Other common building operating costs are allocated	• Other common building operating costs are allocated	• Other common building operating costs are allocated
Issue—Operating Costs		
• For normal operating day, operating costs for all floors occupied will be lower than Alternative 3. Approximately equal to Alternative 2	• For the summer operating day, operating costs for all floors occupied will be lower due to lower energy consumption than Alternative 3. Approximately equal to Alternative 1	• For the summer operating day, operating costs for all floors occupied will be higher due to higher energy consumption than Alternative 1 or Alternative 2, due to less efficient DX compressors
• Overtime operation requires the chiller plant to operate in the summer. With variable-speed fan control and headered supply and return, fans' energy costs equal to Alternative 2. Operation more cumbersome. Fan and chiller plant costs must be allocated	• Overtime operation requires the chiller plant to operate in the summer but otherwise simple. Chiller plant cost must be allocated	• Overtime operation is simplest but probably higher in cost than Alternative 1 or Alternative 2. Single floor tenant cost for cooling tower only must be allocated

and any fans that may be required to deliver air conditioning to the tenant. Most leases include the heating cost as a landlord's cost and, because heating costs in an office building are nominal, there is a lesser problem with allocating that component of operating cost. The only central facility that must operate is the condenser water system and the outdoor air ventilation system.

One of the primary advantages of Alternative 3 is that the cost of energy for air conditioning for any single floor tenant can be directly metered to the tenant on his own electric meter. If electric heat rather than fossil fuel heat is used, that cost can also be placed on the tenant's meter. To express it more directly, the problem is simple and the solution straightforward with Alternative 3. Overtime operation for firms that operate on extended hours is equally simple, with only the cost to operate the cooling tower and any necessary labor being subject to an allocation basis. Alternative 2, again, is more complex in that the costs of operating the chilled-water plant in warm weather must be allocated with only the fan energy, lighting, and small power in the local floor-by-floor fan room on the tenant's meter. If possible, the condenser water flow and temperature to and from a floor should be metered to allocate the condenser water cost.

The issue is a difficult matter, but the use of Alternative 3 with floor-by-floor DX units has achieved much of its application because it provides a solution that appeals to the landlord because the landlord can negotiate a lease with minimal concern with regard to any need to allocate costs. It appeals to the single-floor prospective tenant because the system can be operated when needed and with the knowledge that the costs to operate the system are predictable and under the tenant's control.

Further, because condenser water is required to operate any one unit in a project on an overtime schedule, the provision of condenser water to tenants with supplemental cooling needs for information technology rooms or a limited data center can be easily accommodated through the operation of the cooling tower and condenser water pumps to satisfy both needs.

The marketing advantage in the multiple-tenant developer building with Alternate 3 is clear. In owner-occupied and corporate headquarters buildings, allocating operating costs is not a real issue and, as a result, these buildings more typically use either of the chilled water solutions in Alternative 1 and Alternative 2.

EQUIPMENT CONSIDERATIONS

The decision on which of the three alternative solutions to use in any building—owner occupied or developer constructed—also must involve the nature of the equipment installed in the particular building after the building is completed. These issues are summarized in Table 9.4. These concerns require little elaboration but include the redundancy and operational flexibility, life expectancy, and maintenance concerns of the equipment installed in each alternative.

The developer may well select Alternative 3 because of its marketing advantage even though the maintenance and replacement costs will be the least with Alternative 1 and, to a degree, less with Alternative 2.

The drawback of a lesser degree of equipment redundancy with Alternative 2 and Alternative 3 is rarely considered but is a matter that warrants consideration. There is very little that can be done to mitigate the downtime in Alternative 3 that would occur if a compressor failed in a unit. Fortunately, most units are or can be provided with multiple compressors, which will result in only a partial loss of cooling. Also, the availability of replacement compressor parts, coupled with the relatively infrequent failure and the relatively straightforward means of replacement, have reduced the concern when this alternative is considered for a project.

ARCHITECTURAL ISSUES

The decision on which alternative is chosen will have a significant impact upon the architectural design of the building. Table 9.5 provides an outline summary of the comparative issues that involve the architectural design. Each requires a more detailed discussion.

The building massing changes significantly as a function of the alternative selected. With either of the floor-by-floor alternatives, there is a lesser impact upon the architecture when

Table 9.4 Equipment Considerations

Alternative 1 Central Fan Systems Central Chilled Water	Alternative 2 Floor-by-Floor Fan Systems Central Chilled Water	Alternative 3 Floor-by-Floor DX Systems Central Cooling Tower
Issue—Equipment Maintenance		
• All equipment is installed in central mechanical equipment room with centralized maintenance • Chiller is installed in a central mechanical equipment room allowing centralized maintenance	• Requires more maintenance than Alternative 1, but less than Alternative 3, due to larger number of units with filters, motors, fan drives, bearings, etc. • Chiller is installed in central mechanical equipment room, allowing centralized maintenance	• Requires more maintenance than either Alternative 1 or Alternative 2 due to larger number of units with filters, motors, fan drives, bearings, etc., plus the compressor and condenser equipment on each floor
Issue—Equipment Redundancy and Flexibility		
• Can operate in reduced mode in case of limited failure due to headered multiple fan arrangement. Can handle changing cooling loads and/or uneven cooling loads on a floor-by-floor basis within limits. Can usually turn down system operation to supply air to a single floor	• If unit fails, floor is without air conditioning. Cannot handle changing cooling loads or uneven cooling loads on a floor-to-floor basis without building in additional system capacity at design	• If unit fails, floor is without air conditioning. Cannot handle changing cooling loads or uneven cooling loads on a floor-to-floor basis without building in additional system capacity at design
Issue — Equipment Life Expectancy		
• Life expectancy of equipment is in excess of 25 years	• Life expectancy of equipment is in excess of 25 years.	• Compressor life expectancy is approximately 10 years • Remainder of installation life expectancy is in excess of 25 years

Table 9.5 Typical Architectural Issues

Alternative 1 Central Fan Systems Central Chilled Water	Alternative 2 Floor-by-Floor Fan Systems Central Chilled Water	Alternative 3 Floor-by-Floor DX Systems Central Cooling Tower
Issue—Building Massing Impact		
• Central fan rooms usually require two-story MER and many louver • Chiller plant room usually requires two-story MER	• Local fan room fits within floor-to-floor height of the office floor • Chiller plant room usually requires two-story MER	• Local fan room fits within floor-to-floor height of the office floor • No central chiller plant room required
Issue—Usable Area Impact		
• Takes the least area per office floor* • Maximum usable area per office floor	• Takes a greater area per floor • Less usable area per office floor than Alternative 1	• Takes a greater area per floor. • Less usable area per office floor than Alternative 1
Issue—Gross Area Impact		
• Takes more gross building area than either Alternative 2 or Alternative 3	• Takes more gross building area than Alternative 3 but less than Alternative 1	• Takes less gross building area than either Alternative 1 or Alternative 2

* This depends greatly on the number of floors served from a single duct shaft. While ductwork can reduce in size away from the fan room, it is difficult to recapture this shaft area as usable area.

compared to the central fan system alternative, because any central mechanical space will be limited in size, with the conditioned air for the office floors developed by the local floor-by-floor air-conditioning unit. The need for a more limited central fan room exists with the Alternative 2 or Alternative 3 solutions, but it is significantly less than with Alternative 1. Alternative 1 requires one or more two-story, full-floor mechanical equipment rooms with large areas of exterior louvers, if an air economizer is incorporated, to contain the field-erected supply air systems and the extensive supply and return air ductwork extended from the supply fan to the supply air shafts and from the return air shafts to the return air fan, with the further extension to the supply air system and the spill dampers that allow the air to be expelled to atmosphere. The need for more than one double-high mechanical equipment room for air-conditioning supply units and return air fans is a function of the number of floors, the air-conditioned floor area in the building, and the location of the central mechanical equipment room within the project.

One location that is frequently used for the central mechanical equipment room in a tall commercial building results from the design of the vertical transportation system. As noted in Chapter 12, every high-rise office building will require multiple banks of elevators, each of which will serve separate banks of floors. The floor above the last floor served by any bank of elevators will require that an elevator machine room be provided that will contain the machinery that operates the elevator cabs in the bank. The elevator machine room can be 18 ft (5.5 m) in height (more than a single floor) and will exceed the width of the shaft that contains the elevator cab. The existence of this equipment will frequently dictate that the floor on which it is located can also become a mechanical equipment floor, because potential occupied space is already compromised, so the addition of air-conditioning equipment is easily accommodated. The floor can also serve well as a location for plumbing and high-voltage equipment.

The air distribution from any central fan room in the Alternative 1 approach is limited by the number of floors above and/or below the central mechanical equipment room, the acceptable size of the supply and return air duct shafts, and the area of the individual floors. Though experience on large projects shows that the maximum number of floors from the central mechanical equipment room is limited to approximately 20 to 24 floors, the architecturally acceptable central mechanical equipment room location may be different as a function of the aesthetic considerations for the building (which would affect the number of floors being handled by a given central mechanical equipment room).

For example, if the central mechanical equipment room can be accommodated aesthetically in the middle of a tall building, it could theoretically be possible to satisfy the air capacity for a 40- to 48-story building with a single central mechanical equipment room for the air-conditioning supply and return systems. In a practical sense, this will frequently not be possible. Moreover, the architect (and perhaps the building owner) may well not accept a band of louvers around the middle of the building. They may well prefer that the central mechanical equipment room be located in a penthouse space immediately below the cooling tower and elevator machine rooms on the roof. If this is the case, a second central mechanical equipment room for a 40- or 44-story building would be required, again perhaps immediately above the building entrance lobby area.

In addition, for either Alternative 1 or Alternative 2, a location must be found for the chiller plant room. As discussed in Chapter 9, with the necessary design considerations that plant can be located anywhere from a basement area of the building to a penthouse mechanical space. The clear height of the mechanical equipment room (i.e., the space below the structural steel of the floor above the mechanical equipment room and the slab of the room) that contains the refrigeration equipment can vary from 15 to 18 ft (4.6 to 5.5 m) as necessary to install the refrigeration equipment. The height must be sufficient to allow the relatively clean installation of the refrigeration equipment, vibration isolation, and sound control slabs as well as both the chilled-water and condenser water piping with all of the associated valves and fittings. No central chilled-water plant or space for such a plant is required for Alternative 3.

Usable area and gross building area are also affected by the alternative selected for a project. *Usable area* refers to that available for beneficial occupancy on each office floor. Generally, the central mechanical equipment room uses less space on any office floor than either of the floor-by-floor alternatives. Only shaft space is required, whereas in the floor-by-floor alternative, one or more fan rooms each using between 250 and 450 ft^2 (24 m^2 and 42 m^2) each is required. The variation in area is a function of the size of the unit required to support the capacity requirements of a given floor. However, the central system shafts can, in some cases, equal or exceed the floor area of the fan room, depending on the total area served by the central system.

The double-high mechanical equipment room required for Alternative 1, particularly if considered as two floors, requires more gross building area than either of the local fan room approaches. Also, because of the absence of a central chilled-water system, Alternative 3 will require less gross building area than Alternative 2.

This analysis of usable and gross area should be made on every project before a decision is made on the best solution. Additional usable space will be given favorable consideration by the project real estate professionals. In the United States, the rentable area may or may not be affected by the fan room floor area as a function of the local rules for determining rentable area. This determination, which will differ in various areas of the United States, can be substantively different elsewhere in the world. However, usable area for office occupancy is measurable and can be compared for the various alternatives. It may favor the central air-conditioning supply system.

The following is an example of required area calculation for a centralized fan room compared to floor by floor fan rooms. The example building has 50 floors and the total supply air volume has been calculated at 731,013 cfm (345 m³/s).

For this example, there are three mechanical rooms, one at level 5, one at level 30 and one at level 54. The required floor area for the air handling units is 2600 m² and the required riser area is 4,241 ft² (394 m²), for a total floor area of 32,228 ft² (2994 m²).

A floor-by-floor solution would require 969 ft² (90 m²) area to house a 45,891 cfm (7.5 m³/s) ahu on each floor, the total floor area required would be 46,502 ft² (4320 m²). In this example, a centralized air handling and distribution system would consume less floor area than a floor by floor alternative.

The additional building gross area with the central mechanical equipment room would be factored into the building cost to create the fan room area.

INTAKE AND EXHAUST DISTANCES

The general school of thought is that a minimum distance should be kept between intake and exhaust air paths to avoid short-circuit problems. These minimum distances change, depending on the guidance being read:

- CIBSE (2005) recommends a 33 ft (10 m) separation
- ASHRAE (2013a) recommends 15 ft (5 m) separation for mechanical ventilation
- Rating systems such as LEED[7] and BREEAM[8] have requirements for minimum separation that depend on the credits being pursued

Table 9.6 Required Area for Central AHU System

Level	cfm (m³/s)	Area, ft² (m²)
54	207,650 (98)	(7320) 680
30 up	174,807 (82.5)	6889 (640)
30 down	174,807 (82.5)	6889 (640)
5 up	174,807 (82.5)	6889 (640)
		27,987 (2600)
Total riser area		4241 (394)
Total area		32,228 (2994)

7. LEED requirements are to comply with ANSI/ASHRAE Standard 62.1-2019, *Ventilation for Acceptable Indoor Air Quality*, and to locate intakes more than 25 ft (7.62 m) from designated smoking areas.

8. BREEAM requires air-conditioned and mixed-mode buildings to have intakes and exhausts more than 33 ft (10 m) apart and more than 65 ft (20 m) from sources of external pollution. For naturally ventilated buildings, windows/ventilators need to be more than 33 ft (10 m) from external sources of pollution. Sources of external pollution are defined as highways and main access roads, car parks and vehicle delivery/waiting spaces, and other building/process exhausts.

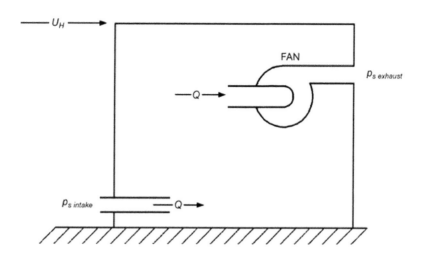

Figure 9.6 Fan setup for a single-zone building.
(ASHRAE 2017a)

These recommendations can form an acceptable starting philosophy, but care must be taken to consider what will happen in reality. Caution must also be displayed with regard to external sources of contamination.

Wind effects can cause exhaust air to attach itself to the building face. This air may then be sucked in any intake louvers it encounters. This may be a particular problem in the case of smoke and kitchen exhausts, which will contain contaminants. High-velocity exhausts may minimize the risk of recirculation, but designers should beware of noise issues that may be introduced.

INTAKE AND EXHAUST FAN PRESSURES

Quantitative estimates of wind effects on a mechanical ventilation system can be made by using the pressure coefficients provided in *ASHRAE Handbook—Fundamentals*, Chapter 24, to calculate the wind pressure on air intakes and exhausts (ASHRAE 2017a). For simplicity, we use the intake coefficient of $C_P = 0.7$ and an exhaust coefficient of $C_P = -0.4$. A simple worst-case estimate is to assume a system with 100% makeup air supplied by a single intake and exhausted from a single outlet. The building is treated as a single zone, with an exhaust-only fan as shown in Figure 9.6. This overestimates the effect of wind on system volume flow.

The surface wind pressures at the air intake and exhaust locations are as follows, where Equations 9.1 through 9.4 are in I-P units and Equations 9.5 through 9.8 are in SI units:

I-P

$$P_{S\ intake} = C_{P\ intake}\left[\frac{\rho_a U_H^2}{2g_c}/2.152\right] \tag{9.1}$$

$$P_{S\ exhaust} = C_{P\ exhaust}\left[\frac{\rho_a U_H^2}{2g_c}/2.152\right] \tag{9.2}$$

$$(P_{s\ intake} - P_{s\ exhaust}) + \Delta P_{fan} = F_{sys}\frac{\rho Q^2}{A_L^2 g_c} \tag{9.3}$$

$$\Delta P_{wind} = (C_{p\ intake} - C_{p\ exhaust})\left[\frac{\rho_a U_H^2}{2g_c}/2.152\right] \tag{9.4}$$

SI

$$P_{S\,intake} = C_{P\,intake}\left[\frac{\rho_a U_H^2}{2g_c}/2.152\right] \tag{9.5}$$

$$P_{S\,exhaust} = C_{P\,exhaust}\left[\frac{\rho_a U_H^2}{2g_c}\right] \tag{9.6}$$

$$(P_{s\,intake} - P_{s\,exhaust}) + \Delta P_{fan} = F_{sys}\frac{\rho Q^2}{A_L^2 g_c} \tag{9.7}$$

$$\Delta P_{wind} = (C_{p\,intake} - C_{p\,exhaust})\left[\frac{\rho_a U_H^2}{2g_c}\right] \tag{9.8}$$

where

ρa = outdoor air density at height h

U_H = approach wind speed at upwind height h, mph (m/s)

For the single-zone building shown in Figure 9.6, a worst-case estimate of wind effect neglects any flow resistance in the intake grill and duct, making interior building pressure $P_{interior}$ equal to outdoor wind pressure on the intake ($P_{interior} = P_{S\,intake}$). Then, with all system flow resistance assigned to the exhaust duct in Figure 9.6, and a pressure rise ΔP_{fan} across the fan, pressure drop from outdoor intake to outdoor exhaust yields

$$(P_{S\,intake} - P_{S\,exhaust}) + \Delta P_{fan} = F_{sys}\frac{\rho Q^2}{A_L^2} \tag{9.9}$$

where

F_{sys} = system flow resistance,

A_L = flow leakage area, and

Q = system volume flow rate.

$$(p_{s\,intake} - p_{s\,exhaust}) + \Delta p_{fan} = F_{sys}\frac{\rho Q^2}{A_L^2 g_c}$$

This result shows that, for the worst-case estimate, the wind-induced pressure difference simply adds to or subtracts from the fan pressure rise. With inlet and exhaust pressures from Equations 9.1 and 9.2, the effective fan pressure rise $\Delta P_{fan\,eff}$ is:

$$\Delta P_{fan\,eff} = \Delta P_{fan} + \Delta P_{wind} \tag{9.10}$$

where

$$\Delta P_{wind} = (C_{p\,intake} - C_{p\,exhaust})\frac{\rho_a U^2 H}{2} \tag{9.11}$$

The fan is wind-assisted when $C_{p\,intake} > C_{p\,exhaust}$ and wind opposed when the wind direction changes, causing $C_{p\,intake} < C_{p\,exhaust}$. The effect of wind-assisted and wind-opposed pressure differences is shown in Figure 9.7.

In addition to flow patterns described previously, the turbulence or gustiness of approaching wind and the unsteady character of separated flows cause surface pressures to fluctuate. Pressures discussed here are time-averaged values, with a full-scale averaging period of about 600 s. This is approximately the shortest time period considered to be a steady-state condition when considering atmospheric winds; the longest is typically 3600 s. Instantaneous pressures may vary significantly above and below these averages, and peak pressures two or three times the mean values are possible. Peak pressures are important with regard to structural loads and mean values are more

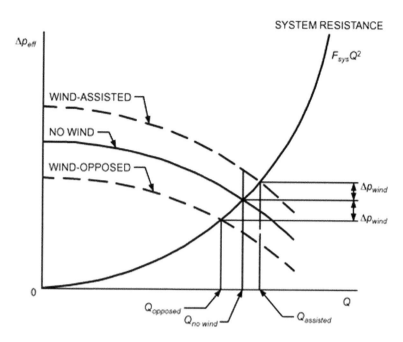

Figure 9.7 Difference in a wind-assisted and wind-opposed pressure.

ACOUSTICS

In any project developed for commercial usage, acoustical criteria should be established for the alternative types of occupancy that are expected in the building. For example, open-plan office space can be designed to meet a noise criteria level of NC 40, whereas private and executive offices or conference rooms should be no higher than NC 35 and could be lower. The acoustical engineer on a project will set these levels, and it is the responsibility of the HVAC designer to work with the acoustician to see that the criteria established can be achieved in the designed installation.

The selection of one of the three alternatives discussed in this chapter will have an effect on the sound treatment and the resultant acoustical level in the occupied areas of the office floors. Regardless of which alternative is selected, it is important that, in addition to establishing the project acoustical standards, the actual designs and equipment selections be reviewed by the acoustical consultant to ensure that the desired levels can be achieved in the final construction. This need for an acoustical consultant is advised on all projects but is particularly necessary with either of the floor-by-floor fan room alternatives for the reasons detailed in the following sections.

Acoustical Issues with Central Fan Systems

With Alternative 1, it is possible to provide a sound criteria level of NC 35 or lower in any office area as a function of the selection of the equipment provided for the chosen air-conditioning system, the design and acoustical attenuation means for both the supply and return ductwork, and the selection of the air distribution equipment, including the air terminals and air diffusion devices to distribute the air in the occupied space.

To provide physical separation of airborne sound transmission between the mechanical equipment room and occupied areas, the construction of slabs both at the bottom and top of the mechanical equipment room (assuming occupied floors above and below the mechanical equipment room) should be, as a minimum, 8 in. (200 mm) normal weight concrete to contain the noise that is generated by the fan equipment in the room. The type of construction used in the mechanical equipment room that contains the refrigeration equipment is discussed in Chapter 7. In either case, the intent is to contain the noise that is generated by the mechanical equipment.

Spaces occupied by office workers on the same level but adjacent to the central mechanical equipment room that contains fans and similar equipment should be separated by a wall with a minimum installed sound transmission class (STC) rating of 50. This can be achieved with a 6 or 8 in. (150 or 200 mm) cinder block wall or gypsum board construction that includes 3 5/8 in. (90 mm) metal stud erected slab-to-slab with batt insulation in the stud cavity and two layers of 5/8 in. (16 mm) thick gypsum board on both sides of the stud. A typical example of this construction is shown in Figure 9.8.

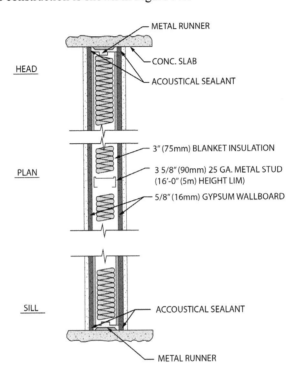

Figure 9.8 A typical mechanical room wall construction.

A further consideration with a mechanical equipment room located above grade in a building is the possibility of noise being carried along the curtain wall at the slab ending or through openings at the mechanical level and back through the glazing installed in office floors above or below the mechanical equipment room. To avert this from happening, the slab endings at the curtain wall on the mechanical level must be sealed properly, and there should be no openings that are not closed along the wall of the mechanical room.

The ductwork from the central air-conditioning supply units must be treated acoustically. Typically, internal acoustic duct lining is recommended 30 ft (9 m) downstream of the supply fans. Some building owners are concerned for environmental reasons about the inclusion of duct lining. This concern may still exist even when the acoustical lining is covered with a material to minimize its fibers from being loosened by the air velocity and carried from the duct distribution system to occupied areas. In these cases, it is necessary to use sound attenuators or silencers. The best location for a sound attenuator is within the built-up air-conditioning system where the velocity of the air through the cooling coil is 500 fpm (2.5 m/s) and the resultant velocity through the attenuator will be quite low. This yields a silencer selection with better attenuation in the space of 3 to 5 ft (0.9 to 1.5 m) with a lower static pressure drop. If a sound attenuator is required, it would be installed in the supply air ductwork at the exit from the equipment room. The velocity in the ductwork can be 2500 fpm (12.5 mps) or higher, but the maximum air velocity for a silencer is 1200 fpm (6.0 m/s) to minimize the static pressure drop through the attenuator. This difference in velocities will require a duct shape transition to satisfy the difference in velocities. The attenuator length will be between 5 and 7 ft (1.5 and 2.1 m), which does not include the duct transition requirement. The combination of the length of the attenuator and the duct transition to accommodate the attenuator will be a significant design complication.

In the central fan room alternative, return air can also be a problem in the floors closest to the central mechanical equipment room where they are in close proximity to the return fan. These several floors may require sound attenuators, acoustically lined elbows at the shaft, or an equivalent sound treatment as the supply fans to prevent transmission of the return fan noise back through the return air shaft to the occupied floor. Finally, both the air-conditioning supply fans and the return fans will require external spring isolation between the fan and the concrete base on which the fan is installed, the details of which should be prepared by the project acoustical engineer.

Acoustical Issues with Local Fan Room Systems

The design issues with local floor-by-floor Alternatives 2 and 3 are subject to wide variation as a function of the proximity of the unit to occupied space, the unit configuration, the type of fan used, and both the supply and return duct arrangements that are possible on the project.

In general, office spaces other than those contiguous to the local fan room can achieve the NC 35 or lower noise criteria possible with Alternative 1. The spaces contiguous to the fan room, assuming the design considerations detailed herein are respected, may only be capable of achieving a sound criteria level of NC 40 to NC 45 up to approximately 10 ft (3 m) from the local fan room wall. The precise distance of higher noise criteria levels will depend on the fan selection, the duct layout in the local fan room, and the construction of the room itself. This slightly higher noise level is usually not a major deterrent to the use of these alternatives for general office space but should be understood by the design team and, especially, by the owner when developing a lease document with any prospective tenant.

The air-conditioning supply systems used with either local fan room alternative can be obtained in either a draw-through or blow-through configuration. These two configurations have different acoustical characteristics and, accordingly, result in different noise control requirements. Today, virtually all projects utilize fan-speed control through a variable-frequency drive rather than variable inlet vanes. This improves the acoustical levels from the unit because the possible turbulence created by the vanes is eliminated. Moreover, because the fan speed is reduced at part loads, the acoustical energy and the resultant noise level will be lower than would be the case at full fan speed. This, coupled with the fact that the system will operate at less than peak design airflow conditions virtually at all times, results in lower noise levels than might be expected if the fan operated at full speed at all times.

A unit configuration that has found application with floor-by-floor systems is a blow-through arrangement with the fan before the inlet side of the cooling coil. The advantage of this configuration is that the fan heat will be removed by the cooling coil after the fan. This configuration, however, is inherently noisier on the unit return air side, with a resultant noisier fan room than would be the case with a draw-through unit. This system arrangement will require treatment to allow return air to transfer back to the local floor fan room while keeping noise from escaping the fan room. The options to achieve these goals include an acoustically lined return air plenum to allow the use of the least amount of acoustically lined return ductwork or special return air treatment, such as an architectural return air transfer wall, detailed subsequently in this chapter.

The unit configuration most frequently used with the floor-by-floor system, however, is a draw-through unit, which eliminates any concern with fan-system-casing radiated or inlet noise. This type of unit also makes it possible to consider return air transfer to the local fan room with simpler return air duct connections than for a blow-through arrangement.

In addition to the arrangement of the unit, the type of fan used will determine the noise control specification for the project. There are three fan choices typically available.

Acoustically, the most desirable fan is a mixed-flow fan. This fan has its loudest sound levels at higher frequencies than either of the other two alternatives. The maximum acoustical noise with the mixed-flow fan occurs between 250 and 500 Hz frequency. Noise in these frequencies is more easily attenuated than would be the case with the lower frequency noise generated, for example, by centrifugal fans.

A plug fan is the second alternative. It is a quieter selection than a centrifugal fan, because it pressurizes an open plenum and is more isolated within the air-handling unit than would be the case with a centrifugal fan. The plenum with plug fans also provides a versatile design option, because the supply ducts can be distributed with multiple taps in differing directions. This can be quite advantageous, particularly where ducts will be routed from the local fan room in multiple directions off a common supply plenum. A variation of the plug fan concept using multiple small fans, a "fan wall", has become more common in an array with inherent fan redundancy and quieter operation.

The third type of fan that has been successfully used is a centrifugal fan. The fan will require less space on its own but the supply duct must proceed in the direction of the fan rotation with minimal deviations in that direction until the airflow is sufficiently laminar to allow a change in direction. In addition, the sound power levels from a centrifugal fan are higher than either of the other two alternatives and may require a sound attenuator in addition to the acoustical lining or increased lengths of supply duct prior to penetration of the duct into the ceiling void above an occupied area.

The only acoustical difference between Alternative 2 and Alternative 3 is the compressor that is provided with Alternative 3 that is not required with Alternative 2. The problem is partially resolved in that the unit manufacturer for Alternative 3 will provide spring isolation for the compressors and possibly acoustical jackets as an integrated part of the unit. The air-handling unit for Alternative 2 or Alternative 3 should be mounted on external springs where occupied areas are adjacent to the local fan room. The spring-on-spring condition between the internal and external isolators is not a problem but, together, they resolve the potential noise from compressor vibration in Alternative 3. With this treatment of isolation of the compressor, the fan noise will predominate and will require the major consideration of the designer in the effort to develop the needed acoustical design details.

The remaining acoustical issues that are common to both Alternative 2 and Alternative 3 are the construction of the partition that forms the fan room wall adjacent to occupied space, the construction of the door that permits access to the fan room, and the control of the airborne noise from the supply fan that can be transmitted by either the supply ductwork or the return air connection provided for the air that is recirculated on the floor.

The wall partition should be provided to achieve a minimum installed STC of 50. The construction, as was the case with adjacencies on the same level as a central fan room solution, can be a 6 or 8 in. (150 or 200 mm) block wall or can have the construction shown in Figure 9.6.

The detailing of the doors can differ as a function of their location with respect to occupied areas and the arrangement of the local floor-by-floor air-handling unit within the fan room. A blow-through unit, which will be acoustically louder than a draw-through unit, will require a higher acoustical rating. The options available for the door to the fan room include a core-filled hollow metal door with perimeter gasketing and automatic drop seals, back-to-back doors with threshold seals, or an acoustically rated door and frame assembly. An example of the detailing of the back-to-back door arrangement is shown in Figure 9.9.

To minimize airborne noise transmission through the supply duct system, it is prudent to include at least 10 ft (3 m) of a straight run of lined supply duct in the local fan room, before the duct penetrates into the ceiling plenum of occupied areas. This is very difficult to achieve in practice, but this is at least as important as the unit selection for overall noise impact. Where the straight length of ductwork is more limited, then the unit selection will be more critical. This straight run of duct is important, as it will not only attenuate fan noise but also will reduce the turbulence of the air and allow the air to even out its flow in the ductwork. If possible, as a function of the space available and the fan type used on the project, the splitting of the supply duct is also beneficial in that the acoustical energy will be distributed into two ducts rather than one. If the fan room and associated space will not allow the installation of two ducts in the fan room, the splitting of the single duct after it leaves the fan room can be beneficial in obtaining a reduction of the acoustical energy in the resulting pair of ducts.

The return air duct from the plenum ceiling should also be lined and have at least 12 ft (4 m) of lining. One method of achieving this goal is to bring the lined return air duct to the floor as the duct enters the fan room, creating a vertical elbow from the ceiling plenum to the fan room. This lined elbow section of ductwork of approximately 9 ft (3 m) will limit the lined extension into the ceiling plenum to about 3 ft (1 m). A further alternative is that shown in Figure 9.10 where a return air transfer wall eliminates the need for return ductwork, in that air passes through a specially constructed, widened fan room wall.

Care must be taken in the duct construction for both the supply and return ducts to ensure sufficient gage sheet metal is used to contain the low-frequency fan noise. This requirement for the use of the appropriate sheet metal gage is especially important where the ductwork has a high aspect ratio to allow the ducts to fit within the space constraints forced by the need to minimize the ceiling plenum depth. The gage of the duct may well be heavier than would be required for sheet metal rigidity as is defined in several sources. This is a major consideration for the first sections of ducts over occupied areas.

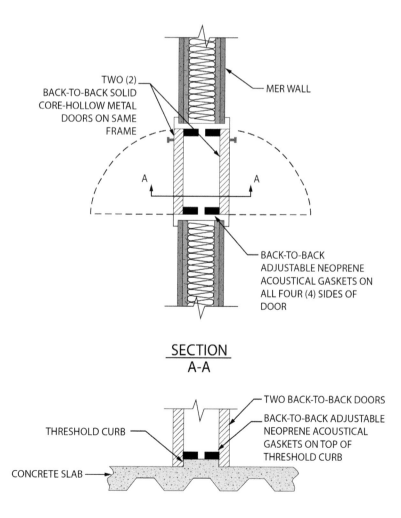

Figure 9.9 A typical back-to-back door arrangement for local fan room.

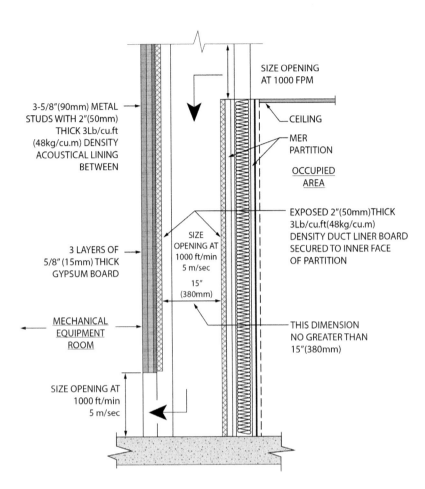

Figure 9.10 A typical return air transfer wall.

CHAPTER 10
Central Heating and Cooling Plants

Many, but not all, tall commercial office buildings will require a central plant to provide chilled water and hot water or steam to meet the cooling and heating needs of the building. If packaged direct-expansion equipment is used on a floor-by-floor basis, as is discussed in detail in Chapter 8, a chilled-water plant will not be required. Similarly, in cold climates, where heat is necessary, if electric resistance heat is used, either along the base of the outside wall or in an overhead fan-powered air-conditioning terminal supplying the periphery of a building, a central hot-water or steam boiler is not required.

Additionally, there are geographical locations where chilled water and/or steam or hot water are available from a central utility. If these sources of cooling or heating are used, a refrigeration or boiler plant will not be necessary.

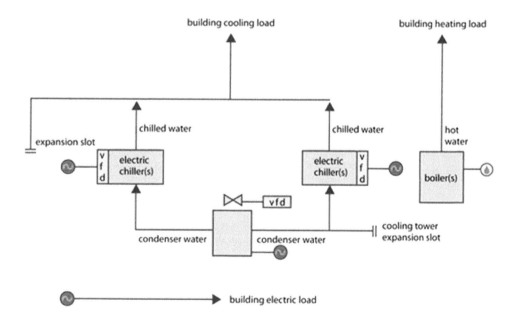

Figure 10.1 Typical heating and cooling plant.

For most other installations, a central chilled-water plant using refrigeration machines and a central boiler plant will be required. Factors that should be considered to allow the most rational decision as to the type and location of the heating and cooling plant include the following:

- Weight, space requirements, and impact on the structural system
- Effect on the construction schedule
- Specific changes in mechanical room detailing and slab construction within which the equipment is located
- Acoustical considerations
- Ease and cost of operation and maintenance
- Available energy sources
- Annual operating costs and possibly the life-cycle costs

The methods of calculating owning and operating costs are discussed in the *ASHRAE Handbook—HVAC Applications* (2019a). Alternative refrigeration machines are detailed in *ASHRAE Handbook—Refrigeration* (2018) and boilers in *ASHRAE Handbook—Systems and Equipment* (2016b). Useful reference information is also contained in the *ASME Boiler and Pressure Vessel Code* (2015).

PLANT ECONOMIC CONSIDERATIONS

A detailed analysis is needed to determine the refrigeration system to be installed in a project. The choices are usually limited to either centrifugal refrigeration machines or absorption machines. Centrifugal machines can be electric drive or steam drive and are almost always water cooled. Absorption machines can be single effect or double effect, but to utilize the double-effect machines with the advantage that results from lower energy costs, high pressure steam is required. The use of high-pressure steam is rare in a commercial project unless the steam is available from a central utility.

There are cases where air-cooled refrigeration machines have been installed in tall buildings, but these are infrequent for a number of reasons. The most important reasons are the limited commercially available sizes of air-cooled refrigeration equipment and the resultant space requirements for this type of equipment. The largest air-cooled refrigeration machine that can be purchased at this time is 400 tons (1400 kW). Tall buildings, by their very nature, are typically large buildings, and the multiple number of air-cooled refrigeration machines that would be required to meet the needs of a large building and the relatively large space they require will usually result in their not being a viable solution.

In addition, air-cooled equipment will probably have higher operating costs because of the higher condensing temperatures developed by the refrigeration equipment. This higher operating cost results from the fact that the refrigerant condensing temperature for air-cooled equipment is a function of the dry-bulb outdoor air temperature, whereas water-cooled equipment will have a refrigerant condensing temperature driven by the lower outdoor air wet-bulb temperature. This operating cost difference will exist even though there is no cooling tower fan or condenser water pump and the motor associated with the pumps that would be required for the water-cooled equipment.

The geographic locations and/or penthouse where air-cooled equipment has found application in larger projects, including tall commercial buildings, would be in areas where water to meet the needs of the cooling tower make-up is either not available or is prohibitively expensive.

The heating plant for either low-rise or high-rise buildings, when electric resistance heat is not used, is selected from the same list of available plants that find application in other types of projects. This would include oil- or gas-fired boilers, boilers that use both oil and interruptible gas as a function of the availability of either fuel or their relative cost, or boilers that use electric energy. These boilers would be used to provide hydronic heat, low-pressure steam which is distributed to spaces in the building, or as supplements to heat pumps or heat recovery systems. The choice of the correct solution for a building is subject to an economic analysis that will consider the space requirements, first cost, and operating expense as a function of the cost of alternative available fuels and possible differences in maintenance costs.

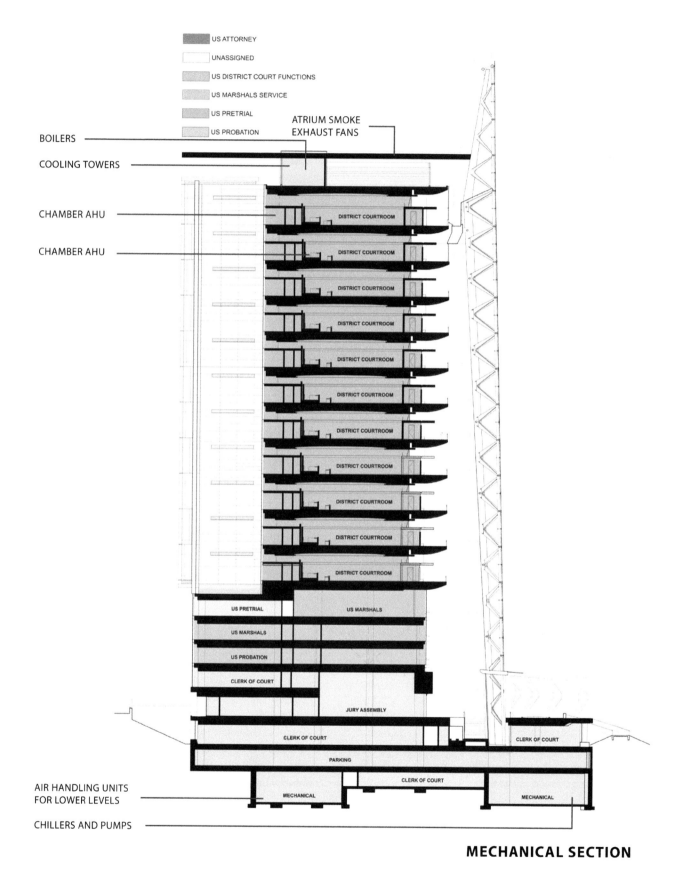

Figure 10.2 A section through a tall building where the chillers are in the basement and cooling towers on the roof.

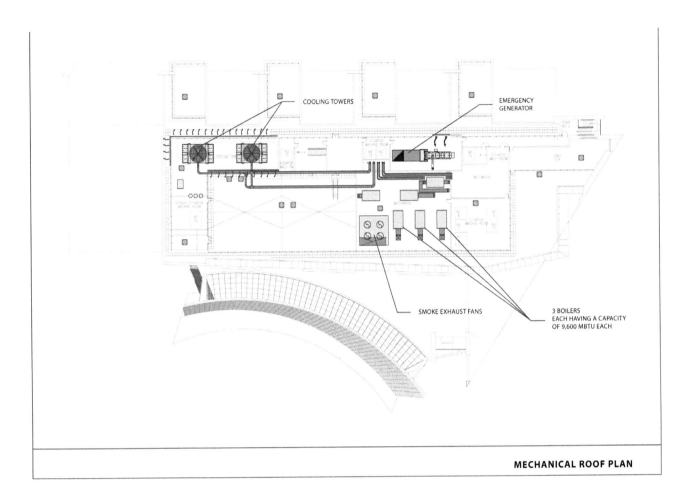

Figure 10.3 A typical roof layout for a tall building.

CENTRAL PLANT LOCATIONS

Further complicating the decision is the location within the building of all equipment. The possible locations will affect structural costs, architectural design, construction time, and availability of the cooling or heating effect in relation to occupancy requirements. Not uncommonly, the latter requirement can be a significant factor in a determination to place central heating and refrigeration plants below grade in certain projects even though this decision may result, in some cases, in design complications and possibly higher overall project costs. The placing of chiller plants and heating plants in floors above grade, up to and including space directly below the roof, is not only common but may be desirable in terms of the simplicity of construction and ease of providing the necessary ventilation air and other services to the equipment. Moreover, the two types of plants need not be installed at the same level in the building, as there is usually no direct interconnection of the two plants.

There is no location of a boiler plant or of water-cooled refrigeration machines that cannot be used in a building. The location is determined through the consideration of several requirements for the equipment. Boiler plants and refrigeration plants can be located in the below-grade levels, in a rooftop mechanical equipment room, or anywhere in between.

If a boiler is installed above grade, fuel (i.e., oil, gas, or electricity) must be brought to the boiler, and a flue, in the case of an oil- or gas-fired boiler, must take combustion products from the boiler to the atmosphere. The location of a boiler plant should be determined by analysis vis-á-vis previously outlined parameters.

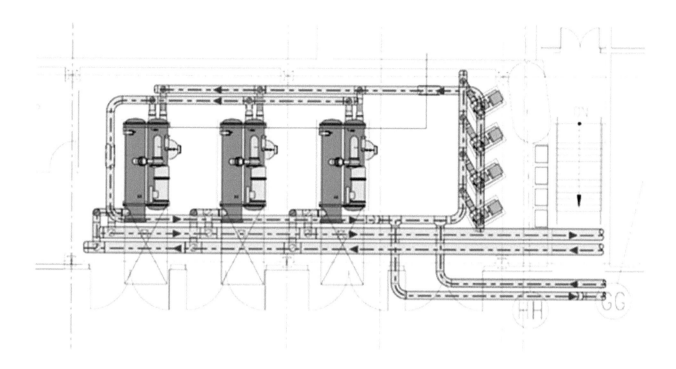

Figure 10.4 A typical multiple chiller layout.

The considerations for the refrigeration plant location are more complex, because the chilled water and condenser water must be pumped to and from the location of the refrigeration plant to the air-conditioning supply equipment that requires it. In addition, the cooling tower and the working pressure of the refrigeration machines (as well as the piping, fittings, and valves discussed in Chapter 11) must be reviewed. Further, electricity or steam must be brought to the machine to provide the energy to operate the equipment.

Regardless of where it is installed, the detailing of the design must include appropriate acoustical design considerations and vibration isolation. Reluctance has been expressed by owners concerning possible noise transmitted from the refrigeration equipment to occupied space on the floors above, below, or adjacent to the plant. This should not be a concern if the architectural, structural, and mechanical designs fully consider the vibration and acoustical requirements of the plant.

CENTRALIZED SERVICES SYSTEMS

Locations

The plant will consist of the following services and equipment located at various locations in the building. The typical arrangement in a tall building is as follows:

- Basement
  - Utility intakes and meter rooms
  - Boiler plant and main pumping systems
  - Water chiller plant and main pumping systems
  - Domestic water pumping systems
  - Switchgear rooms and transformers
  - Uninterruptible power supply (UPS) (emergency generator) equipment
  - Other equipment for garages and other services

- Roof level
  - Flue discharges
  - Elevator motor rooms
  - Cooling towers
  - Ventilation air intakes
  - Smoke discharges

- Midlevels (dependent upon design strategy)
  - Ventilation inlets and/or plants to serve office spaces
  - Water decoupling and booster plant for heating, cooling, domestic, and fire protection systems
  - Switchgear rooms and transformers
  - Elevator motor rooms

- Central systems versus decoupled systems
  - Central system plant reduced in size by use of load diversities
  - Better security of supply
  - Centralized maintenance
  - Reduced room space
  - Maximizing potential energy recovery (primarily from exhaust flows, chilling equipment, standby electrical equipment, and cogeneration equipment, if used)
- Floor-by-floor options
  - Ventilation
  - Cooling and/or heating plants

Systems

- The HVAC plant includes space for boilers, pumps, pressurization sets, HVAC control panels, chillers, water softening plant, and salt storage. HVAC riser space allows for pipework and ductwork.
- Air-handling plant includes space for AHU, toilet vent, and control panels.
- Heat rejection plant includes space for cooling towers/air-cooled condensers.
- Electrical plant includes space for substations, switch rooms, standby generators, UPS, battery rooms, PABX rooms, distribution frame rooms etc. Electrical riser space allows for power and communication cables
- Public health plant includes space for tanks, clarifiers, etc. Public health riser space allows for pipework and drainage
- Fire protection plant includes space for sprinkler tanks, alarm valves, and smoke extract system. Fire protection riser space allows for wet/dry risers, sprinkler pipework, and smoke extraction ductwork.
- Cogeneration (combined heat and power) is an option for all tall buildings, depending on energy charges, electric utility rates, and available space for equipment and fuel storage. In addition, the waste heat can be used for heating in the winter, preheating of ventilation air, heat recovery steam generators for steam-driven turbine generators, and absorption cooling equipment. It also provides for equipment diversity in case of utility interruptions.

CHILLER SYSTEMS

Chiller systems in commercial tall buildings are typically located in the basement because the first floor is valuable lease space and also because floor loading concerns. Advantages include relative ease of access to maintenance personnel, relative ease of replacement, and reduced noise and vibration to other areas of the building. At least two chillers are usually installed to accommodate part loading and partial redundancy. The part-load efficiency of chillers has increased in recent years so that the use of multiple chillers allows at least one of the chillers to operate at full or part-load most of the time to satisfy the cooling load.

Figure 10.5 A typical basement plant room for multiple chillers.

The piping systems normally designed and encountered in the design of tall buildings are discussed in Chapter 11, Water Distribution Systems.

For electric chiller systems, chilled-water and ice storage systems may prove to be economical where peak to off-peak electricity usage rates are relatively large. Thermal storage systems also allow for the use of cold-air distribution systems, which decrease the size of air distribution ductwork, which can in turn decrease the height of ductwork ceiling plenums. A reduction in plenum height can increase the number of stories for the same building height, increasing tenant occupancy.

Thermal storage requires the use of chilled-water, ice storage tanks, or unitary ice storage tanks, which require space in the building, Chilled water or ice storage tanks can be located below ground level or external to the building structure. In either case, they require a large space. Ice storage systems require significantly less space than chilled-water systems. Unitary ice storage systems can be distributed throughout the floors to reduce pumping and piping costs.

CASE STUDY
Lotte World Tower

eoul

Name: Lotte World Tower

Location: Seoul, South Korea

Description: This 1823 ft (555 m) monument to Seoul's skyline reaches heights never before seen in Korea and is one of the top 10 tallest buildings in the world.

Elegance of form was one of the prime objectives, following Lotte's desire to add a beautiful monument to the capital city skyline. The sleek, tapered form of the 123-story tower stands out from the city's rocky, mountainous topography, and is organized around a stacked mixed-use program, including retail, office, residential, and a luxury hotel. The building's top 10 stories are earmarked for extensive public use and entertainment facilities, including an observation deck and rooftop café.

The design melds a modern aesthetic with forms inspired by the historic Korean arts of ceramics, porcelain, and calligraphy. The tower's uninterrupted curvature and gentle tapered form is reflective of Korean artistry. The seam that runs from top to bottom of the structure gestures toward the old center of the city.

The building design is LEED Gold certified, a measure of the client's commitment to environmental responsibility. Sustainable design strategies incorporated into the design include:

Building-Integrated Photovoltaics. Photovoltaic panels and solar energy modules on a rooftop and exterior walls of the building produce 500 Mwh of electricity a year and reduce the CO_2 emissions by 222 tons (201,395 kg).

Wind Power Generation. The tower's systems analyze the environment regarding the surrounding winds and sets up a wind generator with the vertical axis in harmony with the building after considering the beauty, vibration, and noise of the building.

Geothermal System. Using an underground heat exchanger, the ground heat is applied to the air-conditioning and heating system with the benefit of saving electricity of 6675 Mwh a year and reducing CO_2 emissions by 2968 tons (2,692,524 kg).

Heat Pump System Using Han River Water. After exchanging heat from the groundwater, the water is recycled by reducing the load of air conditioning and heating.

Building Function: Hotel, residential, office, retail and observation
Building Height: 1823 ft (555.7 m)
Building Ground Floor Area: 3,273,100 ft^2 (304,081 m^2) (tower), 16,202,849 ft^2 (505,294 m^2) (development)
Architects: Kohn Pedersen Fox Associates (Design), Baum Architects (Architect of Record)
Structural Engineer: LERA (Design)
MEP Engineer: Syska Hennessy Group (Design)

Adapted from a report originally published at kpf.com
https://www.kpf.com/projects/lotte-world-tower.

CHAPTER 11
Water Distribution Systems

The design of the piping for water distribution systems for a commercial tall building differs from the design of these systems for a low-rise building primarily because of the static pressure on the piping system as a result of the height of the building. This condition can affect the design of all of the piping systems in the building, including the domestic water and sprinkler systems, but this chapter of this design guide only addresses the chilled-water, hot-water, and condenser water systems. Domestic water piping is briefly discussed in Chapter 13 and sprinkler piping is similarly covered in Chapter 17.

Chilled- and hot-water systems are always closed systems, whereas the condenser water system is usually an open water system. A closed water system is one in which the pumped fluid is essentially not exposed to the atmosphere at any point. Examples of closed water systems in a building are the chilled-water and hot-water systems for air conditioning and heating. These systems always contain an expansion tank, which can be either an open expansion tank or a closed expansion tank. The open expansion tank is always at the highest point of the particular system.

If an evaporative cooler or dry cooler (commonly referred to as an *industrial fluid cooler*) is used rather than a cooling tower for the condenser water (which handles the heat of rejection from the refrigeration equipment), the piping system would be a closed system rather than an open system. The use of evaporative or dry coolers for an entire large commercial office building is extremely rare. However, they are used in portions of tall commercial buildings as a means of handling the heat of rejection from occupants' supplemental cooling systems that may be installed in spaces needing additional cooling capacity or cooling capacity on an extended operational basis, such as a data center.

As stated in the *ASHRAE Handbook—HVAC Systems and Equipment* (2016b), the "major difference in hydraulics between open and closed systems is that certain hydraulic characteristics of open systems cannot occur in closed systems. For example, in contrast to the hydraulics of an open system, in a closed system the following is observed:

- Flow cannot be motivated by static pressure differences
- Pumps do not provide static lift
- The entire piping system is always filled with water

HYDROSTATIC CONSIDERATIONS

A major consideration in the design of a piping system in a tall building is the hydrostatic pressure created by the height of the building. This hydrostatic pressure affects not only the piping and its associated valves and fittings but also the equipment installed in the building. In the

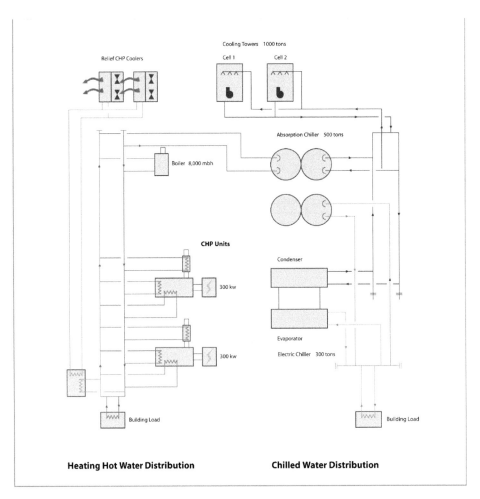

Figure 11.1 A diagrammatic layout of typical heating and cooling distribution systems for tall buildings.

case of the chilled-water system, the equipment involved includes the refrigeration machines, the casings for the chilled-water pumps, the cooling coils installed in the air-conditioning systems, any heat exchangers provided, and, if included as the system of choice, fan-coil units, radiant ceilings, or active beams at the exterior wall of the building. A similar list of devices beyond the pipes, valves, and fittings themselves can be developed for other pumped systems in a project such as a condenser water system or any hot-water system.

Beyond the static increment developed by the hydrostatic height of the building, there are dynamic pressures that are necessarily created by the pumps in any tall building that must be added to the static pressure increment to determine the working pressure on any element in the piping systems for the building. The dynamic pressure at the pump is the total of the following elements:

- The friction loss through the piping and its associated valves and fittings
- The residual pressure necessary at the most remote piece of heat transfer equipment in the project that will allow that piece of equipment to function. This would include the pressure loss through the control valve at the equipment and the friction loss or pressure drop through the equipment.
- Any excess pressure caused by the pumps when they operate at low flow close to the shut-off head of the pump

It is necessary to determine the working pressure of the piping and the equipment connected to the piping at various elevations in the building. This is done by adding the hydrostatic pressure head at the specific location to the dynamic head that can be developed by the pumps at that loca-

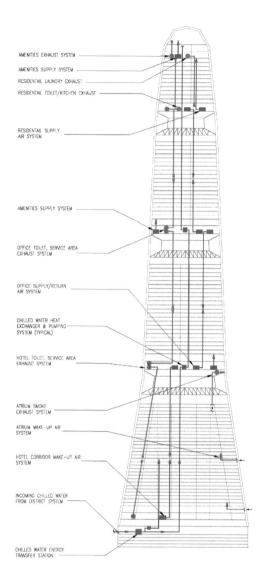

AMENITIES EXHAUST SYSTEM

AMENITIES SUPPLY SYSTEM

RESIDENTAIL LAUNDRY EXHAUST

RESIDENTAIL TOILET/KITCHEN EXHAUST

RESIDENTAIL SUPPLY
AIR SYSTEM

AMENITIES SUPPLY SYSTEM

OFFICE TOILET, SERVICE AREA
EXHAUST SYSTEM

OFFICE SUPPLY/RETURN
AIR SYSTEM

CHILLED WATER HEAT
EXCHANGER & PUMPING
SYSTEM (TYPICAL)

HOTEL TOILET, SERVICE AREA
EXHAUST SYSTEM

ATRIUM SMOKE
EXHAUST SYSTEM

ATRIUM MAKE-UP AIR
SYSTEM

HOTEL CORRIDOR MAKE-UP AIR
SYSTEM

INCOMING CHILLED WATER
FROM DISTRICT SYSTEM

CHILLED WATER ENERGY
TRANSFER STATION

MECHANICAL

Figure 11.2 A typical distribution of water systems for a megatall building.

tion. The considered dynamic head should be the head generated by the pump at or close to shut-off at full pump speed even if variable-speed pumps are used. This is because it is possible to operate the pumps at this shutoff point at full speed. The point is that the working pressure on piping and equipment will be less as the static head at a specific location is reduced.

CHILLED-WATER PIPING ARRANGEMENTS

The arrangement of the piping of the chilled water in any project is subject to alternative approaches as a function of the experience of the designing HVAC engineer, local practices, and the needs of the project. There are basically two alternative approaches that find application in tall commercial buildings. Either of these two basic alternatives is subject to variation by the design engineer, but any specific solution will be a modification of either of the basic concepts.

The first arrangement is one in which the pumps that are associated with the refrigeration machines also distribute the chilled water to the cooling coils and other heat transfer equipment. A flow diagram of this arrangement is shown in Figure 11.3. This figure shows three chillers. Each machine will handle one-third of the total load in the building. It is common on many projects that only two machines will be provided, each handling 50% of the total calculated load. It is also not unusual to include four machines. Two could be rated at one-third of the total calculated load and two rated at one-sixth of the load. This will provide machines for operation at light loads, such as for the overtime needs of a limited data center within a large building. The number of machines and their relative capacity as a function of the total load for a project is a judgment that must be made by the design engineer as a function of the needs of the building and its usage in overtime and on weekends (when there may be partial occupancy). It is not usual to provide spare refrigeration machines in most locations where service from the manufacturer or other service agencies and spare parts are readily available.

In Figure 11.4, in addition to the three machines, there are four chilled-water pumps. Each of the chilled-water pumps is selected for the rated flow through each of the chillers. If the control of the flow of chilled water at the heat transfer equipment in the project is directed by two-way control valves, which is usually the case, the pumped amount of chilled water will vary with the cooling loads in the building. The pumps, therefore, will be variable-flow pumps and will require variable-frequency drives. In addition, the pumps are piped in parallel, as are the chillers, so any machine can operate with any of the pumps. This provides pump redundancy in the event of a pump failure for any reason. The inclusion of the spare pump is relatively common, as pumps will be down for service or repair in a random fashion that cannot be coordinated with the needs of the project or the service requirements of the chillers.

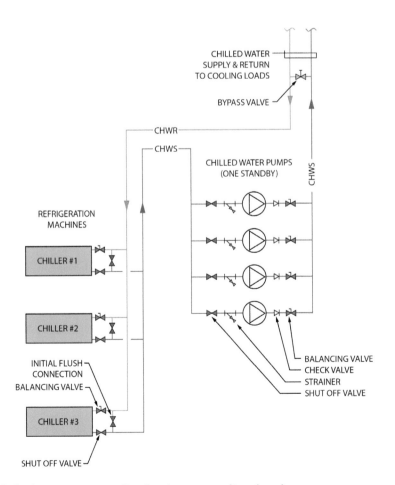

Figure 11.3 Direct chilled-water pump distribution to cooling load.

While not shown, the refrigerant condensers on the refrigeration machines would be piped in a similar fashion where four pumps are provided with three machines and any pump can be used with any of the three machines. These condenser water pumps, however, will not have their flow change with load, so they will not require variable-frequency drives.

The second common arrangement consists of primary and secondary pumps as shown in Figure 11.4. In this arrangement, contrary to the arrangement in Figure 11.3, each chiller is operated with a dedicated primary pump that will operate at constant speed and constant flow. It is possible to pipe both the chillers and the pumps in parallel, adding a spare as is the case in Figure 11.3.

The variable-speed secondary pumps shown in Figure 11.4 distribute the water to the chilled-water coils installed in the air-conditioning equipment as well as the other heat transfer equipment. Proponents of this arrangement point to the fact that the flow through each chiller is constant and will not vary, because the control valves on the cooling coils and heat transfer equipment reduce the chilled-water flow as the cooling load on the coil or on the equipment is reduced. Most chiller manufacturers stipulate a maximum velocity through the cooler of the chiller, which is usually 10 fps (3 m/s), but also require that the flow not be reduced below a stated minimum velocity, which is approximately 3 fps (1 m/s). The piping arrangement in Figure 11.4 will ensure that the flow is constant and eliminate any possible flow problem.

In the arrangement of Figure 11.4, a bypass bridge could be required, at the pumps, when cooling capacity control at each piece of heat transfer equipment is being achieved by two-way throttling valves. Any bypass bridge that would be required in the arrangement shown in Figure 11.4 would be at the secondary pumps. In either case, the system under light load will

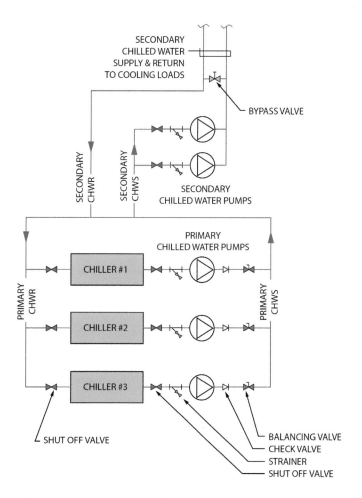

Figure 11.4 Secondary chilled-water pump distribution to cooling loads.

pump more water than is needed at the heat transfer equipment, which will necessitate the inclusion of a bypass bridge to relieve the excess water being pumped. The designs being implemented today, however, usually include variable-speed pumps. With this design, the flow will tend to be proportionate with the load, eliminating the need for a bypass bridge.

IMPACT OF REFRIGERATION MACHINE LOCATION

The decision on which level to place the refrigeration machines and the supporting chilled-water and condenser water pumps can have a cost impact on the refrigeration equipment, the pumps, the piping, and the fittings and valves associated with the piping. The economic impact is due to the change in the design working pressure to which the equipment, piping, fittings and valves will be subjected by the system.

As stated in Chapter 9, the refrigeration plant can be located at virtually any level in a building, from a basement mechanical equipment room to one located on the roof. To illustrate the impact of the refrigeration machine location at various levels in a building, Figure 11.5 shows three alternative chiller locations in a 140-story, 2000 ft (600 m) tall building with secondary pumps at the basement level, two mid-level mechanical equipment rooms with pumps, and cooling coils at the highest level. The expansion tank at the top of the building in all three alternatives is an open tank which is at the highest point in the system. If a closed expansion

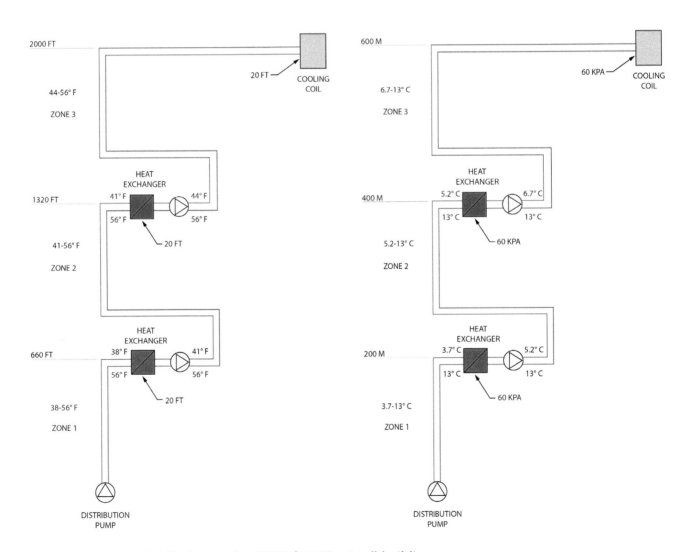

Figure 11.5 Zoned chilled water for 2000 ft (600 m) tall building.

tank were used, the maximum pressure must be established and considered in the determination of the working pressure of the system.

For a 2000 ft (600 m) building there may be as many as four zones, each zone separated by a required pressure break. The next problem to be solved is the distribution of chilled-water temperature. With a 2°F to 3°F (1 to 2 K) temperature approach for each of the heat exchangers in the chilled-water distribution system, the following chilled-water supply temperatures are required in order to provide 42°F (6°C) chilled water at the top of the building:

- 4th zone = 42°F (6°C)
- 3rd zone = 40.1°F (4.5°C)
- 2nd zone = 37.4°F (3°C)
- 1st zone = 35°F (1.5°C)

See spreadsheets at https://www.ashrae.org/tallbuildings for more information.

Therefore, the chillers have to produce 35°F (1.5°C) water in order to provide 42°F (6°C) chilled water at the top of the building. This decreases the efficiency of the chillers (see Chapter 9.)

The working pressure on any equipment or the piping, valves, and fittings at any location in a building is the sum of the hydrostatic height of the water in the piping above the point being considered. The hydrostatic pressure is determined in feet of water. This is the total pressure in feet at the referenced point. To determine the working pressure in psig, this total pressure in feet must be divided by 2.31. This is the conversion factor to convert pressure in feet of water to pressure in psig. To convert m of water to kPa, multiply by 9.81.

For a 2000 ft (600 m) building with four pressure breaks, the pumping power has been calculated as follows:

- 4th zone for 2805 gpm at 180 psi = 83 hp (177 kg/s at 1244 kPa = 62 kW)
- 3rd zone for 5975 gpm at 179 psi = 175 hp (439 kg/s at 1241 kPa = 153 kW)
- 2nd zone for 8987 gpm at 180 psi = 265 hp (701 kg/s at 1242 Pa = 244 kW)
- 1st zone for 10318 gpm at 134 psi = 227 hp (832 kg/s at 930 kPa = 217 kW)

Therefore, the total pumping power is calculated at 906 hp (676 kW). (Note: this assumes the supply and return temperatures are 42°F to 57°F (6°C to 14°C) for the whole height of the building.)

When the supply temperature is corrected to account for the approach to the heat exchangers, the following results are determined:

- 4th zone for 177 kg/s at 1244 kPa = 62 kW
- 3rd zone for 377 kg/s at 1239 kPa = 131 kW
- 2nd zone for 567 kg/s at 1244 kPa = 198 kW
- 1st zone for 651 kg/s at 928 kPa = 170 kW

Therefore, the total pumping power is calculated at 559 kW (749 hp).

The standard working pressure for the coolers and condensers on large refrigeration machines from all of the major manufacturers in the United States is 300 psi (2100 kPa). The machines can be manufactured for any working pressure above 300 psi (2100 kPa) at an additional cost. The incremental increase in the cost of any given vessel becomes larger with each unit of increase in the working pressure. Accordingly, it is necessary for the HVAC design engineer to accurately determine and separately specify the working pressure on both the cooler and the condenser of the refrigeration machines.

It is possible to reduce the working pressure on the refrigeration machine by locating the chilled-water pump on the discharge side rather than the suction side of the refrigeration machine. If this is done, the residual pump pressure on the refrigeration machine water boxes is a minimal value, and the working pressure on the vessel is reduced to the sum of the hydrostatic pressure and this nominal value of dynamic pressure from the pumps after the piping system pressure loss is deducted. This can result in a reduction in the cost of the refrigeration machines, but will not alter the pressure on the pump casing and flanges, which must still be the sum of the static and dynamic pressure.

CHILLED-WATER PRESSURE REDUCTION

The cost of the refrigeration equipment as well as the pipe, fittings, and valves in the tall building will increase as the working pressure on the equipment and piping increases. A means of reducing the pressure on the refrigeration equipment by altering its location to an elevation above the basement has been discussed. This, however, will not alter the maximum pressure experienced by the pipe, fittings, and valves at any location that is used (for example, to extend the piping to chilled-water coils). It is possible, however, to reduce the chilled-water working pressure on both the machines and piping through the use of plate-and-frame heat exchangers, which will segregate groups of floors into separate static-pressure zones.

For example, we can reduce the static pressure on all of the piping, valves, fittings, and heat transfer equipment in a building through the use of flat-plate heat exchangers. The availability of these flat-plate heat exchangers with the ability to provide secondary water within 2°F (1.1°C) or less of the primary water has made the use of secondary distribution systems a viable option that did not exist when commercially available technology was limited to shell-and-tube heat exchangers with an approach differential between the primary and secondary water of approximately 8°F (4.4°C).

In a 2000 ft (600 m) building with the refrigeration machine in the basement of the building, it is possible to break the chilled-water system into three separate zones as shown in Figure 11.5.

The pumping head on the primary chilled-water pump in the basement will not change substantively from that required where no secondary systems were included, because the primary chilled-water pump must now overcome the loss through the flat-plate heat exchanger. In addition, motor-driven pumps are added at each secondary water heat exchanger. Finally, with the addition of the two additional zones and the resultant chilled-water temperature increase, there will be a requisite increase in the amount of water flowing through the systems on the upper floors. Accordingly, while there are benefits in the reduction in pressure, there are partially offsetting considerations that must be analyzed to determine the overall cost effectiveness of the use of the flat-plate heat exchangers to reduce the operating pressure on the equipment, pipes, valves, and fittings at a given level.

The use of flat-plate heat exchangers and their location in a chilled-water piping system is subject to an economic analysis by the design HVAC engineer to determine the first cost of alternative arrangements as well as the operating cost differentials, if any, for any scheme.

The use of a flat-plate heat exchanger to obtain a reduction in the working pressure on the condenser of the refrigeration machines, while feasible, is not often given consideration, because the condenser water piping is usually in a single shaft with minimal if any offsets and a resultantly small number of fittings. Valves are also only installed at the machines and are few in number. This limit in the number of fittings and the smaller number of valves may not be sufficient to offset the cost of the flat-plate heat exchanger and its valving as well as the added pump on the secondary side of the heat exchanger. Beyond that, there will be an increase in the temperature of the condenser water, which will increase the cost of operating the refrigeration machines.

PIPING, VALVES, AND FITTINGS

The working pressure on the piping, valves, and fittings at various levels in a building must allow a proper specification of the piping material. In the United States, with steel pipe, Schedule 40 pipe is the standard wall thickness for pipes up to 10 in. (250 mm) in diameter. For pipes 12 in. (300 mm) and larger, the pipe standard used has a wall thickness of 0.375 in. (9.5 mm). Either of these standards would accommodate the working pressures experienced in any expected pipe diameter in any tall commercial building. The allowable pressures for various pipe diameters can be found in the ASME publications ASME B16.34-1996, ASME B31.9-1996, and *Boiler and Pressure Vessel Code* and in the publications of various pipe manufacturers (ASME 1996a, 1996b, 2015). The valves that are used should be reviewed in the valve manufacturers' literature to ensure their ability to meet the project's requirements.

For steam condensate piping or for condenser water piping, where corrosion is a possible concern, pipe with a heavier wall thickness should be given consideration. This consideration is not needed when contemplating the working pressure on either system.

Piping materials other than steel are often used. For pipe sizes below about 4 in. (100 mm), in the cases of runouts or in open condenser water piping where corrosion is a concern, copper is the usual choice. The use of copper pipe is rare, but the use of copper tubing is common. The limiting factor in the use of copper tubing will usually be at the joints where the ability to handle higher working pressure is restricted.

PIPING DESIGN CONSIDERATIONS

The design of the piping must also take into consideration other factors, including expansion and contraction in the piping and the static and dynamic loads of the piping, as they will be reflected in the structural steel framing system of the building; the need for access to expansion joints and the anchors and guides for the piping, which should be subjected to periodic inspection after the building is constructed; the provision of fire stopping between the pipe and the sleeve located at all penetrations of rated slabs, walls, and partitions; and, if required, seismic restraints on the piping systems and the pumps.

In addition to providing for the expansion and contraction of the piping caused by changes in the temperature of the ambient condition or the temperature of the pumped fluid in the piping, a problem can present itself in concrete buildings. The problem results from the frame shortening that will occur because the concrete shrinks as it cures over time. Concrete-framed structures, through shrinkage or creep, can be shortened over time in the range of 1/8 in. (3 mm) per floor. Although this movement is relatively small, it amounts to about 9 in. (225 mm) for a 70-story building. This condition will require that attention be paid by the designer to provide sufficient flexibility in the pipe above, below, and between anchor points to allow for pipe movement with respect to the structure. To properly design for this condition, the HVAC designer should obtain from the structural engineer the exact amount of movement that the piping system can experience so the system can be designed to accommodate this frame-shortening condition.

EXPANSION AND CONTRACTION

The full range of movement of piping during various operating periods must be anticipated and accounted for by the HVAC design engineer. This analysis must also consider the movement of the piping during the construction phrase. It is of extreme importance that the determination of the movement of the piping be considered in the structural design of the building, because the loads from piping movement can be substantial. These loads can be even greater during construction, because frequently and for long periods of time the piping will be subjected to widely varying outdoor air temperatures, because the building will be neither heated nor cooled.

The HVAC engineer must provide to the structural engineer the expected dynamic loads and the static loads of the piping caused by the weight of the fluid-filled pipe to allow the structural system to satisfy the loads developed by the piping system at the point where the piping is being supported by the building steel.

THE ECONOMICS OF TEMPERATURE DIFFERENTIALS

Traditionally, rules of thumb in the selection of refrigeration machines in the United States have used a 10°F (54°F to 44°F) (6°C [12.2°C to 6.7°C]) or 12°F (54°F to 42°F) (6°C [12.2°C to 5.6°C]) temperature differential between entering and leaving water in the chiller and a 10°F (6°C) differential or 3 gpm per ton (0.054 mL/J) of capacity for the condenser. These guidelines are appropriate for small buildings, where they have little impact on project cost, but can be viewed from a different perspective on large buildings, specifically tall commercial buildings. In projects of this type, the capital costs of the piping, valves, and fittings can be substantially reduced, with a possible penalty in refrigeration machine operating cost, by using larger temperature differentials with a lower flow of water and a consequent reduction in the diameter of the piping.

However, when dividing a building into zones, it is necessary to control the chilled-water supply temperature to provide sufficient approach to the pressure break heat exchangers. For the previous example we chose an approach of 35°F (1.5°C).

So, to obtain 10°F (6°C) chilled-water supply at the 4th zone,

- 3rd zone chilled-water supply temperature = (10°F – 35°F) = 40.1 F [(6°C – 1.5°C) = 4.5°C]

- 2nd zone chilled-water supply temperature = (40.1 F – 35°F) = 37.4°F [(4.5°C – 1.5°C) = 3°C]

- 1st zone chilled-water supply temperature = (37.4°F – 35°F) = 37.4°F [(3°C – 1.5°C) = 1.5°C]

To provide 10°F (6°C) at the top zone, the chiller(s) need to provide 35°F (1.5°C) chilled water. This reduces the coefficient of performance (COP) of the chillers and must be considered when calculating the chilled-water energy consumption.

ASHRAE/IESNA Standard 90.1, *Energy Standard for Buildings Except Low-Rise Residential*, Appendix G states the chilled-water design temperature at design conditions must be 44°F (6.7°C) and the return water temperature must be 56°F (13°C). Obviously, the base case will always be more efficient than the proposed chiller for a high-rise building. A solution to this is to model the base case and proposed case identical to each other, as a high-rise building and to inform the ASHRAE Standard 90.1 reviewer that, at present, Standard 90.1 is not applicable for high-rise buildings.

Regarding pumping power, ASHRAE Standard 90.1 states that pump power must be 22 W/gpm (349 kW/1000 L/s). This is about equal to a pump operating against a 75 ft (22.9 m) head with an efficiency of 60% combined impeller and motor efficiency. It could be argued that section G3.1.3.10 of ASHRAE Standard 90 is based on a 75 ft (22.9 m) head, and that if the total head of the building being considered is higher, then the pumping power can be adjusted accordingly. The same solution is to model the base case and proposed case identical to each other, as a high-rise building, and to inform the ASHRAE Standard 90.1 reviewer that, at present, ASHRAE Standard 90.1 is not applicable for high-rise buildings.

For a 2000 ft (600 m) building with a total cooling capacity requirement of 10,290 tons (36,000 kW), the chilled-water flow at a 10.5°F (6°C) temperature differential would be 22,639 gpm (1428 L/s). If a 15°F (8°C) temperature differential were used, the total flow from the refrigeration plant would be 16,979 gpm (1071 L/s). The resultant pipe size at a 10.5°F (6°C) differential would be a 20 in. (500 mm) diameter at a velocity just below 10 fps (3.0 m/s), whereas with a 15°F (8°C) differential, the resultant pipe diameter would be 16 in. (m) at a velocity just below 10 fps (3.0 m/s). The savings in the piping at the greater temperature differential would be significant. Moreover, while the kilowatts per ton (kW) for the refrigeration machines under both conditions would need to be studied, with the same discharge temperature, the operating energy consumption would probably be unchanged.

For condenser water piping on the 10,290 ton (36,000 kW) refrigeration plant with a 10.5°F (6°C) temperature differential, the condenser water flow would be 22,639 gpm (1428 L/s). If this temperature differential were increased to 15°F (8°C), there would be a reduction in the condenser water to 16,979 gpm (1071 L/s). The pipe diameter for 22,639 gpm (1428 L/s) would be 24 in. (600 mm), and, at 16,979 gpm (1071 L/s), the diameter would be 20 in. (500 mm). Again, this change would result in a significant first cost savings, which would vary as a function of the distance between the refrigeration machines and the cooling towers.

The energy consumption for the refrigeration machines might increase to a marginal degree because the condensing temperature of the refrigerant and the resultant energy usage is in large part, but not solely, a function of the leaving condenser water temperature.

The consideration of higher temperature differentials in both the chiller and condenser of the refrigeration plant is a matter worthy of evaluation on any tall commercial building, because there can be significant savings in the cost of the piping, fittings, and valves that are part of the overall refrigeration plant for the project.

CHAPTER 12
Energy Modeling and Authentication

Nearly all new buildings are required to comply with energy codes, and therefore energy performance calculations are critical. This chapter looks at specifics associated with modeling tall buildings and compliance with various energy codes. It also provides information on the EUI of tall buildings and the expectations when designing and modeling such intricate buildings and systems. It is useful to look at implications of HVAC design of tall building in a broader range of climates, particularly warmer and more humid regions, in which much construction has occurred in the past and will occur in the forthcoming decade.

TALL-BUILDING ENERGY CONSUMPTION

Energy simulation can provide the architect and client with information regarding the massing of the building and the orientation to improve its thermal and natural daylight capabilities. This information would also guide the preliminary energy goals for the building. This is usually determined by ASHRAE/IESNA Standard 90.1, *Energy Standard for Buildings Except Low-Rise Residential*, and other applicable standards and codes. Setting goals also helps outline possibilities in providing efficient building design solutions that consume less carbon than the standards or codes allow. A preliminary report should include any relevant solutions or possibilities for the building and its systems. The report should also remove any nonplayers, minimizing the alternatives so as not to tax the available budget. With the relevant simulation programs, guidance can be provided at an early stage on, for example, glass types and systems. The next plan as the project develops is to analyze the buildings' performance using simulation programs (usually DOE-2 [LBNL 2005]). Once the base line has been determined, energy conservation measures can be assessed. When the base line and alternatives have been developed, probably the most difficult stage emerges: obtaining costs for the different alternatives from the contractor. Should a quantity surveyor be employed, this will simplify matters but not necessarily provide a usable solution.

At the concept phase, it should be possible to define an engineering solution for a building design. The energy consumption of alternatives can be translated into reductions of utility costs and, probably more importantly, be translated into reductions of CO_2 consumption. Carbon trading has begun to emerge, although it is not wholly known by most clients and will continue to develop into energy carbon trading and a reduction of carbon consumption that will be very important for emerging countries in places such as Asia and Africa. There are also many incentives available from utility companies to assist in the production of energy analysis, so it should not be an extra taxation on the design budget. Another reason for being as effective as possible in the analysis phase is to reduce costs.

A framework for understanding key differences between the energy consumption of tall and low-rise buildings is shown in this chapter. The framework presented here describes energy benchmarking data from New York City, but which can be applied to other cities and used as a comparison for energy simulation models.

Solar Gains

Because trees and other buildings rarely cast shadows upon them, tall buildings are exposed to higher levels of solar radiation. In suburbs settings, the solar exposure per foot (meter) of façade is relatively comparable between a low-rise building and a tall building, because little shading can be had from nearby buildings. In cities, this difference in shading is more significant in low-rise buildings versus tall buildings. Low-rise buildings in cities can be significantly shaded. Tall buildings may have a little of shading from nearby building; this is especially true for the higher floors. Increased solar exposure in cities increases cooling energy in the summer and may it decrease heating energy in the winter.

Increased solar gains from reflections off surrounding buildings are also probable, though not as problematic as the decreased shading from surrounding context in tall buildings. These heightened reflective solar gains led to a 2.6% increase in heating and cooling energy from the first floor to the top floor of the Freedom Tower (Ellis and Torcellini 2005; Leung and Ray 2014).

Mean Radiant Loss

In the same way that tall buildings are exposed to more solar radiation than low-rise buildings in urban environments, they are also exposed to more of the sky from increased sky view factors (SVFs) compared to low-rise buildings. Higher SVFs increase infrared radiation to the sky, which increases heat loss during cold winter nights. Low-rise buildings in urban environments predominately radiate to surrounding buildings at much higher temperatures than the sky, resulting in lower heat loss. Although infrared radiation to the sky increases heating energy during the winter, it helps lower cooling energy in the summer.

Thermal Conductance

The overall conductance (U-factor) of glazing and façade assemblies increases with elevation because of increased external wind speeds. The significant influence of local wind velocities on U-factors is well understood in the industry; the National Fenestration Reporting Council has specified a standard exterior wind condition of 12.3 mph (5.5 m/s) for U-factor calculations (NFRC 2017). The commonly used wind profile relationship suggested by ASHRAE predicts local wind velocities as an exponential function of elevation (ASHRAE 2013c). In a dense urban environment, a local wind speed of 12.3 mph (5.5 m/s) at an elevation of 33 ft (10 m) is predicted to lead to local velocities of 26 mph (11.6 m/s) at an elevation of 984 ft (300 m) (ASHRAE 2013c). These increased wind speeds at higher elevations decrease the boundary layer along the façade and lead to greater heat transfer rates between the building and environment as the floor elevation increases.

Air Characteristics and Air Quality at Different Elevations

In addition to changing wind speeds, other important environmental factors also change with elevation. Air temperature drops with elevation, exposing the façade to different outdoor conditions at different elevations (Leung and Weismantle 2008). There is an average difference of 3.5°F (1.85°C) between the 5 and 931 ft (1.5 and 284 m) elevations of the Freedom Tower in New York City. This temperature gradient's effect on annual heating and cooling highly depends on the specific climate under consideration. As cities continue to grow, removing ground-level pollutants through city-scale ventilation becomes more important. Tall buildings help increase the standard deviation of building heights in a city and have been shown to increase pedestrian purging rates and lower ground-level pollutants by increasing both the horizontal and vertical mean flows (Hang and Li 2010). Aerosols reduce the transmittance of air by absorbing some solar energy. Calinoiu et al. 2013 found a 20% reduction in solar energy for high levels of aerosol.

Water vapor has a significant impact on infrared radiation and is known to decrease with altitude (Calinoiu et al. 2013; Egan 1994). Two sources of measured New York data confirm variations in water content with altitude. The National Oceanic and Atmospheric Administration observed a decrease in dew-point depression from 6°F to 5°F (3°C to 2.4°C) with an elevation gain from 26 to 567 ft (8 to 173 m) (NOAA 2013).

Infiltration

Although many energy modelers use constant infiltration rates, they are undoubtedly a function of external conditions (Emmerich and Persily 2011). Ng et al. explored this difference by modeling various types of buildings with both an EnergyPlus program that assumed a constant infiltration rate and a CONTAM model that calculated infiltration rates based on dynamic pressure differences, which accounted for changes in external and internal conditions (Ng et al. 2013). They found a 200% and 600% increase in total infiltration sensible loads for cooling and heating, respectively, from using the constant EnergyPlus model compared to the dynamic CONTAM model, reinforcing the well-accepted notion that infiltration rates highly depend on external conditions. Furthermore, when considering only the effect of wind, they found up to an 800% increase in infiltration rate from $0.1 \ h^{-1}$ at 4.4 mph (2 m/s) wind speeds to $0.8 \ h^{-1}$ at 18 mph (8 m/s).

Chapter 4 also explains how wind speeds vary with vertical height, and these should be accounted for when modeling infiltration in tall buildings

HVAC Pumping

Both external and internal heat loads determine an important factor of a building's energy consumption. In tall buildings the pumping energy required to distribute heating and cooling water through the height of the building can consume a large portion of energy. Typically 300 psi (2100 kPa) fittings are the maximum commonly used in tall buildings. The static pressure is only present when the pumps are switched off. When the pumps are running, the only pressure to be overcome in the system is the friction resistance of the piping, fittings, coils, and heat exchangers. There is also a temperature differential change to accommodate the temperature differential across the heat exchanger; this is typically 1.5 K.

For more information on pumping considerations, see Chapter 11.

Elevator Energy

Although the energy consumption of elevators is typically negligible in commercial buildings, it is often significant in tall buildings. Depending on height, climate, and program, elevators can consume anywhere from 5% to 25% of the total building energy in tall buildings (Al-Sharif 1996; Sachs 2005; Liu et al. 2010). Tall buildings have higher elevator energy consumptions compared to low-rise buildings, because elevators travel longer distances in tall buildings and generally at higher speeds.

EXISTING BUILDING ENERGY BENCHMARKING AND TRANSPARENCY POLICIES[9]

The Energy Efficiency Improvement Act of 2015 requires an overview of key benchmarking and transparency (B&T) policy and implementation attributes, and a study to summarize known performance impacts of state and local energy B&T policies on privately owned buildings (Energy Efficiency Improvement Act of 2015).

This section focuses on the 24 state and local jurisdictions, home to more than 65 million Americans, that require owners of privately owned commercial buildings, multifamily buildings, or both to comply with a B&T policy. These jurisdictions are:

---

9. This section provides partial text from "Evaluation of U.S. Building Energy Benchmarking and Transparency Programs: Attributes, Impacts, and Best Practices," a report by Mims et al. of Lawrence Berkeley National Laboratory (2017). The text has been modified slightly for this information to integrate smoothly into this book; otherwise the content remains as originally published.

- Atlanta
- Austin, TX
- Berkeley, CA
- Boston
- Boulder, CO
- Cambridge, MA
- Chicago
- Denver
- Evanston, IL
- Kansas City, MO
- Los Angeles
- Minneapolis
- Montgomery County, MD
- New York City
- Orlando
- Philadelphia
- Pittsburgh
- Portland, ME
- Portland, OR
- San Francisco
- Seattle
- Washington, D.C.
- State of California
- State of Washington

Thirteen other jurisdictions require that only publicly owned buildings comply with a B&T policy:

- State of Alabama
- Cook County, IL
- State of Delaware
- State of Hawaii
- State of Michigan
- State of Minnesota
- State of New York
- State of Ohio
- State of Oklahoma
- State of Oregon
- Salt Lake City
- West Chester, PA

The number of B&T policies are growing quickly. In 2016 alone, seven cities passed benchmarking ordinances:

- Denver
- Evanston, IL
- Los Angeles
- Montgomery County, MD
- Orlando
- Pittsburgh
- Portland, ME

Building sizes benchmarking and transparency policies vary widely in terms of the sizes of buildings that must comply. For example, Austin's B&T policy covers the greatest range of sizes for commercial and multifamily buildings: commercial buildings 10,000 ft^2 (930 m^2) and larger and multifamily units with five or more units. Most of the policies cover commercial and multifamily buildings greater than 50,000 ft^2 (4645 m^2), while some set the threshold for compliance at 25,000 ft^2 (2322 m^2). Market size and of building owner sophistication for each category of building are factors that help jurisdictions determine the appropriate building size thresholds for their policy. The lower the threshold size for compliance, the more buildings will be required to participate. Thus, in determining the size thresholds for the policy, jurisdictions weigh potential trade-offs—more buildings mean more city resources are needed for data collection and verification, outreach, help center support, and enforcement. New York City expanded its coverage to buildings with areas greater than 25,000 ft^2 (2322 m^2) in 2018, capturing an additional 10,000 properties, though the increase in area covered is relatively small. Staff from the City of Austin reported that when they reduced the original threshold from 75,000 to 35,000 ft^2 (6967 to 3251 m^2) and then down again to 10,000 ft^2 (929 m^2), they discovered that each building size strata had a different owner profile. Owners of smaller buildings typically had much less time and resources to devote to energy management than owners of larger buildings. These different strata would likely benefit from different types and levels of effort for outreach and technical support.

The New York City government, with the purpose of reducing greenhouse gas emissions and fighting against climate change, adopted a pack of local laws for large buildings. The laws (Local Laws 84, 85, 87 and 88) require large building owners to keep a record of their energy and water consumption data which will then be used for developing better energy efficiency strategies (Phoenix Energy 2019).

It is estimated that buildings are responsible for nearly 70% of the city's greenhouse gas emissions. This proves the urgent need for the implementation of the above mentioned local laws. Starting from the moment of their enactment, all the required buildings will have to submit the corresponding energy and water consumption data. Failing to meet the requirements may result in certain penalties.

The requirements differ from law to law and every building owner must know the details regarding them such as: what are the exact demands of these laws, how to comply with them, when are the deadlines, what are the amount of penalties, and so on.

- Local Law 87 requires building owners to carry out an energy audit and retrocommissioning every 10 years.
- Local Law 84 requires large building owners to submit benchmarking data (energy and water usage reports).
- Local Law 133 requires midsize building owners to submit benchmarking data (energy and water usage reports).
- Local Law 33 requires building owners to display energy letter grades and benchmarking scores at the entrance of their buildings in a visible place (Phoenix Energy 2019).

INTERNATIONAL EXPERIENCES[10]

International B&T efforts largely center on building energy rating schemes and associated building labeling policies and programs. The European Union (EU) first launched its Energy Performance of Buildings Directive in 2002, ramping up to full compliance for all member states by 2006. The directive provided for the establishment of building energy rating schemes and associated energy performance certificate (EPC) labels for residential, private commercial, and public buildings. A number of non-EU countries have developed their own energy rating or labeling schemes as well. Rating schemes vary by jurisdiction for a number of reasons, such as variation in building stock and climate, and the ability of the government to mandate regulations. Rating and labeling policies vary in regard to three key program components: 1) which buildings are targeted (e.g., new versus existing, residential vs. commercial); 2) key requirements (mandatory versus voluntary, timing of the transparency); and 3) type of rating (e.g.,

---

10. This section provides partial text from "Evaluation of U.S. Building Energy Benchmarking and Transparency Programs: Attributes, Impacts, and Best Practices," a report by Mims et al. of Lawrence Berkeley National Laboratory (2017). The text has been modified slightly for this information to integrate smoothly into this book; otherwise the content remains as originally published.

asset-based versus operational) Several international rating and labeling schemes (such as those in Australia, France, and Germany) have similar key provisions as the B&T policies in the United States—the policy is mandatory, uses an operational rating scheme, and covers private commercial or multifamily buildings.

Table 12.1 provides examples of building rating schemes implemented by countries that are members of the International Partnership for Energy Efficiency Cooperation (IPEEC).

The Energy Performance Certificate (EPC) is the key disclosure and transparency vehicle for the Energy Performance of Buildings Directive (EPBD). The EPC provides information about a building's energy performance to potential tenants and buyers. The EPC is intended to spur demand for better performing buildings or rental units, in turn increasing market values and influencing building owners to renovate their properties. The directive requires EU member states to ensure that building owners provide EPCs to prospective tenants or buyers as part of the property transaction process. The EPCs must be produced when a covered building is constructed, sold, or rented, and must contain key information, such as an energy efficiency rating and comparison to peer properties. The directive also requires countries to maintain an EPC database. Some countries, such as Ireland, have developed data visualization tools much like those in the United States to disclose the information to the general public, rather than just to participants in the sale or lease transactions. Others, such as Germany and Austria, have stronger privacy concerns and only allow data access to officials directly involved and occasionally for research purposes. The EPBD requires the EPC to be physically displayed in a prominent, visible location on large buildings that are frequently visited by the public. This requirement applies both to public buildings larger than 2690 ft^2 (250 m^2) and to any building larger than 5382 ft^2 (500 m^2). European Union member states have implemented the display requirement differently. For example, Greece, Ireland, and the United Kingdom have implemented a simplified approach that requires all large buildings, whether public or private, greater than 2690 ft^2 (250 m^2) to display the EPC.

GENERAL CONSIDERATIONS

Energy comparisons of design options generally involve relatively small changes in overall energy consumption. Accurate models are required to resolve the differences in chiller, pump, and fan energy consumption resulting from changes in design parameters.

Table 12.1 Examples of IPEEC Member Building Rating Schemes

Country	Scheme Name	Mandatory	Asset Based	Operational	Private Commercial	Multifamily
Australia	Commercial Building Disclosure	Y		X	X	
Brazil	PGE Edifica		X		X	X
Canada	Energy Star		X	X	X	
	Realpac Energy Benchmarking Program			X	X	
China	China 3-star Building Energy Efficiency Program		X	X	X	X
EU	Energy Performance Certificates (EPCs)	Y	X	X	X	X
France	Diagnostic de Performance Energetique	Y	X	X	X	X
Germany	Energieausweis	Y	X	X	X	X
India	Star Ratings for buildings			X	X	
Italy	Certificazione Energetica	Y	X	X	X	X
Japan	CASBEE		X	X	X	X
Russia	Energy Passports		X		X	X
South Korea	Certificate of Building Energy Efficiency		X	X	X	X
United Kingdom	EPCs	Y	X		X	X
United States	Energy Star (National)			X	X	X
	Commercial Building Energy Asset Score		X		X	X
	Energy Start (Local Ordinance)	Y		X	X	X

COOLING PLANT

A key issue in evaluating energy consumption of retrofit systems is the possible increase in chiller energy caused by lower fluid supply temperature, increased dehumidification, and reduced economizer availability. To properly assess this issue, the simulation program must accurately model the cooling plant, because the difference in energy consumption between alternative cooling plants is often small.

The chiller performance curves used to describe the cooling plant must apply to the specific chiller and chilled-fluid temperatures in question. In particular, if the effects of reduced fluid supply temperature are to be evaluated, the temperature dependence of the chiller performance must be accurately represented.

Thermal Storage

As discussed previously, accurate simulation of retrofit plants is difficult. Most programs cannot model the interaction between chiller and storage performance, the effects of chiller-upstream or chiller-downstream configuration, or the performance impacts of chiller-priority, storage priority, and demand-limiting control strategies.

However, for a designer to adequately evaluate alternative design options, the simulation program must be capable of modeling the differences between those options.

Pump Energy

Pump energy constitutes a significant fraction of the annual energy consumption of many cooling systems. Differences in pumping energy are important in comparisons involving retrofit systems with high chilled-fluid temperature ranges.

Pump energy is difficult to model in detail with most simulation programs. Typically, pumps may be specified with a constant energy consumption whenever chillers are operating or a variable consumption proportional to the percentage of full load. The constant consumption input corresponds to chiller primary pumps and condenser water pumps that operate at constant volume when chillers are on. The variable consumption input corresponds to secondary distribution pumps that operate at variable volume as the load varies. The cubic relationship between power and flow may or may not be considered. Variations in pump operation with the mode of storage operation are also difficult or impossible to model.

Most programs simulate air distribution systems and central cooling plants separately, and cannot model the interactions between cooling coil performance and chilled-fluid temperature. Generally, programs implicitly assume that the system temperature range will be constant over the entire range of part-load operation, although this is rarely true in actual systems.

More details on pump energy can be found in Chapter 12.

SUPPLY FAN ENERGY

The modeling of supply fan energy consumption is straightforward and is easily accomplished with most simulation programs. For accurate comparisons, designers should specify the appropriate fan total pressure for the systems simulated.

Many programs supply generic part-load performance curves for supply fans, which may or may not be accurate. For example, a commonly used part-load curve for variable-speed drives shows 5% fan power at 20% fan volume, whereas in fact most drives will not modulate below 30% of full speed. Modelers should confirm with variable-speed drive suppliers that the curves used correctly represent the drive characteristics.

Modelers should also verify how the simulation treats fan system diversity. Some programs assume that the fan's design flow is equal to the sum of the peak zone flow requirements, which is not true in a system designed for diversity. A model making this assumption will treat a fan designed for 75% diversity, and operating at 100% flow, as if it were at 75% of full flow. This error causes an underestimate of fan energy and of fan energy savings for cold air distribution.

ECONOMIZER CONTROL

Economizer control sequences compare the outdoor air temperature or enthalpy with another quantity to determine whether outdoor air can be used for cooling.

An enthalpy economizer cycle uses outdoor air for cooling whenever its enthalpy is lower than that of the return air. Other variations compare the outdoor air dry-bulb temperature with that of the return air or with a fixed changeover temperature.

Modelers should specify an economizer control option that realistically represents the control that will be used by the system simulated. The fixed changeover is the simplest and most commonly used method. The enthalpy economizer maximizes energy savings, but it requires special attention to calibration or it can result in improper control and increased energy consumption.

Programs that do not calculate the actual return air condition but make an assumption about the space or return air humidity cannot accurately model an enthalpy economizer with cold-air distribution.

SUPPLY AIR RESET CONTROL

A supply air reset sequence resets the supply air temperature to the highest level below some maximum that will satisfy the zone with the highest cooling load. In some systems, this strategy is often used to decrease excessive dehumidification energy, to increase economizer availability, or to maintain a higher level of room air circulation. As loads vary, there may be a relatively large number of hours when the supply air temperature can be reset.

Modeling of supply air reset control is dependent on scheduling of zone loads. In a typical simulation, occupancy schedules are given as general averages for blocks of zones. Lighting and equipment heat gains are commonly described in terms of average watts per unit floor area. All similar zones will have the same loads for each hour, except where exterior exposures differ.

In a real building, loads vary as people move in and out of zones, turn lights and equipment on and off, and possibly open and close window shades. The actual occupancy and equipment density schedules will show much more variation between zones and over time than the simulation.

Real buildings also show more interaction between exterior and interior zone loads than is typically reflected in simulations. There may be mixing of return air in common plenums, airflow through doorways, or even common open spaces served by both interior and exterior zone distribution.

To accurately simulate the impact of a supply air reset strategy, a model should consider differences between "identical" zones and include some variations in individual zone load schedules. If possible, the model should also account for interactions between interior and exterior zones.

NEED FOR ACCURATE PROFILE

An accurate 24-hour design load profile is essential to the success of a model.

Generic load profiles for various building types are sometimes offered as an aid for sizing systems. These generic profiles are useful for initial screening studies, but they should never be used for final sizing and design. Even if the peak load is calculated accurately, assuming an incorrect load profile shape can lead to serious undersizing of cooling capacity.

VAV systems meet changes in the cooling/heating load by varying the supply airflow rate. In general, the VAV system maintains the supply air at a constant supply temperature and reduces or increases the airflow between preset maximum or minimum flows to meet the space loads. The supply air temperature is set at 55°F (13°C) for conventional systems. It is also possible to reset the supply air temperature in a VAV system to prevent overcooling of a space.

VAV systems generally consist of a main air handler and a number of VAV terminals, each with a damper and controller to vary the airflow rate to the appropriate zone. Some types of VAV systems are described as follows:

- **Cooling-only interior systems.** This system throttles the air at the terminal boxes and modulates the airflow rate with inlet vanes, frequency inverters, or some other means.

- **Combined interior and perimeter systems.** In this arrangement, cooling-only terminals for the interior zones are combined with reheat VAV terminals for the perimeter zones on the same system.
- **Separate interior and perimeter systems.** In this arrangement, the VAV system meets the cooling and ventilation requirements, and a perimeter system meets heating or cooling requirements caused by heat transfer through the building envelope.
- **Multizone systems.** This system has a single central air handler with a number of hot and cold deck dampers in the discharge for different zone ducts. Each zone duct is a separate main duct. Different zone load requirements are met by mixing hot and cold air through the zone dampers at the main air handler. VAV terminals are used to vary the air volume in the zones.

The flow rate through each VAV terminal is controlled by a zone thermostat. The terminal is fully open at the maximum zone load. As the load decreases, the zone control thermostat will cause the VAV damper to begin to close and increase the pressure drop across the damper. This increases the duct pressure, which produces a reduction in system airflow. The throttling ratio, the ratio of the actual flow rate to the design flow rate, depends on the ratio of the ventilation and cooling requirements. The system throttling ratio will not be equal to the zone throttling ratios due to the differing loads and ventilation requirements. Fan bypass, discharge dampers, inlet vanes, or variable-speed fan control can be used for duct pressure control.

CASE STUDY
Ping An Finance Center

Shenzhen

Name: Ping An Finance Center

Location: Shenzhen, China

Description: Ping An is the physical and iconic center of Shenzhen's growing central business district. With more than 100 floors of office space and a large podium with retail and conference space, the project also connects to neighboring commercial and residential properties and public transportation.

The stainless steel and glass tower rises from the site, anchoring the development. Its four façades are sheathed in chevron-shaped stainless-steel piers that extend from the lower part of the building. The podium includes nine floors of retail shops that terrace away from the tower to form an amphitheater-like green space. The building is also defined by a central atrium, which serves as a public vestibule and allows daylight in, creating a welcoming space for meeting, shopping, and dining.

Building Function: Office, retail, and observation deck
Building Height: 1965 ft (599.1 m)
Building Floor Area: 4,153,990 ft^2 (385,918 m^2)
Architects: Kohn Pedersen Fox Associates (Design), CCDI Group (Architect of Record)
Structural Engineers: Thornton Thomasetti (Design), CCDI Group (Engineer of Record)
MEP Engineers: J Roger Preston Limited (Design), CCDI Group (Engineer of Record)

Report courtesy of KPF.

CHAPTER 13
Vertical Transportation

As noted in the introductory portions of this guide, the construction of tall buildings only became possible with the development of the elevator safety braking system and the elevator itself, with the resulting ability to move people expeditiously through the multiple levels of a tall building. Generally, the HVAC designer does not have a significant involvement with the elevators other than to provide cooling in the elevator machine room to ensure that the controlling electronics of the elevator system are maintained at an appropriate temperature to allow their reliable operation and, if required by code, to vent the elevator shafts and the elevator machine room to the atmosphere. In tall, supertall, and megatall buildings, however, the final core design generally results in one or more elevators confined within a single shaft. This creates significant problems with respect to the "piston effect" caused by the compression of the column of air ahead of the elevator, and stack effect, either positive or negative, depending on the time of year or climatic conditions of the region. Recently, the advent of naturally ventilated buildings has also created situations where the involvement of the HVAC designer is critical in developing a comprehensive solution for the building.

THE BASIS OF THE SYSTEM CONFIGURATION

Every tall building will require a vertical transportation system. The vertical transportation system will always include elevators and may include escalators. Escalators, when included, will meet the limited and special needs that may develop in a building, to allow the efficient transferring of people from an entrance level to the main lobby that exists on the floor above the entrance level. Escalators are also frequently included to move large volumes of people to cafeteria levels if they are located below the entrance lobby level. In addition, escalators will be required if a sky lobby with double-deck elevators, discussed later in this chapter, is part of the design for a building. In most tall buildings, escalators will not be required.

The selection of the elevators, including their arrangement within the core, is of critical importance to the architect. While there are rules of thumb, discussed later, that will indicate, for concept design purposes, the number of elevators required based on the area or diversified population in a building, the application of these rules of thumb is not appropriate in the actual design of a tall commercial building due to the multiple arrangements and types of elevators available and the inherent complexity of the possible solutions that can be used in the actual design. The need for an independent, experienced elevator consultant is a matter that must be understood by the developer who is putting together the design team. Once a building is finished with a given arrangement of elevators, it is not possible to significantly alter or improve the performance of the system that has been installed. Except for minor tweaking, it cannot be changed insofar as the arrangement, the number of cabs, and the floors that are served by each cab are concerned.

The configuration of an elevator system, which will include a determination of the number of elevators and the arrangement of the cabs in banks, their individual capacity with regard to the number of people that can occupy a cab at one time, and the speed of the elevators for a specific project, will be determined by several considerations. These will include the number of floors in the building, the populations on alternative floors, the location of special-use facilities such as a cafeteria, and the type of occupancy for which the building will be constructed. A corporate or single-occupancy building could have an alternative elevator system specified when compared to a multiple-tenant developer building.

The populations for alternative building types (e.g., general office use, with diversified occupancy or executive spaces) have been developed by vertical transportation consultants and companies that manufacture elevators based on the usable space in a building and an analysis of the actual populations in multiple buildings. These studies indicate there will be approximately one person for each 150 to 160 ft^2 (14 to 15 m^2) of usable floor area. Special areas such as a trading floor will be more densely occupied and can be as dense as 70 ft^2 (6.5 m^2) of usable area per person. Moreover, densities in Europe and Asia will usually be designed for greater populations than in the United States, in that staff will typically be allocated less working area per person than would be the case in the United States.

The population density for elevator calculations as determined by these densities is different from those used in the HVAC load calculations. The HVAC loads use the peak number of people that will be experienced in a limited space, not a diversified population over a space of multiple floors. This is a significant difference, because the HVAC load calculations for general office space will usually be one person per 100 ft^2 (9.3 m^2).

The rules of thumb alluded to previously, which can only be used by the architect to determine a preliminary potential number of elevators required when he addresses the conceptual design of the core for a project, would be to allow one elevator for each 40,000 to 50,000 gross ft^2 (3700 to 4600 gross m^2) of the building or one elevator for every 225 to 250 building occupants. These rules of thumb should be used with the understanding that a more accurate determination of the number of elevators by an elevator consultant in his traffic analysis may well alter the quantity of elevators for the project.

Once the population of a building is determined, the elevator consultant who is configuring the system can determine the number of elevators and the floors they will serve, the speed of the elevator, and the platform size of each cab and their resulting capacity in pounds, which will be converted into people in the cab. The determination will be based on generally accepted standards in two separate categories. Important information for banks of elevators includes the following:

- Handling capacity expressed as a percentage of the total population that is served by the bank of elevators that will be moved in 5 minutes

- Interval in seconds, which is the average time that an elevator will take to be dispatched from the main lobby or terminal floor during the heaviest time of peak elevator usage, or average waiting time, used with a destination selection control system, which is the average time a person waits for their assigned elevator at the main lobby or terminal floor during the heaviest time of peak elevator usage.

The handling capacity for an office building will usually be allowed by the elevator consultant to vary from a low of 12.5% to a high of 15%, with the lower number being acceptable in a developer building and the higher percentage being the standard used in an owner-occupied building.

Traditionally, buildings designed to an average interval that will be acceptable in an owner-occupied building will generally have an average interval for an elevator be 25 seconds or less and in a multiuse developer building 30 seconds or less. Today, however, the performance parameters associated with average waiting time and average time to destination are the determining factors in proper elevator design. This is due to the fact that the next departing elevator may not be that person's assigned elevator.

The determination of both the handling capacity and interval involves a series of assumptions based on experience. These will start with the population served in an elevator bank, the population that will be using the elevator at the peak time of usage during the day (usually in the morning up-peak period when occupants are arriving at work and little traffic is going down), the number of people on each trip in each car during this peak usage time, the number of cars in the bank, the number of probable stops the elevator makes at this peak time, and an assumed speed of the elevator. The calculations or traffic analyses using these assumptions are made in a series of iterations with changes in the floors served by the bank, the number of cars in the bank, the capacity of each elevator, and alternate speeds at which the elevator can travel.

ALTERNATIVE ELEVATOR CONFIGURATIONS

In tall commercial buildings, as defined in this design guide, multiple banks of elevators will be required to meet the handling capacity and interval criteria that have been established for office buildings. There are also other accepted standards that will affect the elevator configuration. These are as follows:

- In the United States, for office buildings, the platform size for first-class office buildings should have a capacity between 3500 and 4000 lb (1600 and 1800 kg). In most cases, the platform dimension should have greater width than depth to facilitate the entering and leaving of passengers.
- The handling capacity and average waiting time and average time to destination of each bank in a project should be relatively equal, but neither criteria should ever differ in a bank-to-bank comparison by more than 10%.
- The maximum number of elevators in any one bank is generally limited to eight and they should be arranged as four opposite four to make the necessary movement from the call button to any responding elevator as direct as possible.
- If four or six elevators are determined to be acceptable, they should also be arranged in facing sets of two or three.

The arrangement of eight, six, and four elevators in a bank is shown in Figure 13.1.

The requirement for relative parity in the handling capacity and interval from bank to bank in a given property will usually result in an unequal number of floors served by each bank. This results from the longer travel distance for the banks serving upper floors and the inherently longer travel time to complete a round trip. Accordingly, the banks serving the upper floors frequently serve fewer floors to reduce the round-trip travel time and maintain approximate parity in the average waiting time and average time to destination.

With these guidelines in hand, it is possible for the elevator consultant to select and configure the elevators for a building. This may involve a process of give-and-take with the architect who is incorporating the elevator selections into his core design, but through the process of alternative selections of elevator systems with different platform sizes, speed, and the number of floors served, a mutually acceptable solution will be determined.

CONFIGURATIONS FOR SUPERTALL AND MEGATALL BUILDINGS

Over the past several decades, innovations in the available elevator types have become available to meet the special needs of the supertall building. Two alternative conceptual configurations are available from the major elevator manufacturers. These are (1) a system using a sky lobby approach and (2) a system using double-deck or multideck elevators.

SKY LOBBY CONCEPT

In the sky lobby concept, high-speed, high-capacity shuttle cars transport passengers from the entrance level to a sky lobby located at the point where the passengers transfer to a second bank of elevators that serve the local floors above the sky lobby. Figure 13.1 shows in cross

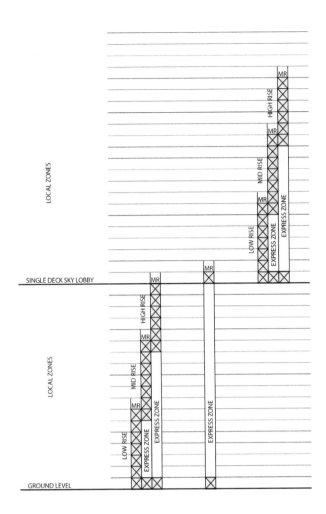

Figure 13.1 A multideck elevator combination.

section an arrangement of elevators for a building with a single sky lobby. The lower half of the building is served by local elevators configured with low-rise, mid-rise, and high-rise groupings. An express shuttle is available to take building occupants to a single-level sky lobby where they will have a second arrangement of low-rise, mid-rise, and high-rise local elevators. This configuration effectively has two standard buildings one on top of the other.

This process in a supertall building of 80 or 90 stories or more could be repeated with passengers being express carried to a second sky lobby from the entrance level where they transfer to the bank of elevators that serve the floors they are going to in the building. In this case, the result would be a building that, in effect, would resemble three standard buildings being stacked one on top of the other, each of the buildings having its own independent local elevator system served from the entrance level by the express shuttle elevators.

DOUBLE-DECK ELEVATORS

An alternative to the sky lobby that has found application in tall buildings is a double-deck elevator. In this alternative, a dramatic reduction in the area required by the elevator shafts in the building core is possible. Each elevator is two cabs high and each cab serves every other floor. Initially upon departure from the main lobby, one serves all of the even number floors, the other every odd number floor. The two floors at the entrance level are connected by escalators to allow passengers access to the cabs serving their desired destination floors. After the elevator makes its first stop in response to a "landing" call, the operational system changes and

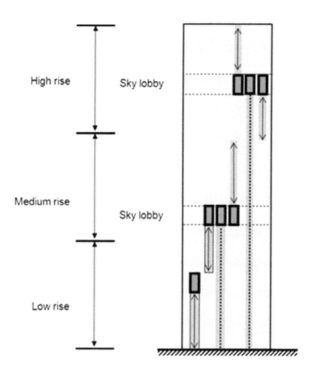

Figure 13.2 A double-deck elevator system.

allows either cab to serve an even or odd numbered floor. This results is a system where the two elevator cabs use a single hoistway, which in turn results in a more efficient core design for the project, because the number of elevator shafts is reduced. This benefit is obtained through a substantial premium in the cost of the elevators. Figure 13.2 shows in cross-section the double-deck arrangement in a building with local floor stops.

This arrangement of double-deck elevators serving local floors has had limited applications and has usually been installed in a single tenant building with a high density of population or a building where the saving in shaft space is considered of prime import. The most common application of double-deck elevators has been in supertall buildings in combination with the sky lobby concept. In this case, the shuttle elevators to the sky lobby will be double-deck elevators. When the vertical transportation system is provided in this configuration, escalators will be required at the entrance level to allow people entering the building to efficiently proceed to the correct level of the elevator. Escalators will also be required at each sky lobby to simplify the movement up or down to the proper bank of local elevators to take a passenger to his local floor destination. This typical configuration of the double-deck elevator with a sky lobby is shown in cross section in Figure 13.3. One of the historical limitations of double-deck elevators has been the need for all floors to be the same distance apart. Systems are now available where the main lobby floor to floor dimension can be up to 6 ft (1.83 m) greater than that of the typical floors. The system automatically adjusts as the car is traveling so that the two cabs are the proper distance apart prior to the first stop.

Two independent cabs operating in the same shaft dates back to the 1920s, when Sprague's dual elevator system operated in a 20-story Pittsburgh building. It was taken out of service in 1931. A system with two elevators using the same hoistway did not operate again until 2002 (Barrington 2014).

Each car in a multiple-car elevator system has its own counterweight and separate safety and drive equipment but common guide rails and shaft doors. There are four levels of safety controls to prevent car collisions; these include an independent controller that constantly mon-

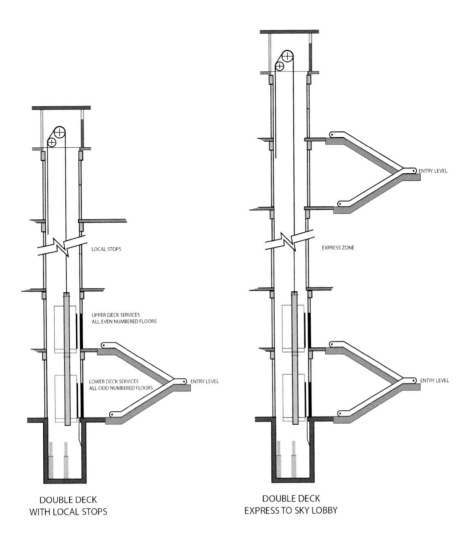

DOUBLE DECK
WITH LOCAL STOPS

DOUBLE DECK
EXPRESS TO SKY LOBBY

Figure 13.3 A double-deck elevator system.

itors the position and direction of each elevator car. Cars can safely travel toward or away from one another. A one-way clutch ensures all elevator cars move only in one direction at a time. Further safety measures include independent brake systems, automatic monitoring of minimum safety distances, emergency stop function if the safety distance is breached, and automatic engagement of the safety device in the unlikely event of multiple safety system failures.

Using up to three cars in a shaft can save space in a tall building by reducing the need for additional shafts. Shaft space can be repurposed to lay IT cables or for HVAC systems. Multiple-car systems can also allow a building to provide different types of service, such as using the top car to service upper floors and penthouses, while using the bottom car to service lower floors or as a service car (Barrington 2014).

The destination selection control system is an essential part of a multiple-car system. Before entering the cab, the passenger selects their destination via a touch screen and is assigned the most suitable car. Waiting times and stops en route are minimized. Energy consumption is also reduced by minimizing trips.

Destination selection control systems can also be adapted to the needs of building owners. For example, access to specific floors can be regulated by entering a code or reading a radio frequency identification (RFID) chip in an access control card (Barrington 2014).

Figure 13.4 A multideck twin elevator system.

SERVICE ELEVATOR

For all large commercial office buildings of an area in excess of 250,000 ft^2 (23,000 m^2), the inclusion in the design of a dedicated service elevator with its own service lobby should be given strong consideration. All buildings with an area greater than 300,000 ft^2 (28,000 m^2) should include a dedicated service elevator. The sizing of the platform for a service elevator should, because of the nature of its particular usage, differ from the platform size of a passenger elevator. The platform should be greater in depth than width and should have an entrance door that will accept the largest broken-down piece of equipment that will be in the building. Figure 13.5 shows the typical dimensions for a 6000 lb (2800 kg) service elevator.

The platform dimension for the service elevator, however, may well need to be modified from an ideal size to one that will conform to the structure framing, which can be driven, in large part, by the passenger elevators. When a dedicated service elevator is provided, it must have a dedicated service lobby on each floor to allow its use in delivering materials to meet the needs of a specific floor. The final requirement for the service car is that it should serve all floors, including mechanical equipment room floors, in the building.

The use of a passenger elevator as a swing car, which can be converted on an as-needed basis to a service car, is usually not appropriate in a tall commercial building. This is due to the inherently large total area of that type of building and the adverse impact on the handling capacity and interval that will occur when a passenger elevator in a given bank is used as a service car. Moreover, if a passenger elevator is used as a swing service car, the fact that there are multiple banks of elevators serving the several floors will mean that the service car will not be available on all floors of the building and will usually not stop at the mechanical floors. While avoiding the use of passenger elevators as a swing cars is not a requirement, this use can cause significant issues that should be given consideration in arriving at the configuration of the service elevator system.

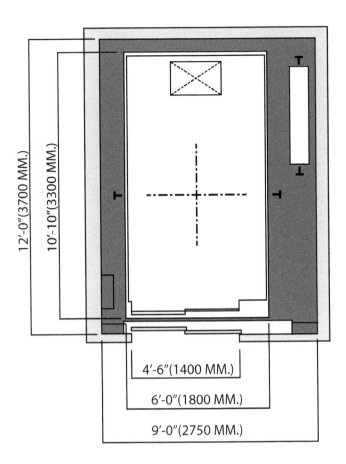

Figure 13.5 A typical layout of a service elevator.

HIGH-RISE RESIDENTIAL ELEVATORS

As described by Popp (2013), modern high-rise residential buildings cover a wider range of amenities and variations than traditional apartment buildings (Figure 13.6). Often, they are the primary residence and home, small communities within themselves, with retail levels hosting basic services such as dry cleaners and food stores. Whether they are serviced apartments associated with a major international hotel brand, owner-occupied condominiums that are only occupied during certain times of the year, or timeshare rentals, each type of residential building requires a different elevator solution.

Tall and supertall residential properties require special design features for elevator systems. For example, the Burj Khalifa features three sky lobby levels where residents and visitors transfer from an express elevator to local elevators, and which also provide opportunities for amenities including pools, restaurants, and roof garden access.

Supertall buildings use a sky lobby strategically located to divide the building into two or more shorter buildings stacked on top of one another. Each of these buildings is then served by express shuttle elevators between the ground level and the sky lobby. Residents then transfer to local elevators, thereby minimizing waiting and trip times. The different zones also provide the opportunity to offer different qualities of residences, with different entry lobbies.

The main lobby and the elevator system represent essentially the front doors of each residence, and as such must be architecturally consistent with the character of the lobby and market position of the property. The elevator should meet the specific needs of the property, with appropriate waiting and trip times consistent with the quality and location of the property. The

160 and above	Mechanical	
156–159	Communication and broadcast	
155	Mechanical	
139–154	Corporate suites	
136–138	Mechanical	
125–135	Corporate suites	
124	At the Top observatory	
123	Sky lobby	
122	At.mosphere restaurant	
111–121	Corporate suites	
109–110	Mechanical	
77–108	Residential	
76	Sky lobby	
73–75	Mechanical	
44–72	Residential	
43	Sky lobby	
40–42	Mechanical	
38–39	Armani Hotel suites	
19–37	Armani Residences	
17–18	Mechanical	
9–16	Armani Residences	
1–8	Armani Hotel	
Ground	Armani Hotel	
Concourse	Armani Hotel	
B1–B2	Parking, mechanical	

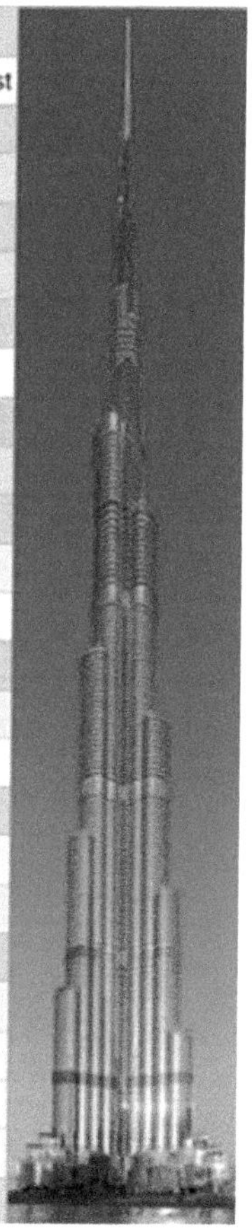

Figure 13.6 The different floor levels of the Burj-Khalifa in Dubai.
(Popp 2013)

systems must be efficient and reliable, particularly in very exclusive properties where the elevator opens directly into the residence. Properly designed elevator systems complement and enhance the asset value of the property.

Elevator systems must also address special needs including, but not limited to, the following:

- resident security
- visitor access
- deliveries
- discreet penthouse access
- resident move-in/move-out
- accessibility for the mobility impaired
- stretcher accommodation
- discreet maid service

The elevator system should be designed based on the late afternoon/early evening peak five-minute two-way traffic condition. This reflects the most demanding traffic period, when residents return from work and leave for evening activities. Target performance requirements are based on the location of the property, the type and quality of the property, the number and type of residential units (one-bedroom, two-bedroom, etc.), and the projected number of persons per each type of unit. Next, determine the appropriate average interval and required handling capacity, as a percentage of the theoretical residential population. These values then allow calculating the number, capacity, and speed of the elevators required.

Separate parking elevators from the garage levels to the main lobby provide security for residents by requiring a physical transfer between the parking garage elevators and the residential tower elevators. This also improves the efficiency of the tower elevator systems, particularly where subways and public transportation are typically used as opposed to private automobiles. Properties with valet parking are often provided with special automobile elevators serving between the ground level and parking levels. In some designs, the automobile elevators serve the residential floors, allowing residents to park on their floors.

In some cases, depending upon the amenities provided (e.g., publicly available health club facilities, restaurants), separate, dedicated elevators may be required to prevent unwanted public access to residences.

Dedicated service elevators are needed to accommodate resident move-ins/move-outs. These elevators typically have front and rear entrances, with the front entrance serving the typical floor residential corridor and the rear entrance at the dock level, allowing for direct loading/unloading. The rear entrance may require special attention to stack effect and/or piston effect mitigation, because this entrance usually opens into unconditioned dock areas. This elevator is typically also used to meet the stretcher accommodations required by code, and it should be large enough to accommodate items up to and including grand pianos, especially in high-quality residential properties.

Preventing wind noise caused by elevators in single shafts traveling through the building is critical and often requires special design considerations. Mechanical and electrical noise and vibration caused by the elevator equipment, particularly in post-tensioned construction, must also be addressed. Proper design of the hoist machine and controller isolation, often with the assistance of an acoustical consultant, is essential to ensure that all residences are habitable. Machine rooms must be accessible without going through penthouse residences.

HVAC INVOLVEMENT WITH VERTICAL TRANSPORTATION SYSTEMS

The HVAC designer generally has limited involvement with the vertical transportation system except in buildings requiring stack effect and/or piston effect mitigation. These concerns have become more pronounced with the advent of the use of natural convection to moderate building temperature. Most often, HVAC designers are called upon to provide adequate cooling to the elevator machine room and to vent the elevator shaft so that it will conform to the codes regarding the elevator system. The need for the elevator machine room at the top of each shaft for each cab may well result, as discussed in Chapter 8, in the use of the floor on which the elevator machine room is located as a mechanical equipment room for air-conditioning and plumbing equipment, including fans, coils, heat exchangers, refrigeration machines, and boilers. In this case, providing cooling and any required venting of the shaft to the atmosphere is more greatly simplified than if the area around the elevator machine room were used for general office occupancy.

ELEVATOR MACHINE ROOM COOLING

The elevator machine room, as well as machine spaces associated with modern machine-room-less elevators, has cooling loads that consist of not only the electric motor that drives the hoisting mechanism for the elevators but also extensive heat-generating electronic controls for the elevators. The electronic components will require that the elevator machine room be cooled in hot weather to a maximum temperature of 80°F (27°C), be heated in cold weather so the space temperature will not drop below 60°F (16°C), and must be considered as active loads. Relative humidity should not exceed 85% noncondensing. One means of maintaining the temperature between these allowable levels is to provide a packaged DX condenser water unit in the elevator machine room, but, because of possible significant operational availability restrictions on the use of a water-cooled unit, the HVAC designer is cautioned to review that alternative with the building developer. The use of a packaged DX condenser water unit may well be necessary for a low-rise or mid-rise elevator bank for which the elevator machine room is in the middle of the building, unless the elevator machine room location results in the use of the remainder of the floor as a mechanical equipment room. For the elevator machine room for the elevator bank that serves the top of the building, it is possible to use air-cooled DX equipment, which will not require the operation of the condenser water system on a 24/7 basis.

The ultimate size of the water-cooled or air-cooled DX unit will be determined by the information provided by the elevator manufacturer who is selected as the provider of the elevators for the project. For the initial design stages, the necessary general information to allow the project to be designed and bid upon can be provided by the elevator consultant. The amount of cooling as the electronic devices and motor drives for the hoist have evolved has increased significantly. With current elevator designs, the DX unit may require 10 to 15 tons (35 to 52 kW) or more of capacity in a single elevator machine room.

ELEVATOR HOISTWAY AND MACHINE ROOM VENTING

All elevators that are installed in the United States must conform to ASME A17.1, *Safety Code for Elevators and Escalators* as it is modified by the locally applicable building code. These modifications can vary by jurisdiction, with many areas modifying the code by stated amendments of the A17.1 code (ASME 2013).

One of the requirements of most codes is the inclusion of a vent opening at the top of each elevator shaft that is 3.5% of the plan area of the shaft. The rationale for the opening is not entirely clear, but it was probably originally intended to allow the venting of smoke during a building fire. Regardless of the reason for its inclusion, the HVAC project design, where the vent is required, must provide a duct that connects the vent to the atmosphere. This vent is generally provided with a fail-safe fire-rated damper, preventing the loss of conditioned building air or exacerbating stack effect during nonemergency conditions. Similar requirements exist for elevators with speeds of 700 fpm (3.5 m/s) in single shafts. This is simple at the top of the building, but for a low-rise or mid-rise elevator (unless the elevator termination floor is a mechanical equipment room), the connecting duct must be extended to the nearest mechanical equipment room and then to the atmosphere.

When designing supertall buildings, where elevator speeds are greater than 1400 fpm (7 m/s), vents at the top and bottom of the shafts may be required by code to facilitate the rapid escape of the compressed column of air ahead of the direction of car travel as well as the inrush of air by the vacuum created behind the car. Under many codes, for a building that is fully sprinklered, the need for the vent and its extension to the atmosphere may be waived for passenger elevators. The vent is still required for a dedicated service car, but this is normally easily handled, since the service car will be serving all floors in the building and the extension of the vent opening is a simple task where the elevator terminates at the top floor of the building.

SMART ELEVATORS[11]

Much like smartphones and smart TVs, elevators are becoming more high-tech. As skyscrapers continue to rise to even more dizzying heights, elevator manufacturers must make adjustments to safely and quickly transport passengers. Smart elevators are among the new wave of advancement in our industry. A passenger pushes a button to set his or her destination and an indicator will direct them to a specific elevator that will transport him or her to that floor the fastest. This advanced routing is a more efficient way of moving passengers, especially during high-traffic hours in busy office buildings or hotels. These elevators can be programmed to operate differently at certain periods throughout the day.

Elevator manufacturers have developed intuitive elevator technologies for increasing the overall commuter experience. Intuitive elevator technologies include smart grouping and destination-based models with modern aesthetics. Smart grouping technology organizes commuters by grouping them based on their floor/zone preferences; for example, passengers going to the same destination are assigned only to those elevators that serve that group of floors or zones. This results in much faster and much better-organized service, i.e., in a 50-floor building, this smart grouping can reduce overall traveling time by 40 percent, when compared with conventional systems. It can also reduce energy consumption by up to 27 percent.

---

11. This section provides text originally published by Schwartz (2018) and Jacob (2018). To integrate smoothly into the book, the content has been updated to conform to this book's style; otherwise, the content is as originally published.

Elevators on the Internet

Sensors gather data about usage and other factors, which can affect wear and tear on parts and machinery. That information is then transferred to a cloud-based platform where it is processed and analyzed to predict when maintenance might be needed. Accurately predicting future problems could allow the elevator technicians to make repairs before there is a breakdown.

Another benefit is that companies would be able to service some aspects of elevators remotely, which can help save money and time when repairs are needed (Schwartz 2018).

Collected data is sent to the Cloud and analyzed. If operational anomalies are detected, then the information is compared with all available legacy data from the entire elevator database of the supplier. Then a comparison is made to determine whether similar readings have indicated that a component is about to fail. This all takes place in a matter of seconds, and service engineers receive messages on their smart devices in real time indicating which components need to be replaced. Engineers can then effectively address and rectify the issue before the elevators break down, thereby reducing downtime. Continuously monitors and analyzes all elevator's data such as following:

- What is the status of all its embedded components?
- How quickly the elevator is accelerating?
- How quickly the door is closing?

Virtual Reality Diagnostics

In collaboration with Microsoft, a leading manufacturer is developing a virtual reality headset that might change the way mechanics do elevator repairs. These devices allow mechanics to diagnose a problem without climbing tens of floors or dangling in a lift shift. Once the mechanic puts the glasses on, he or she can use hand motions to go close-up and explore the engine and individual parts. The view can also be widened, allowing the mechanic to do a virtual "walk through," looking for places where repairs or replacement are needed.

Energy Efficient Elevators

Interest in saving energy remains high in real estate and construction. Energy efficient buildings are designed to use less energy, and the trend has spread to elevators as well. How is an elevator classified as "green?" It relates to not only energy consumption, but also the materials, processes, and technologies used, as well as interior paints, flooring, control panels, lighting, and HVAC systems.

Elements of energy efficient elevators:

- Machine-room-less (MRL) technology with machinery housed directly in the elevator shaft
- Gearless traction design, which can use up to 80% less energy than hydraulic lifts
- Drive systems that recover and regenerate energy
- Precision traffic control to cut down on elevators with fewer passengers (which use more energy)
- Computerized systems that reduce the number of light-load trips
- In-cab sensors and software that will "go to sleep" when occupied, turning off lights, ventilation, music and video
- Destination dispatch control software that batches elevator stop requests. This reduces the number of stops and even reduces the number of elevators required in a building

Destination Controls

Calling an elevator is no longer simply pressing a button and waiting for it to arrive. new, high-tech features "allow building managers to more intelligently group and assign passengers to elevators, move people more rapidly to their destination, adjust passenger flow in real-time and personalize touchscreens and kiosks."

Elevators can be dedicated to high-traffic areas to more adequately answer passenger demands. Building managers will be able to control everything remotely from anywhere in the building.

The Fastest Elevators in the World

Cities all over the world are competing to having the tallest skyscrapers, and a similar race is happening regarding the speed of the elevators that serve them. The Shanghai Tower holds three Guinness World Records for the world's fastest elevator, the tallest elevator in a building, and the fastest double-deck elevator. It travels at 67 feet per second. The elevator in the Guangzhou CTF Tower (1739 ft [530 m] tall) makes its trip from floor 0 to 95 in only 45 seconds.

Watch out for the Jeddah Tower in Saudi Arabia, which will become the tallest building in the world in 2019. That building's elevators will use "ultrarope," a carbon-fiber cable that has incredible lift power. It will enable the machine to travel over 33 feet per second, reaching the highest livable floor in 52 seconds.

These and other innovations in the world of elevators mean it's an exciting time for our industry. We look forward to the next wave of emerging technologies, many of which will influence the daily operation of new elevators around the world.

Interactive Touch Panels

Manufacturers now include interactive touch panels in elevators to provide passengers entertainment, cab indicator functionality, system monitoring, and emergency call technology all as a measure to increase commuters' comfort.

Cable-Free Smart Elevators

With the help of cross-industry innovation, elevator suppliers have developed cable-free elevators that can move both vertically and horizontally. These elevators are typically made of carbon-fiber-reinforced plastic and are powered by linear motors that can move cabs up and down, forward and backwards, and left or right on magnetic rails. Cable-free elevators are energy efficient and reduce carbon footprint impacts dramatically.

Automated Vehicle Storage and Retrieval Technology

This uses elevators and other related systems to transport vehicles using robotic lifting systems. This is an untapped market which is not dominated by most major suppliers. These facilities require advanced and connected elevators to run the facility efficiently and effectively. The technology offers maximized parking capacity by optimum utilization of space, ensures vehicle safety, and provides convenience to customers. These parking systems are used for both renovation and new construction projects. Automated parking technologies are environmentally friendly because car engines are shut off when cars are stored or retrieved in this parking system; in addition, even search time for parking spaces is eliminated because of a robotic system that doesn't involve any human interaction. This automated parking technology is apt for densely populated areas, including business parks, railway stations, subway stations, office buildings, trade centers, hotels, and others.

CHAPTER 14
Plumbing Systems

PLUMBING SYSTEMS

The plumbing systems designed for any building fall into several discrete categories including the domestic water system, which will provide both hot and cold water to various fixtures and water-consuming equipment installed throughout the building; the sanitary system, which will be connected to water closets, lavatories, drains, etc. in the building and will drain the waste from these fixtures to a sewer system external to the building; and a stormwater system, which will collect rain water or melted snow and pipe it to an appropriate disposal point, usually a public sewer.

All of these systems are part of the mechanical designs for a project, but none other than the domestic water system have any involvement with the HVAC design. This involvement is limited to providing makeup water to the chilled-water, hot-water, and condenser water systems and the possible heating of the domestic hot-water system by a hot-water boiler that is included as a part of the HVAC system. The makeup water is required because of the small amount of leakage that can occur at several locations in the HVAC piping systems, including the pumps, and, more important, the loss from evaporation. The major element of evaporation occurs in the condenser water system at the cooling tower. The possible heating of the domestic water is discussed later in this chapter.

The tall commercial building presents essentially two problems in the design of the domestic water system. The first is to provide a means to develop and maintain adequate pressure at the plumbing fixtures in the highest portion of the building. The second is to provide a means to avoid exceeding the pressure requirements on fixtures and equipment in the lower reaches of a building.

Water is supplied to the fixtures either through gravity house tanks or pressure boosting systems. To limit pressure to acceptable levels, the building is divided into multiple vertical zones. This is accomplished by tanks or pressure-reducing stations that limit the zones to 11 floors (assuming 11.4 ft [3.5 m] floor height) or 15 floors (assuming 8.2 ft [2.5 m] floor height) while maintaining the pressure at the lowest floor of the zone at an allowable value that will permit any connected water fixtures to operate properly. This maximum pressure is usually between 80 to 85 psi (550 to 586 kPa).

The domestic water system is used to fill the chilled-water, hot-water, and condenser water systems. This can be accomplished through the expansion tank or the cooling tower at the top of the building. In addition, domestic water is provided to the condenser water system on an ongoing basis to replace the water that evaporates in the cooling tower as it adiabatically cools the condenser water. The HVAC engineer must provide to the plumbing designer the amount of water that will be required on a peak cooling day for cooling tower makeup. This will become a key component of the plumbing engineer's estimate of the project's total water requirements that will be provided to the municipal water authority in a request for service availability. The remainder of the estimate of the daily water consumption will be based on the water consumed per capita per day for various purposes in the building. These estimates will be made by the plumbing engineer.

The means of providing the limited amount of hot water to restrooms and janitorial connections can vary as a function of the building use and type of tenancy, but the piping system must accommodate the same pressure problems as cold water in a tall building as well as the minimum and maximum pressures that are necessary to operate the fixtures at the lavatories in

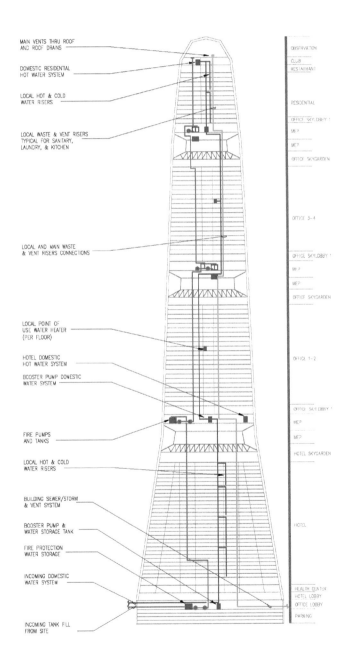

PLUMBING / FIRE PROTECTION

Figure 14.1 A typical water distribution for a megatall building.

the restroom. In central domestic water heating, the plumbing engineer will furnish the HVAC engineer the hourly energy load for the domestic hot water and the expected peak hot-water demand load. The energy load is used to size the boiler that will be provided in the HVAC design documents as the heat source for the hot-water heater and capacities of hot-water tanks. The demand load, representative of the peak domestic flow rate, will be used to size the steam or boiler water piping to the domestic hot water heater.

As an alternative, it has become quite common to install a separate electric hot-water heater on every floor or every third or fourth floor of a commercial building. This allows the project's needs to be met at lower first cost than would be the case with a central domestic heating solution. If a separate electric hot-water heater is included in the design, there will be no interface required between the HVAC and plumbing drawings to provide domestic hot water to the project.

GRAY WATER SYSTEMS

Today the term *gray water* has come to mean water that is derived from hand sinks, showers, bathtubs, and clothes washers and can be reused, after simple appropriate treatment, for irrigation and toilet/urinal flushing. *Appropriate treatment* means some form of settling, filtration, and secondary treatment usually with ultraviolet C-band radiation and chlorine injection.

Gray water recycling and reuse can be very cost effective at offsetting the use of potable water in a once-through arrangement (i.e., toilet flushing). Balancing the amount of gray water collected versus the amount needed to flush the toilet and urinals on a daily basis is a somewhat scientific and artful exercise. In general, the following guidelines should be considered when evaluating a project for gray water use:

- Does the project have a large number of plumbing fixtures to contribute gray water? Usually, bathtubs, showers, hand sinks, and clothes washers are appropriate candidates. Kitchen sinks, dishwashers, and other like appliances are not appropriate for this use.
- Because gray water system requires large number of hand sinks, showers, etc., office-type occupancies are generally not good candidates for gray water collection and reuse. However, very large office buildings can offer adequate gray water plumbing fixtures to make this concept viable. High-rise dwelling occupancies (apartments, condominiums, hotels) are the best choice as they have a large number of appropriate fixtures for this purpose.
- Is the project located in a municipality that is receptive to, and interested in, water conservation and reuse protocols? Many local authorities may be reluctant to entertain the use of gray water recycling for any number of reasons: unfamiliarity with the concept, not specifically in their building code, political and/or trade resistance, etc. It is incumbent upon the gray water system designer to clearly and concisely discuss the gray water system with the authorities and review with them the collection, filtering, and treatment protocols to be employed in the system.

A gray water system must consist of at least the following major components:

- A collection tank with a conical bottom and settling screen to allow any grit in the incoming water to settle out and be drained off.
- A pump sized for the necessary water flow from the collection tank to the filters.
- A filtering medium, such as cartridge-type filters in increasing filtering capability (e.g., from 100 μm down to 1 μm), in however many steps the system designer feels is appropriate. This decision will be influenced by the quality of the waste stream, space available for the filtering medium, and cost of filter products. Other filtering types are available and should be considered by the designer based on the above concerns. Regardless of the filtering medium chosen, it is good practice to have two filters in the line, one for duty and one for standby.
- A final means of clarifying and adding some level of disinfection to the cleaned waste stream. This could be an ultraviolet light operating in the C-band radiation level (UV-C), some form of chlorine injection, or, perhaps, both. Other means can also be considered with the local authorities to satisfy any concerns related to the quality of the water as it enters the building system.

- A clean water holding tank to receive and keep the cleaned water prior to routing it to a pressure booster pump to distribute the water to the toilets and urinals in the building. Some building codes may stipulate that the cleaned water cannot be held for more than 72 hours in the tank. You may need to satisfy the local building official, via calculation, that your design will comply.
- A system to monitor, control, and modulate the flow in and through the system and out to the building. A test port will also be needed to draw sample water from the clean tank for lab analysis.
- Most building codes will also require that the piping used to distribute the gray water through building be unique or identified such that there will be no misunderstanding that this piping system is not part of the potable system. Piping that is plastic and is purple or orange usually is required. Additionally, some identifiers or labeling protocols attached to the pipe may also be required. Depending on the project location, multiple language labels may be needed.
- The gray water system should be located in a dedicated room with adequate lighting, floor drains, and a service-style sink for routine maintenance. Storage should be provided for test bottles, log books, operations manuals, and other such items.

A properly designed and installed gray water reclaim system will dramatically reduce potable water use and, by extension, water utility costs. This will reduce the impact on the environment as the energy used to treat "new" water is avoided. Reducing electrical consumption reduces our carbon footprint, which reduces greenhouse gases,

BLACK WATER

Black water, sometimes referred to as *reclaimed water*, is water that contains human excrement and kitchen wastes and generally requires high levels of treatment before being pure enough to discharge into rivers or streams or to be reused.

In some countries, the reuse of black water is again being studied to allow reclamation, on-site, of as much of the water waste stream as possible. Australia is actively pursuing the use of on-site, small-scale black water treatment and reclaim systems to help offset the use of potable water for irrigation and toilet/urinal flushing in the urban setting. There has been good progress and success in applying this small, local, on-site solution to black water treatment and Australia is developing guidelines for use by the various states and territories. In addition, black water recycling is worth considering for those developments without sufficient metropolis sewage network support.

The primary health risks associated with reclaiming and recycling black water are the microbial pathogens in wastewater from sewage effluent. Major pathogen groups include the following:

- Bacteria
- Viruses
- Protozoa
- Helminths

Any on-site treatment protocols must take these pathogen groups into consideration and be able to produce effluent water that is "fit for the intended purpose." Note that "fit for the intended purpose" could mean anything from irrigation of crops all the way to plumbing fixture flushing.

In the United States, on-site black water treatment systems are not yet developed to the point where individual states are willing to license or accept this protocol without further study and analysis. Only primary treatment plants that accept black water and related waste streams from a very large area are designated as acceptable treatment points.

One very important point to be considered with any type of on-site black water treatment system is the space required for this equipment. By necessity, this equipment is large, somewhat complicated, and requires on-going maintenance. How this equipment relates to the intended operation and "fit for the purpose" approach should be developed using the hazard analysis and critical control point (HACCP) system. This analysis approach consists of the following eight activities:

- Communication and consultation
- Establish (develop) the context
- Identify the hazards/risks
- Analyze the risks
- Evaluate the risks
- Treat the risks
- Monitor and review the hazards/risks
- Record the risk management process

The HACCP system is the International Standard for Food Safety. When best practices are followed, users and consumers can be assured that it is safe to work with and be exposed to recycled water, that food irrigated with recycled water is safe, and that there are no adverse environmental effects from the use of this recycled water.

Equipment size, system maintenance access, odor control, disposal of sludge waste and the need to provide periodic cleaning of the component pieces may make an urban environment an inappropriate location for a black water reclaim system as urban sites are historically constrained in available free area. Also, the need to maximize rentable area within the building is paramount to the owner/developer. Local ordinances, codes, health regulations, and vendor support/maintenance will all serve to temper the decision to use black water reclaim strategies.

CONDENSATE RECOVERY

In almost all modern buildings today, HVAC equipment is used to provide a conditioned indoor environment while using large amounts of energy to cool, filter, and dehumidify the air in these structures. This is especially true for buildings located in hot and humid climates around the world. International engineering organizations, such as ASHRAE, have developed IAQ standards that stipulate substantial requirements for outdoor air to be introduced into a building's air-conditioning system. Internal loads and additional outdoor ventilation air all generate considerable latent loads on these systems and exacerbate the already difficult moisture control problem. A manifestation of this load is the liquid water condensate that is typically drained away from the air-conditioning equipment and routed to the nearest sanitary drain.

Condensate Water Quality and Uses

As described in AWE (2010), this condensate water is basically equivalent to distilled water: it is mineral free and has nearly zero total dissolved solids (TDS). However, condensate water should never be used for human consumption, because it may contain heavy metals from contact with coils and other HVAC equipment. The lack of minerals also makes it corrosive to most metals, especially steel and iron.

Because of the water's low-mineral quality and lack of sanitizers (e.g., chlorine, chloramine), it is excellent for irrigation for plants not intended for human consumption. Although condensate water does not contain biological pollutants commonly found in rainwater, such as bird feces, there is a slight risk of lead contamination from solder joints in evaporative coils building up to dangerous levels in soil continually irrigated with the water.

One of the best uses for condensate water is as makeup water for cooling towers (AWE 2010). The amount of water needed for makeup in a cooling tower is highly dependent on the TDS contained in the water supply. The greater the TDS level of the source water, the greater the water use of the cooling tower. Condensate water can be used instead of potable water, and it has virtually no minerals. Thus, the cooling tower will require less makeup water.

It may also be possible to use condensate water for water-cooled equipment, decorative fountains and water features, evaporative coolers, rinse for washing vehicles and equipment, laundry operations, and industrial processes. Some new air conditioners use condensate water to help cool the hot condenser coils. The variety of uses for condensate water is expected to grow as the need for water efficiency intensifies in the future.

Below are the effective methods of condensate water uses in the modern buildings:

- Use as cooling tower makeup water (after treatment)
- Use as water closet flushing (after treatment)
- Use for decorative fountains
- Use as a cooling medium
- Industrial cleaning applications (after treatment)

Table 12.1 shows the condensate water quality and the acceptable range for each parameter to use for domestic purpose. The table indicates that the water quality of condensate drain water would be acceptable for a domestic or industrial application and consumption with minimal treatment for biological contaminants.

Design Considerations

Condensate water is distilled, pure water when it forms on the condensate coils of an air handler. However, it can pick up bacterial contamination during formation and transport. As with any water stored in a tank, it must be considered unsafe for human contact without the addition of chlorine or ozone.

Chlorine injectors are relatively simple to add to tanks when the water will be used for fountains or aboveground irrigation systems. Treatment is not necessary if condensate water goes directly to cooling towers where biocide procedures will prevent a problem. Treatment is a must if condensate water is used as alternative water resource for toilet flushing as it may come in contact with humans during operation.

An additional design consideration is that the condensate is more corrosive than ground or surface water because of its high purity. Materials that are rated for steam condensate and other high-purity water should be used in system components.

DOMESTIC WATER SYSTEMS

The plumbing for tall buildings needs several special considerations in comparison to that for other types of buildings. As described in Megri (2011), high-rise plumbing typically uses vertical piping systems for water distribution and drainage/venting. The advantage of vertical piping systems is that they are generally more economic and need less maintenance than horizontal piping systems in high-rise projects, using fewer supports, hangers, and inserts and requiring less horizontal space in ceiling plenums for drainage sloping. The disadvantage of vertical piping is multiple penetrations through structural slabs, each of which must be sealed to protect the building pressurization and to prevent vertical migration of fire and smoke. The

Table 14.1 Condensate Water Quality and Acceptable Range of Each Parameter for Domestic Use

Parameter	Condensate drain range	Acceptable range
Conductivity	60–100 µS/cm	0–400 µS/cm
Dissolved oxygen	5–8 mg/L	5–11 mg/L
Turbidity	0.4–0.7 NTU	0–1 NTU
Nitrates	0–1 mg/L	0–45 mg/L
Chlorides	1–3.2 mg/L	0–250 mg/L
pH	5.5–6.5	6.5–8.5

location of the penetrations is important to the building structure and the function of the fixtures. Lightening the overall building structure (e.g., with post-tensioned beams and slabs) limits placement possibilities for slab penetrations (Larson 2007).

Pressure Requirements

As noted by Megri (2011), model plumbing codes and ASPE (2000) limit the pressure supplied to a fixture to P_{max} = 80 psi (551 kPa). Steele (1984) set a more conservative P_{max} = 70 psi (482 kPa). Note that for each 1 ft (0.3048 m) of elevation change, there is a 0.433 psi (2.98 kPa) static pressure change, which is relatively small compared to sprinkler/standpipe fire protection at P_{max} = 175 psi (1207 kPa) (NFPA 2010). The maximum pressure required at fixtures is typically not higher than 25 psi (172 kPa), even for the most demanding fixtures (e.g., flush valve water closets).

The pressure needed by the water booster pumps at the base of the system can be calculated as follows:

$$P_{r,h} + P_s + P_f = P_R - P_{min} = P_{pumps}$$

where

$P_{r,h}$ = residual pressure at highest fixture

P_s = static pressure

P_f = friction losses

P_R = required pressure

P_{min} = minimum available pressure

P_{pumps} = pressure required by booster pumps

To avoid noise problems, pipe erosion, water hammer, and damage to fixtures and equipment, Megri (2011) recommends limiting water pressure in order to limit water velocity below critical values (~10 fps [3 m/s]). In many successful high-rise designs, pressure is controlled either by reducing valves on each level where pressure exceeds the code maximum or branching from the higher pressure riser to make a pressure zone. In this pressure zone, a central pressure-reducing valve and subriser meet the minimum pressure required at the highest level and the maximum pressure allowed at the lowest level. Typically, to avoid excessive pressure, buildings taller than 100 ft (30 m) require multiple water distribution zones.

Significant considerations in water distribution system design include the following:

- Building height
- Available municipal water pressure
- Pressure requirements at different floors
- Flow demand
- Booster pump capacity and control
- Pipe and valve materials
- Riser locations
- Pressure zones
- Pressure-regulating stations
- Water heater location, storage capacity, and recovery
- Domestic hot-water circulation or pipe temperature maintenance
- Space requirements
- Economics
- Energy efficiency
- Acoustics

COLD-WATER DISTRIBUTION

Tall buildings can use several pumping schemes (Megri 2011):

- Single zone: Tank at the top with fill pump at the bottom. The most common system (used in the early 1900s) uses roof tank(s) with constant-speed pumps operated by a level switch in the tank. As a predetermined water level in the tank is approached, pumps either turn on to fill the tank(s) or turn off when the tank is full (Larson 2007). Tanks also provide water storage for fire protection. Water is distributed using a gravity downfeed system.

- Multiple zones: High-zone tank and low-zone tank. Multiple tanks serve multiple zones as needed. Gravity tanks at different floors provide distribution. The tanks must be sufficiently elevated to provide adequate pressure at the first floor connected.

- Multizone cold-water distribution with multiple pumps: Multiple booster pumps with constant-speed, constant-pressure controls are used, with one pump for each zone.

- Pressure-regulating valves: The building is separated into zones. With a pumped system, the supply pressure to the lower zone is controlled by pressure-regulating valves (PRVs); pump discharge pressure is set for the supply to the upper zone. An alternative is to use a tank as the source, controlling the lower zone pressure with a PRV. Many new systems use PRVs inserted off a common high-pressure express main and/or installed at each floor where the pressure exceeds code maximum.

- Variable-speed pump systems: To provide constant water pressure in the building, various control schemes can be used to maintain the desired pressure with varying flows.

HOT-WATER DISTRIBUTION

When domestic water distribution is separated into zones, providing domestic hot-water becomes more complicated; centralized distribution can be problematic. One simple approach is to provide water heating specific to each zone or locally on each floor. Alternatively, a centralized recirculation system can be used, requiring PRVs on the return, although PRVs in the return circuit may have pressure reduction problems. Other multizone hot-water recirculation systems have multiple dedicated heaters, with one or more pumps.

It is important that hot- and cold-water supply are fed from the same water source, to prevent a scalding hazard.

DRAINAGE AND VENTING

The following are important design considerations for drainage and venting (Megri 2011):

- **Terminal velocity:** Water drainage flow (1/3) tends to attach to the piping wall, forming a hollow cylinder of water with a core of air (2/3) in the center, opposed by pipe friction forces.

- **Stack offsets:** When fixture layouts change and stacks must be offset (at an angle higher than 45°), a large slug of water can quickly develop. These fluid and air fluctuations can be controlled by using yoke vents, relief vents, and vent connections at the bases of stacks.

- **Expansion and contraction:** Temperature variations cause expansion or contraction of stacks. This can be avoided by installing soluble gaskets in the caulked joints.

- **Suds pressure:** Washing machines, dishwashers, laundry trays, and kitchen sinks can create additional pressure from the significant amount of suds produced.

- **Venting:** The objective of the venting system is to remove excess air from the drainage system, thus neutralizing the pressure within the system.

CASE STUDY
Shanghai Tower

Name: Shanghai Tower

Location: Shanghai, China

Description: Sited adjacent the neighboring Jin Mao Tower and Shanghai World Financial Center in the heart of the Lujiazui Finance and Trade Zone, the 2073 ft (632 m) Shanghai Tower is China's tallest building. The tower's transparent, spiral form showcases cutting-edge sustainable strategies and public spaces that set new standards for green community. Shanghai Tower houses Class A office space, entertainment venues, retail spaces, a conference center, a luxury hotel and cultural amenity spaces in its 127 stories. The tower has been awarded a China Green Building Three Star rating and a LEED® Platinum Certification from the U.S. Green Building Council.

The Shanghai Tower has a total construction area of about 5,815,000 ft^2 (540,000 m^2) of built enclosed area, of which 4,100,000 ft^2 (380,000 m^2) is above grade and 1,715,000 ft^2 (160,000 m^2) is below grade. It is the second tallest building in the world.

Shanghai Tower Structure. Shanghai Tower's asymmetry was designed in such a way that wind loads were reduced by 24%, generating savings in both building materials and construction process. The design of the building saved more than $55 million in building materials.

Shanghai Tower inner layer has a triangular exterior layer that constantly shapes the building façade from all directions. The building contains a double-skin façade that creates nine atrium sky gardens, cylindrical buildings stacked one atop the other, that are being used as plazas and reunions. Both skin façades are transparent establishing a connection between the buildings' interior and Shanghai's urban fabric.

The Shanghai Tower features many green aspects, such as:

- The inner glass of the building's façades uses 14% less glass than a building occupying the same area but using a square design.
- The glass façade minimizes energy consumption.
- Two skin layers form the building façade and create thermal buffer zones that improve IAQ.
- Some of the building's parapets are designed to collect rainwater that is then used for heating and A/C systems.
- The spiral shape creates an asymmetrical surface that reduces wind loads.
- Water treatment plants recycle gray water and stormwater for irrigation and toilet use.
- A 38% water consumption reduction is achieved by having interim water storage tanks distributed within the tower allowing the water pressure to be maintained by gravity.
- Two chiller plants, strategically located in the building, reduce the energy required to pump chilled water.
- On-site power is generated by wind turbines located directly beneath the parapet.
- Shanghai Tower's owners aim to register for a high level of building certification from the China Green Building Committee and the U.S. Green Building Council.

Shanghai Tower Construction Facts. The project may be one of the most challenging buildings of the world and, knowing this, the development team attempted to mitigate this through the following measures:

- All of the Tower's mechanical equipment has been distributed throughout the Tower to provide design and cost efficiency.
- The space design to locate all electrical and mechanical equipment is also used as a life safety refuge area.
- The core of Shanghai Tower is made of a 30 square meters concrete core.
- The massive concrete core also interacts with four super columns.
- Shanghai Tower foundation is made of a six-meter thick mat supported by 947 bore piles.
- The building is designed to save 21.59% in annual energy costs compared to the ASHRAE 90.1-2004 baseline.
- It has a 2000 KW natural gas-fired cogeneration system that provides electricity and heat energy.
- Shanghai Tower has two independent curtain walls, the outermost one designed as a non-thermally broken aluminum extrusion encasing 26mm laminated low-iron glass.

Outdoor Design Criteria. Outdoor atmospheric temperature range from 27°F (−2°C) to 95°F (35°C), with an annual average temperature in the urban district of 64°F (18°C). Humidity levels vary daily but are constant through the year. Annual precipitation is more than

1440 mm (56 in.). Fifty percent of the annual precipitation falls in the flood season between May and September. There are many northwestern and southeastern winds throughout the year. The building receives an average of 1547 hours of sunlight annually.

Energy Performance. The main feature considered for the exterior wall performance is based on a bio-climatic concept of a passive atrium system, where two skins are located in such a way as to create a large, full-height atrium space capitalizing on all the benefits that captured air—and the natural convection of air—can provide. Although a completely passive "greenhouse" effect could not be used alone for the atrium, there is minimal need for additional cooling and heating, and total thermal stresses and energy use in office spaces and the hotel are significantly reduced, as confirmed in energy modeling. Zones 1 through 8 have three atria per floor that function together with an exterior and interior glazed skin to provide the level of thermal comfort desired for a built environment in Shanghai (Zone 9 is designed without either interior curtain wall or atrium spaces). This is done with a great degree of efficiency, with only the first 15 ft (4.5 m) of atrium mildly conditioned with the use of a perimeter Fan Coil Unit that either heats or cools—primarily during weather extremes—leaving the majority of the atrium to be ventilated with a combination of natural updraft and regulated top exhausts, as well as with spill air on the first and last floor of each zone. The whole system (inclusive of other LEED strategies in the building) creates about 21% energy efficiency, compared to ASHRAE 90.1–2004 in LEED Rating and about 12.5% over China's nationally recognized Three-Star Rating. Seven percent of total efficiency is achieved as a result of various features used for exterior skin design

Building Height: 2073 ft (632 m)

Building Floor Area: 5,815,000 ft^2 (540,000 m^2) (enclosed area), 4,100,000 ft^2 (380,000 m^2) (above grade) 1,715,000 ft^2 (160,000 m^2) (below grade)

Architects: Gensler (Design), Tongji Architectural Design (Group) Co Ltd. (Architect of Record), East China Architectural Design and Research Institute (Peer Review)

Structural Engineers: Thornton Thomasetti (Design), Tongji Architectural Design (Group) Co. Ltd. (Engineer of Record), China Academy of Building Research (Peer Review)

MEP Engineers: Cosentini Associates, Aurecon (Design), Tongji Architectural Design (Group) Co. Ltd. (Engineer of Record), WSP/Parsons Brinkerhoff (Peer Review)

Report courtesy of Gensler Architects.

CHAPTER 15
Life Safety Systems

Every tall commercial building constructed in the United States should include design details and operating systems that, in total, constitute a life safety system. The requirements for both the design details and operating systems that should be included are defined in the building code that applies in the building's jurisdiction. The building code should address construction details of the building, outline minimum criteria for the means of egress from the building in the event of a fire or other emergency, and should specify protective features and systems that must be included to achieve the level of protection that can reasonably be provided to allow adequate egress time and protection for building occupants who may be exposed to a fire or the smoke generated by a fire.

UNIQUE FIRE SAFETY PROBLEMS IN TALL BUILDINGS

From the perspective of life safety systems, tall buildings (1) are beyond the reach of fire department aerial equipment, (2) pose a potential for significant stack effect, and (3) require unreasonable evacuation time.

The HVAC engineer is primarily concerned with the design of the smoke control system, but the HVAC engineer must also understand how the entire life safety system functions and the concerns that the other design professionals must address to provide an integrated total system. Accordingly, other facets of the system beyond smoke control are outlined in this chapter.

CODES AND STANDARDS

The design of the life safety systems for any building is a multidisciplinary effort involving the architect and structural engineer as well as the HVAC, electrical, and fire protection engineers. The architect will be concerned with the location and details of the fire stairs and areas of refuge as well as the fire rating of the shafts and internal separation of spaces in the building. The structural engineer will specify the fire-retardant material that will protect the structural system. The remaining elements of the life safety systems that constitute the fire management systems will be designed by the HVAC, electrical, and fire protection engineers.

Each of these areas of design will be governed by the local building code and, frequently, by reference to fire protection standards that have been developed in the United States by the National Fire Protection Association (NFPA). These standards are applicable to many facets of a building's design, specifically those of concern to the mechanical and electrical design trade (the fire alarm systems, the fire standpipe and sprinkler systems, and the smoke detection and smoke control systems). The critical NFPA standards are provided in the Bibliography.

The details of the rationale for these standards and many of the details of current fire suppression technology and practices are provided in the *Fire Protection Handbook* published by NFPA (2008). This book is periodically updated to be consistent with the continually evolving practices developed in fire technology. The book is also an excellent source for material on matters beyond the issue of fire suppression. While not all jurisdictions completely adhere to the recommendations in this book, it is the single most valuable resource on state-of-the-art fire technologies.

Several complications may present themselves when applying these NFPA standards and the code that references them. First, while many local codes will adopt specific standards by reference, others may include modifications to portions of the standards that apply. Second, the authority having jurisdiction, as designated by the governing authority, will have the responsibility of interpreting both the standard and the applicable building code. Their interpretation can well differ and may be more restrictive than would be the case through a literal reading of the standard or the code by the design team. It is therefore imperative that the design professionals involved in any tall commercial project review the interpretation of both the applicable NFPA standards and the building code with both the building department and the fire department in the area. It will be their readings of any applicable standard and the code that the design professionals will be faced with applying in a project design.

Finally, in the United States, there are major insurance carriers that have design criteria that can be more restrictive than either the NFPA standards or the building code and, if the building is being constructed by an entity that desires to comply with the requirements of one of these insurance carriers, it will be necessary that the design be completed to meet the stated requirements of these agencies.

Modifications to building codes are always being considered. For example, discussions currently are taking place in New York City to increase the width of stairwells to 68 in. (1727 mm) to allow simultaneous two-way travel with the occupants proceeding down to exit the building and the fire department personnel going up to fight the fire. This change has not been incorporated into the codes of the City of New York but is included in this design guide to indicate that changes are always possible and under discussion by various governmental agencies. It is therefore prudent that the design professionals on any project be cognizant of impending changes and allow for the inclusion of the appropriate design details on any project.

COMPONENTS OF FIRE MANAGEMENT SYSTEM

The HVAC designer should work with the electrical and fire protection engineers to specify an integrated fire management system. Among the several features and systems that must be designed by this group of design professionals, to provide for the fire management portion of the total life safety system for a properly engineered high-rise building, would be the following: (1) a detection system that will include manual fire alarm boxes, a system of smoke detectors, and flow switches and supervisory switches in the fire standpipe and the sprinkler piping systems; (2) fire standpipe and automatic sprinkler systems; (3) a smoke control system; (4) an emergency electric power system; (5) an automatic elevator recall system; (6) communication and alarm notification systems; and (7) a central fire command center.

DETECTION SYSTEM

A key element in the detection system is a system of smoke detectors. They are not required in all areas of a commercial office building but rather should be installed in locations initiate system responses. These responses can include the altered control and/or shutdown of specific fans and the recall of elevators. Both of these control functions are discussed later in this chapter. The activation of a smoke detector can also activate stair pressurization fans.

Smoke detection system design is a joint responsibility of the electrical and HVAC trades, because the smoke detection system and the wiring of the entire system will be completed by the electrical contractor, but the installation of any smoke detectors that are required at system fans or in the ductwork will be completed by the sheet metal contractor. This involvement of two trades requires close coordination in the design documentation so that each trade understands its responsibility and that there are no conflicts in the definition and detailing of the efforts of each contractor.

Smoke detectors should be installed where required by NFPA 90A, *Standard for the Installation of Air-Conditioning and Ventilation Systems* (NFPA 2018a), and as detailed in the building code. The NFPA standard requires detectors in the return air connection on each floor for buildings using either a central air-conditioning supply system with a capacity greater than 2000 cfm (3398 m^3/h) or a local floor-by-floor air-conditioning system with a capacity greater than 15,000 cfm (25,485 m^3/h). Smoke detectors are also required downstream of the filters in each supply system to shut down these fans in the event of a filter fire or smoke being brought into the building from the outside. Building codes will typically require smoke detectors on the ceiling of each elevator lobby and in mechanical equipment rooms, transformer and telephone equipment rooms, and similar spaces, unless the room is protected by an automatic suppression system such as sprinklers.

The second component of the detection system involves the sprinkler system. All new high-rise office buildings erected in the United States under the model building codes are required to be fully sprinklered.

For the purpose of monitoring sprinkler system performance, water flow devices will be required in the horizontal sprinkler piping on every floor to locate water flow from any activated system. Water flow devices are also required in the vertical fire standpipe distribution system. All control valves in the fire protection system are equipped with supervisory switches that will indicate building operating personnel to any unauthorized operation. The supervisory switches on the control valves are included to alert the building staff to an unauthorized valve closure so that the system is functional.

An alarm from any water flow switch will be transmitted to an approved, proprietary alarm receiving facility, a remote station, a central station or the fire department, or to various combinations of all of these possible receptors. In the installed system, all flow and supervisory switch signals will be recorded on a fire alarm control panel located in the central fire command center, which will be manned at all times. Devices are also installed at the fire pumps to indicate operation, power failure, and abnormal pressure in the pump discharge.

The final component of the early detection system is the manual fire alarm boxes. Manual fire alarm boxes should be provided as required by code, which as a minimum will be at the point where occupants of a building will normally exit a floor and enter the fire stairs. This will allow an occupant who has observed a fire and is exiting the floor to initiate a fire alarm signal at the central fire command center. The fire command center will provide visual indication of the location of the manual fire alarm box to allow building personnel to locate the point of the alarm initiation to report to the local fire department. The control of fans, elevators, and other building components will usually not be automatically initiated with the actuating of a manual pull station.

The activation of the smoke detector in the elevator lobby will cause the elevator to be called to its appropriate floor, as determined by the location of the fire, as is discussed later in this chapter. An alarm condition from any water flow switch control valve at a floor will activate the various components of the communication system, place all equipment required by the local fire department to prevent the spread of smoke in operational mode, and activate the elevator control system. The activation of the other components in the fire alarm system, such as the sprinkler supervisory switch, should not initiate a full-scale fire response.

FIRE STANDPIPE AND SPRINKLER SYSTEMS

There are separate purposes behind the installation of fire standpipe systems and sprinkler systems. The standpipe system provides a water supply to each floor for use by the fire department to fight a fire. It requires a constant flow of water for as long as the firefighters have a need for the flow. On the other hand, a sprinkler system provides the best means of automatic protection from fire.

Standpipe systems are required in all tall commercial buildings as defined in this design guide. In general in the United States, most applicable codes require a standpipe as a function of the area of the floors in a building and/or the height of the building. The height and depth of the floor relate to the maximum practical distance from which a fire can be fought externally from extension ladders and exterior equipment. Accordingly, for buildings greater in height than 75 ft (23 m) (if that is the code-mandated maximum), it is necessary to extend a riser up the stairwell and maintain a supply of water in the riser at all times so that the firefighters need only connect a hose to a standpipe at every floor.

Generally, in an actual fire condition, the hose is connected by the firefighter one floor below the fire. This connection is made with a hose that may be brought to the location of the fire or may be permanently installed in the building in a cabinet adjacent to the fire standpipe (this is the reason for the recent International Fire Code (IFC) requirements that the fire department valves be located at the intermediate landings of the stairwell. The permanent connection of the fire hose to the fire standpipe riser is determined by the operative building code governing the building. The use of the hose immediately adjacent to the stair and door also provides a line for the fireman to follow as an escape guide route in the event of dense smoke. By following the hose, the fireman will be brought to the floor below the fire, which should be clear of smoke.

The amount of water supplied to the standpipe system is defined in the applicable code. It should be related to the number of fire hoses used simultaneously, but the amount of water that must be available and the arrangement of the pumps and piping can vary from jurisdiction to jurisdiction. The city fire department will usually require that they have an unlimited source of water available from the standpipe system to fight a fire. Major urban areas do not usually have a problem meeting this requirement. Under these conditions, it may be necessary to provide an acceptable quantity of water within the building.

The means of distribution and the capacity of any storage tanks in a building will also be different depending on the code in use. The designer should check that the design for a given project will not only comply with the NFPA but also with the local code and the authority having jurisdiction in his interpretation of the code.

While the fire standpipe system permits the fire department personnel to extinguish a fire that has developed in a building, the best way to provide means of early protection from fires is a sprinkler system. The sprinkler system in any space, including all areas of a commercial office building, should be designed, unless modified for example by an owner or insurer, in accordance with NFPA 13, *Standard for the Installation of Sprinkler Systems* (NFPA 2019). This standard establishes alternative occupancy classifications that are applicable only with regard to the sprinkler design. The alternative classifications in NFPA 13-2002 should not be confused with occupancy classifications established in building codes and that govern other matters than the sprinkler design (such as exiting requirements and fire ratings of partitions, walls, and slabs).

The alternative NFPA occupancy classifications for a given space are determined by the type, amount, and arrangement of combustibles and the potential severity of a fire based on the burning characteristics of these combustibles in the space. In an office building, NFPA considers the quantity and combustibility of material of all office space, including data processing areas and any restaurant or food service seating areas or conference rooms, large presentation spaces or auditoriums, to be low and any fire to have relatively low rates of heat release. Accordingly, NFPA places all of these spaces in its lowest classification for sprinkler design, *light hazard*.

If an office building contained a full service restaurant kitchen, that space would be considered an ordinary hazard (Group I) space and would be subjected to different design standards than the office space with the light hazard classification.

The design classification, whether light hazard or ordinary hazard, will govern the schedule of pipe sizes, the spacing of the sprinklers, the sprinkler discharge densities, and the water supply requirements for the space, with more stringent requirements being applied in the ordinary hazard spaces.

NFPA code for all office building spaces also will allow the combination of the fire standpipe and sprinkler piping into one, single standpipe. This is not true of many codes in Europe, which require separate pipe risers for the fire standpipe and sprinkler systems.

SMOKE CONTROL SYSTEMS

The control of mechanical ventilation systems in a tall commercial building is needed to remove smoke from the area within which a fire has developed and to limit smoke from other areas that will allow the occupants to reach a place of safety. The means to achieve these goals is a function of the architectural design of the building and the specific systems that are provided for the project. The HVAC design engineer is responsible for the design of the smoke control systems that uses fans that are installed as part of the air-conditioning system in the building or fans that are installed solely for smoke control.

For the most exhaustive treatment of practical information and methods of analysis for smoke control, the reader is referred to the 2012 publication *ASHRAE Handbook of Smoke Control Engineering* (Klote et al. 2012), which is copublished with NFPA, International Code Council (ICC), and the Society of Fire Protection Engineers (SFPE). In addition, *ASHRAE Handbook—Applications* (2019a) has a chapter on fire and smoke control, and the *ASHRAE Transactions* papers listed in Bibliography include several papers that address this issue. Additional information is contained in NFPA Standard 92, *Standard for Smoke-Control Systems* (NFPA 2018b).

When there is a fire in a tall building, there is a tendency for smoke generated by the fire to spread from the area of the fire to other areas of the building. This is caused by the natural buoyancy and volumetric expansion of smoke, the stack effect that is directly related to the outdoor air temperature and the height of the building, the wind currents around the building that will alter the air movement taking place in the outdoor air and spill dampers and ultimately can affect the movement of both air and smoke within the building, and the operating mode and performance of the fans in the building.

To obtain the necessary control over smoke spread to occupied spaces, the fans in the building must be operated without recirculation of the return air transported from the area of a fire to a mechanical equipment room. If that air were recirculated by the air-conditioning supply systems, it could carry the entrained smoke back to occupied sections of the building. A key concern, therefore, is to operate building fans in a manner that will overcome any stack effect so that smoke-laden air is not distributed from the fire area to occupied building sections not in the actual fire zone.

The exact method of control and fan operation must be reviewed with the local authority having jurisdiction. Many fire departments will require the building fans to automatically shut down and to have the fans' subsequent start-up and control governed by the firefighters at the job site in response to the specific situation observed in the building.

In tall commercial buildings, each floor is usually considered a smoke zone. In the event of a fire, the fan systems should be operated to keep the floor on which the fire occurs in a negative pressure relationship to the floors above and below it in order to limit smoke spread to adjacent floors. This process of containment can be enhanced by maintaining one or two floors above and below the smoke zone floor in a positive relationship to the smoke zone floor through an altered operation of the fans that supply these floors.

The method of obtaining the negative pressure on the smoke zone floor and a positive pressure condition on the floors above and below the smoke zone floor will differ as a function of the type of system used in the project. The alternatives are central air-conditioning systems or floor-by-floor air-conditioning systems. These alternatives were discussed in detail in Chapter 8 of this design guide. The smoke control operation of these two alternative approaches must be discussed separately, because the solutions differ for each approach.

SMOKE CONTROL WITH CENTRAL AIR-CONDITIONING SYSTEMS

In this approach, the conditioned air is delivered to occupied areas by large built-up air-conditioning systems that supply multiple floors and are installed in a central mechanical equipment room.

As was noted in Chapter 8, it is recommended that two-position dampers (i.e., open or closed) be installed in both the supply and return air duct stubs at each point that conditioned air is introduced on each floor and at each point that return air is extracted from the ceiling plenum by a duct stub on each return air connection of each floor. These dampers have the capability of being opened or closed remotely through the building management system to regulate supply and return air for a particular floor.

With these specific capabilities in mind, a method of fan control that has been used is to have the supply fan go to 100% outdoor air (i.e., using no return air) or have the return fan go to 100% spill (i.e., exhausting all return air out of the building) and modify the floor dampers to pressurize adjacent floors to contain the fire within its known location while removing the smoke being generated from the fire floor. This would mean closing the damper in the supply duct to the fire area and opening the damper in the return (exhaust) duct from the same area. In areas adjacent to the fire region (i.e., the floor or floors immediately above and below the fire floor), the supply fan would inject 100% fresh air and the return air (exhaust) ducts would be closed. These actions would effectively pressurize areas above and below the fire floor as well as the stairwells and elevator shafts and remove as many products of combustion from the building as possible without contaminating areas adjacent to the fire.

The variable-frequency drive on the supply and return fans would operate to control the supply and return fans to ensure the proper degree of air movement by the respective fan. The return air fan must extract at least 6 to 8 ach from each fire floor. As noted, this scenario depicts but one possible operating mode of the fan systems, and the experience of the HVAC designer and the requirements of the fire department may result in alternative modes of fan operation.

SMOKE CONTROL WITH FLOOR-BY-FLOOR AIR-CONDITIONING SYSTEMS

The fan arrangement with the air-conditioning systems installed on a floor-by-floor basis is different from the central air-conditioning supply system just discussed. Here, to properly control smoke on a fire floor, it is necessary to provide a smoke exhaust shaft to each local fan room that terminates in the same central fan room that contains the supply fan that supplies outdoor air to the local fan room. The smoke exhaust shaft to which this smoke exhaust fan is connected should be sized, as should the fan itself, for between 6 and 8 ach for the largest floor in the vertical stack of floors to which the duct is connected. Each duct connection to the smoke exhaust shaft must contain a two-position (open or closed) damper. The effect is that a control similar to that of the central fan room alternative can now be effected.

In the event of a fire on a particular floor, the duct connection to the smoke exhaust riser on that floor opens, and the duct connection to the smoke exhaust riser on all other floors remains closed. The smoke exhaust fan is started, with return air from the fire floor only being exhausted to the atmosphere. Supply air to the floor or floors above and below the fire zone can be operated with 100% outdoor air to again pressurize the floor, effectively restricting the smoke-laden air.

An example of how the unit on the fire floor could operate is shown in Figure 15.1.

The units on the one or two floors above and below the fire floor will operate as shown in Figure 15.1. For these units (1) the outdoor air for smoke pressurization and the outdoor air for normal operation of the unit will both open, (2) the return air damper and the smoke exhaust riser damper will both close, and (3) the supply unit will operate with 100% outdoor air. To ensure sufficient outdoor air, all of the other floor-by-floor units using the outdoor air riser must be shut and the outdoor air riser must be sized to provide sufficient air to the number of floors on which the supply units will operate with 100% outdoor air.

SMOKE CONTROL IN ATRIA

An architectural feature of many buildings is the inclusion of an atrium to enhance the aesthetics of the building. The inclusion of an atrium presents special conditions of smoke control that are usually covered within the code for the jurisdiction within which the building is located. Until recently, codes in the United States have required rate of smoke removal for an atrium in terms of air changes per hour over the total volume of the atrium and any open, connected areas. The latest research has determined that this approach of air changes over a period of time is not an appropriate solution for a smoke control design for an atrium. Accordingly, both the *International Building Code* (ICC 2012) and NFPA 5000, *Building Construction and*

Safety Code (NFPA 2018c), use a performance-based design approach detailed in NFPA 92, *Standard for Smoke Control Systems*, and as discussed in *Handbook of Smoke Control Engineering* (Klote et al. 2012).

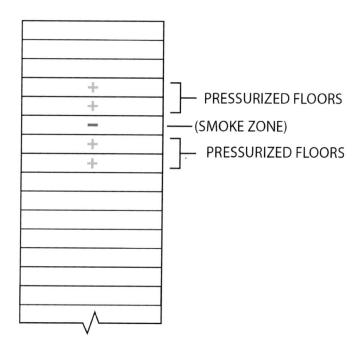

Figure 15.1 Pressurized floors above and below the smoke zone.

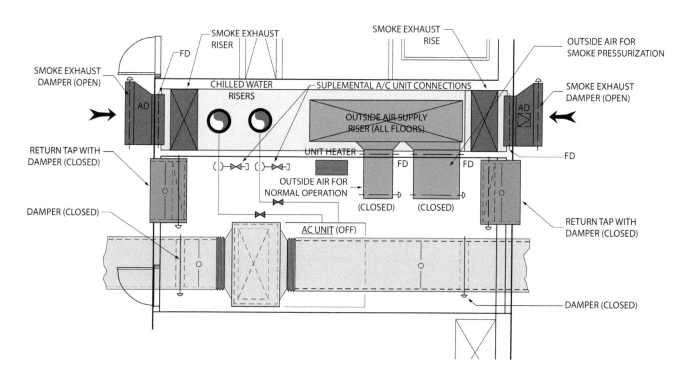

Figure 15.2 Floor-by-floor air-conditioning unit layout.

Figure 15.3 A large modern atrium.

Tall commercial buildings that contain an atrium must have a smoke control system. Generally, this is accomplished through the use of mechanical fans. Natural venting of these spaces is not normally a viable alternative. Under the *International Building Code* and NFPA 5000-2015, the fans that are installed in an atrium must function so as to contain the height of the accumulated smoke layer in the upper portions of the atrium at a minimum of 10 ft (3 m) above the walking surfaces of the means of egress from the smoke zone. The calculation of the fan capacity that will obtain the goal of a 10 ft (3 m) smoke-clear area above the egress level is established in the building code. The means of analyzing the plume configuration and exhaust fan capacity are detailed in NFPA 92 and in *Handbook of Smoke Control Engineering*.

The system must also be configured to provide a natural or mechanical supply of outdoor air or air from spaces adjacent to the smoke zone to replace the air that is being exhausted.

The action of the designed system for the atrium is intended to maintain an environment that will provide a means of egress for the occupants of the building while providing ongoing conditions that will enable firefighting personnel to enter the space and both locate and control the fire.

STAIRWELL PRESSURIZATION

Most building codes will require that the fire stairwells in a tall commercial building be pressurized to keep them smoke free in the event of a fire in the building. The smoke-free atmosphere is required for three reasons: (1) the stairs will be an area of refuge for building occupants who are directed to leave a fire floor or floor in proximity to the fire floor, (2) the stairs are an essential element in the escape route for the controlled evacuation of people from the building, and (3) the stairs will be used by the firefighters as they attempt to control and extinguish the fire.

The stair pressurization system must be capable of maintaining a pressure differential between the stair and any floor that is sufficient to limit smoke-laden air from entering the stairwell. The pressure differential will have a minimum and maximum value which, in the case of the lower value, will be sufficient to limit smoke from entering the stairwell and, in the case of the maximum value, will still allow the door to be opened by occupants trying to enter the stair. The minimum value stated in the NFPA 101, *Life Safety Code,* is 0.05 in. of water (12.4 Pa) in a sprinklered building (NFPA 2018d). For a door 7 ft tall by 3 ft wide (2.1 m tall by 0.9 m wide), this would yield a pressure of 5.5 pounds (24 N) against the total surface of the door. NFPA 101-2000 limits the force that will be required to set the door in motion in a new building to 30 lb (133 N), which, for the same 7 ft tall by 3 ft wide (2.1 m tall by 0.9 m wide) door, would equate to a pressure of 0.27 in. of water (67.2 Pa). This maximum allowable value need not be the basis of the design and frequently the maximum pressure will be between 0.05 and 0.15 in. of water (12.4 and 37.3 Pa). However, the minimum and the maximum pressure will be established in the design specifications, and this range of pressure differentials will need to be maintained in the stair pressurization system.

For the tall commercial building, it is necessary to inject outdoor air into the stair at multiple levels of the stair. There is not full agreement on the number of floors between the points of injection, but three floors or less is probably a prudent recommendation.

The fans that bring the outdoor air into the stair will usually be located in mechanical equipment rooms at more than one level in the building to limit the size of the vertical duct attached to any fan installed to pressurize the stairs. Moreover, the air must be brought from a location that will eliminate contamination with smoke-laden air being expelled from the building. Alternative means have been used to maintain the pressure in the stair between the allowable minimum and maximum values. One successful means of maintaining the pressure differential involves the installation of a series of barometric dampers, one on each floor, to open when the maximum pressure is reached. The barometric dampers and the associated jumper duct will relieve excess air from the pressurized stair to the ceiling plenum adjacent to the stair. The jumper duct will require fire dampers that are necessary to retain the fire rating of the exit stairs. The quantity of air being delivered by the fan under this arrangement would be constant and would be determined by consideration of the number of floors served by the fan, the tightness of the stair, and the maximum number of doors that can be opened at any point of time.

An analysis with a network model can be used to evaluate if a pressurized elevator is capable of being successfully pressurized between the minimum and the maximum design pressure differences. If the analysis shows that successful pressurization is unlikely, the building can be modified or an alternate system can be used. Some alternate systems include the following: (1) stairwell compartmentation, (2) stairwell pressurization with fire floor exhaust, and (3) stairwell ventilation. For more information about stairwell pressurization, see Chapter 15 of the *Handbook of Smoke Control Engineering* (Klote et al. 2012).

ELEVATOR PRESSURIZATION

The elevator pressurization systems discussed in this section are intended to limit smoke from flowing from the fire floor through an elevator shaft and threatening life on other floors. Usually, pressurized elevators are in buildings that have pressurized stairwells, and buildings that have both usually need an engineering analysis done with network modeling.

Design of pressurized elevators is much more complicated than design of pressurized stairwells, but there are a number of systems that can deal with this complexity. The reasons for this complexity are as follows: (1) the building envelope is often not capable of effectively handling the large airflow resulting from pressurization, and (2) open exterior doors on the ground floor can cause high pressure differences across the elevator shaft at the ground floor. The basic elevator pressurization system consists of only providing supply air to the elevator shaft, but in many situations the basic system cannot maintain successful pressurization.

An analysis with a network model can be used to evaluate if a pressurized elevator is capable of being successfully pressurized. If the analysis shows that successful pressurization is unlikely, the building can be modified or an alternate system can be used. Some alternate systems include the following:

- Exterior vent system
- Floor exhaust system
- Ground floor lobby system
- Enclosed elevator lobby on each floor

Depending on local codes, an alternate system may need code approval. See Chapter 15 of the *Handbook of Smoke Control Engineering* for more information about pressurized elevators.

REFUGE FLOOR

Within less than the past two decades, the concept of refuge floors has emerged as a potential life safety strategy for tall buildings. The basic concept and variations of refuge floors should be understood by the designer of mechanical engineering systems, because there are significant implications for the configuration of mechanical systems and for the project costs for the mechanical and related systems. Because of the significant expenses (both initial construction costs and the loss of potential revenue over the life of a building), there are more cost effective and sustainable concepts that can be implemented without a decrease in safety of life, and these should be considered by the design team and, where appropriate, reviewed as potential alternatives early in the project design process with the authorities having jurisdiction.

In brief, the concept of a refuge floor is that the building occupants in a tall building would leave the floor that they occupy and descend the stairs to a designated, otherwise completely unoccupied floor where they would assemble to await further instructions or remain prior to using the stairs again (or using elevators) to evacuate the building.

In some jurisdictions, there has been use of open-air refuge floors. But the challenge has been preventing the smoke from a fire on a lower floor from rising along the outside of the building and entering into the open-air refuge floor, compromising the safety of those assembled there. Although there have been some creative attempts in studying wind movement and deriving designs for architectural features such as wind baffles, the complex variations of air and smoke movement created by wind direction make the use of open-air refuge generally undependable. In addition, an open-air refuge floor is not an optimal solution in locations where there might be temperature extremes.

An enclosed refuge floor is more common, in which an entire floor is normally left completely open and unfurnished. With regards to real estate use, this becomes extremely inefficient and costly, particularly as the number of refuge floors increases due to the height of the building and the number of occupants. Refuge floors can easily reduce the amount of rental area within a building by 3% to 6%. The probability that they will ever be needed during the life of a building is extremely low, making them extremely unattractive with regards to sustainability as well as operations and maintenance expenses.

In jurisdictions that use refuge floors, the codes frequently require that the mechanical system for the refuge floor must be completely independent of all other parts of the building. This essentially results in the doubling of the capacity of the mechanical system, because a refuge floor is usually required to be able to accommodate the entire population of all the floors immediately above it (but below the next refuge floor up).

Therefore, for instance, where refuge floors are required every ten floors, a typical refuge floor would need to accommodate the building occupants from the nine floors above it. In moving those nine floors of occupants to one floor, each refuge floor becomes an assembly floor, with a significant density of occupants. Building codes typical require designs to accommodate one occupant for every 100 ft^2 (10 m^2) on a typical floor, but the gathering of occupants of nine floors onto one refuge floor would create a density of 11 ft^2 (1 m^2) per occupant. The mechanical system dedicated to that floor would need to be designed to accommodate that many occupants. In a hot climate, that would necessitate keeping many occupants cool during their duration on the refuge floor.

If the circumstances of the fire require or cause the mechanical system to shut down, the density of occupants on the refuge floor would experience an accelerated decrease in the quality of the air to be breathed and an accelerated increase in the temperature of the air on the refuge floor (as compared to a situation where most of the occupants were permitted to remain on a typical floor, where there would be nine times the amount of air for each of them to breathe during their wait). It can be expected that such a decrease in the quality of air and increase in temperature will make the occupants waiting on the refuge floor anxious and compel them to want to leave.

As noted previously, a refuge floor is in effect an assembly floor on a high-rise building, but, because there are no increases in the number of exits or of stairs, they often can be an assembly area that might not have an adequate number of exits, as compared to a conventional assembly area. The inability of occupants to quickly leave a refuge floor that is overheating could create further undesirable anxiety among the occupants on the refuge floor.

When possible, a more effective approach is for occupants on compromised floors to evacuate via the stairs (or using elevators that have been design and built to accommodate occupant evacuation during fires). Then those on uncompromised floors should evacuate in an orderly and prioritized manner managed through training and through proper use of communications systems by the fire department or other authorities.

There is a valuable place for refuge floors, and that is their thoughtful and judicious use (but not an overuse) of them in supertall and megatall buildings as an intermediate gathering place from which occupants can be shuttled to the ground floor to exit the building in a safe, effective, and orderly manner. Elevators designed for occupant evacuation during fires have been referred to as *life boat* elevators and have been effectively incorporated into the designs some of the tallest buildings in the world. However, such use should not be mandated by code, but arrived at by considering these elevators as one of the many tools available as part of an overall fire and life safety strategy developed by the design team in concert with the authorities having jurisdiction and with the local fire department.

Refuge Floors in Asian Projects

Many Asian projects require refuge floors. A short description of refuge floors is contained in the appendix. A refuge floor is a protected floor that serves as a refuge for the occupants of the building to temporarily assemble and rest in case of fire.

In general, refuge floors should be provided in all buildings (except for a domestic building or a composite building not exceeding 40 stories) exceeding 25 stories in height, at not more than 20 stories and 25 stories respectively for industrial and nonindustrial buildings from any other refuge floor, or above the street or the open area.

For domestic buildings or composite buildings exceeding 25 stories (but not exceeding 40 stories in height), the main roof of the building may be regarded as a refuge floor.

Every refuge floor should comply with the following requirements:

1. There is no occupied accommodation or accessible mechanical plant room, except fire service water tanks and associated fire service installation plant rooms, at the same level as the refuge floor.

2. The net area for refuge should be not less than 50% of the total gross floor area of the refuge floor and should have a clear height of not less than 7.5 ft (2300 mm).
3. The minimum dimensions of the area for refuge should be at least 50% greater than the width of the widest staircase passing through the refuge floor.
4. The area for refuge should be separated from the remainder of the building.
5. The area for refuge should be open-sided above safe parapet height on at least two opposite sides to provide adequate cross ventilation; the open sides should comply with the requirements of fire resisting construction.
6. Any staircase passing through a refuge floor should be discontinued at such a level so that the exit route is diverted to pass over part of the refuge area before the stairway continues downwards.
7. Every part of the area for refuge should be provided with artificial lighting providing a horizontal luminance at floor level of not less than 300 foot candles (30 lux) and backed up by an emergency lighting system providing a horizontal luminance at floor level of not less than 20 foot candles (2 lux). The design of the emergency lighting system should comply with the regulations.
8. A refuge floor should be provided with such fire service installation and equipment as may be required.
9. A refuge floor (other than a roof) should be served by a firefighter's elevator. The elevator doors should not open onto the refuge floor in normal operation and should be locked at all times until automatically released on actuation of the firefighter's switch.

THE EMERGENCY/STANDBY GENERATOR SYSTEM AND THE LIFE SAFETY SYSTEM

The interface details between the HVAC and electrical designers in the design of the generator plant for a building are discussed in Chapter 16. This chapter is concerned with the technical means of providing power to the life safety system as required by the model building codes and NFPA. The NFPA requirements are provided in the NFPA 70, *National Electric Code®* (NEC).

The distinction between an emergency and a standby generator is not a function of the equipment used to provide secondary electrical capacity. Rather, it is determined by the loads that are being operated by the generator. Specifically, the NEC recognizes three classifications of load that will need to be or can be connected to a secondary power system:

- Emergency loads, which are addressed in the NEC in Article 700. These are the loads that are considered essential to the life safety of people and are required to permit safe evacuation of the building. Included are load items such as the fire command station (including its lighting), the fire alarm system, communication systems, egress lighting (including the main lobby in the building), exit signs, fire pumps, elevators, elevator cab lighting, and other equipment that if not in receipt of backup power, could result in a hazard to building evacuees.
- Legally required standby loads, which are addressed in the NEC in Article 701. These are loads that are required to assist firefighting and rescue operations. Included are load items such as smoke exhaust or pressurization fans, sump pumps, sewage ejector pumps, and other mechanical equipment that could be used by firefighters or rescuers, as well as loads that if not in receipt of backup power, could result in a hazard to rescuers.
- Optional standby loads, which are addressed in the NEC in Article 702. These are loads that the building operation may choose to provide with backup power for business continuity purposes. As noted in Chapter 17, this could involve telecommunications or data processing equipment and the HVAC systems that allow this equipment to operate by maintaining the critical environment for the spaces within which the equipment is installed.

The NEC requires that the generator plant supplying the emergency and legally required standby loads be automatically started with full power in a specified period of time. The emergency loads must receive backup power 10 seconds after a loss of power. The legally required standby system must be capable of accepting electrical loads within 60 seconds of the failure of the normal electric service. The source of power may be separate for each category but usually a single generator plant will supply both the emergency and legally required standby loads so that the 10 second delivery of power for the emergency loads will govern if the secondary source is the generator plant.

The secondary source need not be a generator plant. For example, the fire alarm system must be installed so any data collected by it will not be lost when a failure of the primary electric source occurs. The data collected by the system can only be protected by the inclusion of a battery system to protect the volatile memory of the fire alarm system during the short period of time for the transition of the system electric power to the generator plant. While it is possible to use a battery backup as the sole secondary source, this is complicated by the time frame for which the batteries must provide the power. As a result, the generator plant will be used and the batteries will only be employed for the secondary source of power until the generator is on line.

It is also possible to use battery pack units as the secondary source of power for egress lighting fixtures and exit signs, but the available power from the generator is usually the source of power for these fixtures in a new building. In recent projects, some owners, in a reaction to possible external threats, have also placed the egress lighting on both emergency power and battery packs as well.

The approved secondary source of power (aside from battery systems) are oil-fired diesel generator sets or oil-fired gas turbines. The use of oil-fired gas turbines is not common. In part this is a result of the 20 to 40 seconds gas turbines require to provide power after being started. This exceeds the time limit for power to the emergency loads, which would require battery packs at all lighting fixtures and exit signs and uninterruptible power supply (UPS) power to the other emergency loads if a gas turbine were to be used. In addition to this limitation, an oil-fired gas turbine generator set is more expensive than a diesel generator set of equal size. Further, gas turbines are only available in a limited number of units whose capacity could be used to meet the secondary power requirements of tall commercial buildings. Where oil-fired gas turbine generators have found application is in existing buildings where the generator is to be installed on an upper floor where the structure has limited ability to handle additional structural loads. In these cases, the lighter weight of the gas turbine as compared to a diesel engine may well lead to the use of the gas turbine as a more cost-effective solution.

Spark-plug-energized diesel engines or gas turbines using natural gas as a fuel rather than oil are not permitted under the model building codes, because the code requirement is to have the fuel source for the generator captive to the building. This requirement is in the building codes so that in the event of a disaster that interrupted both the electric and natural gas service to the building, the performance of the life safety system would not be compromised.

The model codes and the NFPA also state that the capacity of the emergency/standby power system must be capable of supplying power to all of the equipment that must be operational by the life safety system at a given point of time. Where a backup power supply system is required to serve emergency loads, it is permitted to also serve legally required standby loads, as well as optional standby loads, as long as there is a load-shedding capability to assure that life safety loads are given priority.

With the inclusion of permitted load shedding, this does not mean that all connected equipment be simultaneously operational. For example, not all elevators in a building would be required to operate at the same time. The elevator needs would be met by conforming to the building code, which, in the event of a power outage, would usually permit the operation of any one elevator at a time in each bank, with the other elevators in the bank being operated sequentially after the first elevator is brought to its agreed terminal floor. The elevator design would then permit a second and then the additional elevators to be operated in the bank until all elevators and their passengers are at the terminal level in the building. However, the emergency/standby generator would only be sized to handle the largest electric motor in a given bank of elevators.

What is therefore required to determine the capacity of the emergency/standby power system is to determine what equipment will need to operate at any given point of time and select the generator to provide that required capacity. As noted in Chapter 14, this necessitates that the electrical design engineer obtain from the HVAC, fire protection, and elevator designers their secondary electrical needs and review these requirements along with the needs of the equipment on the electrical drawings. This will allow the electrical designer to determine the size of the generator plant that must be provided for the project.

It is possible on very large projects (with high optional standby loads beyond the life safety system) to install a separate generator to meet the needs of the life safety system and a separate plant of one or more generators for the special optional loads. This could maintain a higher degree of protection and isolation for the life safety generator while avoiding the complication of the interface with the conventional building loads.

ELEVATOR RECALL SYSTEMS

Any detailed analysis of life safety for the occupants of a high-rise building indicates that the proper control of the elevator system in the event of a prospective fire catastrophe is to return the cabs to the lowest floor that they serve (in the case of mid-rise or high-rise elevator banks) or to the lobby level (in the case of low-rise banks). There are several reasons for this strategy. First, it removes the elevators from the building egress system, forcing the prospective users to go to the area of refuge designated for them. This will help control and direct the flow of people through the building. Second, it has been determined that some fire-related deaths in high-rise buildings have been the result of people trapped in the elevators and ultimately asphyxiating by smoke inhalation. Third, and most important, this system places the entire elevator system under the control of the fire department, who can use the elevators for controlled evacuation and ultimately for the overriding benefit of the largest number of people in the building.

The means for causing the elevators to return to their terminal floor would be the activation of specific alarm device(s) included in the total system (e.g., smoke detector located in the elevator lobby or sprinkler flow alarm).

If a fire and power failure occur simultaneously, the emergency generator must be capable of operating at least one elevator serving every floor in the building at all times with a means to transfer the emergency power to all of the elevators in any bank. This will allow the elevators that are operating at the time of the power failure to be brought down to a terminal floor and effect a controlled evacuation of the elevator passengers.

The use of the elevators in the above-specified fashion requires the active cooperation of the elevator manufacturer and the fire control people but gives great benefit to the building's occupants. It recognizes that the elevator use in the building must be controlled by the people who know what is happening in the event of a building fire situation. It allows the elevators to be used, not only for building evacuation, but also for the quickest possible movement of the firefighting personnel to the area within the building where they can do the most good in controlling the fire.

COMMUNICATION SYSTEMS

The life safety system for the high-rise office building is required by code to have a voice alarm/public address communication system to allow the occupants of the building to be informed of any emergency that may develop as well as the action they must take to exit to an area of refuge. The voice alarm/public address system will operate from the central fire command center. The voice alarm system will generate an audible trouble signal when activated by the operation of any smoke detector or sprinkler water flow device. The system will also be configured to allow the fire department to communicate from the fire command center with both the occupants and the firefighters in various locations in the building. The system will provide the ability to selectively make announcements on office floors but also in elevators, elevator lobbies, and exit stairways.

In addition to the voice alarm/public address communication system, a two-way fire department communication system must be provided in tall buildings for the exclusive use of the fire department. It will allow firefighters to establish two-way communication throughout the building, which will allow firefighters in the building to provide the status of the emergency to the central fire control center personnel. These two-way communication devices are installed in every elevator, elevator lobby, and fire stair.

CENTRAL FIRE COMMAND

A central fire command center is required in every tall building. It will be provided in a location that will be approved by the fire department. A ground-floor location in close proximity to the elevator control panel is usually required. The purpose of the central fire command center is to provide a location where the firefighting personnel can operate during a fire or other emergency. The central fire command center will provide visual confirmation and status of all of the building alarm systems and status and operational control of all of the smoke control systems. The fire command center will also provide the ability to selectively communicate within the building to any area and to fire department locations external to the building. Accordingly, the central fire command center will contain the following:

• Voice fire alarm system panels and controls
• Fire department communication systems controls
• Fire detection and alarm system annunciation panels
• Elevator status and cab locations
• Sprinkler valve and water flow status indication
• Controls for unlocking all doors in fire stairs
• Emergency generator status indication
• Fire pump status indication
• Status and operational control of all building fans, dampers, and systems
• Status and operational control of all floor dampers
• A telephone for fire department use for external communications

The obvious purpose of the central fire command center is to allow a single point within the building to be the rendezvous and control point for the fire department and building personnel. It is the brain and the heart of the ultimate fire response achieved by the building. Its organization, both internally and in terms of the functions that are possible, should be carefully reviewed and analyzed by the designer of the overall system with the local fire department.

FIRE SAFETY RESPONSE PLAN

Having established the fire management approach that is used in the high-rise building, the difficulty of evacuating a building under a fire emergency must be recognized and addressed. During the normal workday, when people desire to leave the building, they will use the vertical transportation system, which will consist of elevators and possibly escalators to get them to the street level. During a fire, as was discussed, the elevators will usually not be available, because they will have been returned automatically to their terminal floor and will be under control of the fire department. Further, even if available, the elevator system is not capable of handling the mass of people who attempt an exodus under these circumstances. Elevators are not installed in any building with the capacity to permit rapid evacuation of substantial portions of the population of the building under emergency conditions.

If the occupants of the building cannot be evacuated vertically, they must be trained to move to areas of refuge that have been established within the building. Typically, these would be stairwells or other designated fire-safe areas that will be three or more floors beneath the fire floor. From these areas, people can be removed from the building on a controlled basis by the fire department. Accordingly, every high-rise office building will be required by NFPA 101-2000, *Life Safety Code*, and by the building code to have in place a fire safety organization and fire response plan. The plan would involve detailing for the building fire marshals all emergency procedures that will be followed in the event of a fire, posting of all areas of refuge that should be used by occupants in an emergency, and requiring regularly called fire drills to ensure proper understanding of what is to be done in the unfortunate event of an actual fire condition in the building. Only through proper and regular rehearsal of procedures by the building fire marshals with all building occupants under nonfire conditions will the occupants be fully capable of proper response to an actual fire. The people who live in the building must know that their safety is contingent upon their following the fire safety plan, which will involve going to their designated area of refuge when a fire alarm is sounded. This reaction can only be achieved through the dissemination of the fire response plan and periodic drills that follow the plan.

An additional point not to be overlooked is the inherent conflict between the use of stairwells as areas of refuge and the security system in the building. Quite frequently, as part of a building security system, the stairwell doors, to the limit allowed by code, will be locked from the inside to prevent exit from the stairs on any floor other than the main lobby floor. For example, in New York City, under a nonfire condition, an unlocked reentry door must be provided on every fourth floor, and it is not possible to enter an office floor from a stair on any of the three floors between the reentry floors. These are not proper restrictions under fire conditions for either the occupants or firefighters who must be afforded reentry paths from stairwells to any floor in the building. Accordingly, means must be provided to automatically open the secured doors, where installed, if any of the building fire detection devices are actuated.

CHAPTER 16
High-Rise Residential

In most modern tall, supertall and megatall buildings, a substantial portion, if not all, of the building is residential. Many clients and owners request natural ventilation opportunities for these residential spaces. Most buildings will operate in "mixed mode," that is, the residences either can be conditioned by a mechanical conditioning system or by natural ventilation. This chapter outlines the ventilation and comfort compliance required for residences conditioned by natural ventilation and is based on the forthcoming *ASHRAE Natural Ventilation Design Guide* by McConahey and Simmonds.

INDOOR DESIGN CONDITIONS

Many state and national building standards use the following or similar language to identify minimum occupied conditions: "Indoor design temperature and humidity condition for general comfort applications shall be determined in accordance with ANSI/ASHRAE Standard 55 (ASHRAE 2017b) or *ASHRAE Handbook—Fundamentals*, Chapter 8 (ASHRAE 2017a), except that winter humidification and summer dehumidification shall not be required."

Occupancy Periods

We assume the residences will be occupied for 24 hours per day. There are three main groups of residents:

- Working residents, who are normally at work during the working week and only home in the evenings through early morning and weekends.
- Family residents, who are intermittently home during the day and weekends.
- Full-time residents, who do not work or work from home and are mostly in their residence 24 hours a day.

There may also be long periods when the individual residences are unoccupied where the control system can shut the residence down.

Lighting

The average load for lighting is estimated at 0.5W/ft^2 (5 W/m^2).

Occupants

For most spaces, it is assumed that one person occupies 50 ft^2 (5 W/m^2) of floor space. The type of work the occupants do in a standard space produces 250 Btu/person (70 W) sensible and 200 Btu/person (60 W) latent heat. The occupants will have a clothing value of 1.0 clo, and an activity level of 1 met (equal to 18.4 Btu/h·ft^2 [58.2 W/m^2]) to be used for thermal comfort calculations per ASHRAE Standard 55.

VENTILATION

ANSI/ASHRAE Standard 62.1 (ASHRAE 2019b, Table 6-1) provides the ventilation requirements and falls under the mandatory requirements section in most international, national, and state code requirements (Pérez-Lombard et al. 2011). Within a building, all enclosed spaces that are normally used by humans must be continuously ventilated during occupied hours with outdoor air, using either natural or mechanical ventilation.

Natural Ventilation

Natural outdoor ventilation may be provided for spaces where all normally occupied areas of the space are within a specific distance from an operable wall or roof opening through which outdoor air can flow. The sum of the operable open areas must total at least 5% of the floor area of each naturally ventilated space. The openings must also always be readily accessible to the occupants.

Airflow through the openings must come directly from the outdoors; air may not flow through any intermediate spaces such as other occupied spaces, unconditioned spaces, corridors, or atria. Also, high windows, operable skylights, and other operable openings need to have a control mechanism accessible from the floor (CEC 2015a, 2015b, 2017).

Air Leakage

Manufactured fenestration products and exterior doors shall have air infiltration rates not exceeding 0.3 cfm/ft^2 (0.5 m3/h·m^2) of window area, 0.3 cfm/ft^2 (0.5 m^3/h·m^2) of door area for residential doors, 0.3 cfm/ft^2 (0.5 m^3/h·m^2) of door area for nonresidential single doors (swinging and sliding), and 1.0 cfm/ft^2 (1.69 m^3/h·m^2) for nonresidential double doors (swinging), when tested according to NFRC-400 or ASTM E283 at a pressure differential of 75 Pa (or 1.57 lb/ft^2), incorporated herein by reference (CEC 2015a).

Stack Effect

Stack-effect-driven airflows in tall buildings compromise smoke control and fire safety, adversely affect IAQ and comfort, as well as increase operating costs for space conditioning energy (see Chapter 5).

COOLING AND HEATING SYSTEM ALTERNATIVES[1]

There are many different types of HVAC systems that can be chosen for a residential development, and many different reasons for choosing them. Some drivers involve the design of the building itself – height, visibility of equipment, and proximity to surrounding buildings – while others entail the developer's preference – initial installation cost, aesthetics, and long-term maintenance and life cycle costs. These, and many other variables, factor into the decision-making process. In this section, we will strive to de•ne the different HVAC systems and explain the pros and cons of each.

Systems breakdown into two major categories- centrally-fed and decentralized.

Centrally fed systems utilize a central heating and cooling plant to distribute to the entire building. They are mostly used in high-rise residential buildings. These systems are more expensive to install and are usually more sophisticated to operate and maintain. A major drawback of centralized generation systems is that usage cannot readily be individually metered;

---

1. The following section provides partial text from the article "Multifamily Residential HVAC Systems: How do you Decide?" by O'Connor and Ellowitz (n.d.).To integrate smoothly into the book, the content has been updated to conform to this book's style; otherwise, the content is as originally published.

therefore, the centralized generation energy costs must be included in any rental fee calculation.

Decentralized systems provide separate heating and cooling equipment for each unit and are less expensive to install initially. The maintenance of these systems is relatively simple, but because there is a system for every unit, service calls can be frequent occurrences. These systems also tend to have a shorter life span than centralized systems. A great benefit of all decentralized systems is that they can be easily individually metered at the unit, whether gas-fired or run by electricity.

Decentralized HVAC systems are a common choice for low-rise residential buildings, especially when • rst cost is a factor. The systems typically consist of an air handler in the units and a remote condensing unit with compressor offering location • exibility as it can be installed in the unit and vented "through wall," or located on a balcony, on grade, or on a • at roof if the building design allows it. Because the air handler and condenser are typically separate units, these are often referred to as split systems, or "splits." Based on the high-end nature of this building, a decentralized system has not been considered.

The centrally fed fan-coil system is the preferred/proposed system.

Centralized Systems

There are three centralized system choices that are appropriate for the weather conditions commonly found in Los Angeles; four-pipe vertical stacked fan-coil units, two-pipe vertical stacked fan-coil units, and vertical stacked water source heat pumps.

A four-pipe vertical stacked fan-coil system carries the highest initial cost, but generally provides the highest degree of comfort control for the resident. It requires a mechanical room. The major components include a boiler, chiller, cooling tower, and pumps. Hot and chilled water are distributed from the mechanical room to fan-coils located inside the living units via two pairs of dedicated supply and return pipes – one for heating, one for cooling.

One of greatest advantages of this system is that it allows the unit occupant to switch from heating to cooling at will. Because the system runs on four pipes – two self-contained systems – hot water and cold water can be available in each unit simultaneously during transitional seasons. With a four-pipe system, the occupant in Unit A can run the air conditioner while the occupant in Unit B runs the heat, without affecting each other's' comfort level.

The two-pipe vertical fan-coil system is similar to the four-pipe system described above, except there are only two pipes to deliver EITHER heat hot- OR chilled- water. Because hot and chilled water share the same piping and pumps, cooling and heating cannot be provided simultaneously. The building owner must change the system over every spring and fall to the appropriate heating or cooling mode. Manual or electric valves are used to isolate the cooling and heating systems. Two-pipe fan-coil systems also require mechanical rooms, but on a slightly smaller scale than four pipe systems.

The advantage of this system is that the initial piping costs are significantly less than the four-pipe system. So, while the two-pipe system does not offer the same • exibility and level of comfort control, the upfront cost differential is often substantial enough to persuade the developer to choose the two-pipe system.

The water source heat pump system is one of the most popular centralized systems for mid to high-rise residential HVAC because it offers some • exibility for simultaneous heating and cooling but is a lower initial cost alternative to the four-pipe system. In this two-pipe system, condenser water, held at a temperature between 60°F and 90°F, is continuously looped through the building via risers to stacked heat pumps in the units. The configuration is similar to the two-pipe fan-coil system but, instead of a chiller, the system utilizes individual compressors at each unit for cooling. A remote cooling tower is used for system heat rejection from the condenser water loop. The boiler component is the same, and there are still valves required for spring and fall seasonal changeovers. Operationally, compressors located in the individual unit heat pumps either withdraw heat from (heating mode) or reject heat to (cooling mode) the condenser water loop. Therefore, as long as most of the building occupants are not calling for the same thing, simultaneous cooling and heating can happen. Another bene• t of this system is

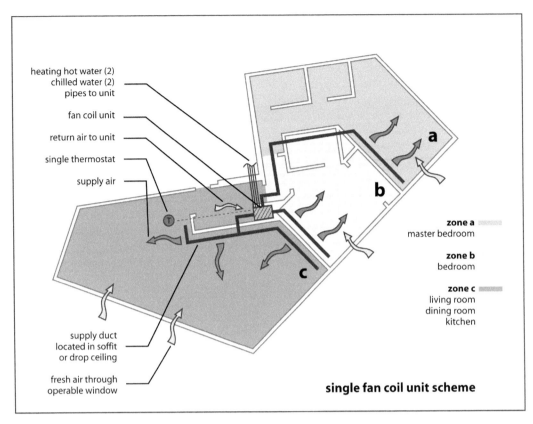

Figure 16.1 Residential single fan-coil unit conditioning system.

that individual compressors allow more of the utility costs to be the responsibility of the residents than with other centralized systems.

For controllability, energy efficiency/heat recovery, acoustical, and maintenance/service requirements, the design approach for this project is a 4-pipe fan-coil unit system serving the residential tower.

The following schemes represent the fan-coil unit options available.

Figure 16.1 shows a single fan-coil unit as a conditioning system for a residence. Figure 16.2 shows a multiple fan-coil system as a conditioning system for a residence.

For both fan-coil systems, each residence may have a single four-pipe fan-coil unit to provide heating and cooling. The supply air is ducted to the different rooms, the air volumes of which are determined by manually operated dampers. Temperature control comes from a single thermostat. Outdoor air is generally ducted to each residence. Heating and cooling water is piped to each residence. The chillers and boilers can be installed on mechanical levels. The chilled-water temperature is often controlled to 55°F to 60°F (13°C to 15.5°C) to avoid having to install condensate drains from each fan-coil.

If the spaces are to be naturally ventilated, then it is recommended to install contact switches in the operable windows which stop the fan-coil from operating when open to conserve energy.

Single Fan-Coil Unit with VVT Scheme

Figure 16.3 shows a single fan-coil with variable volume terminal (VVT) system as a conditioning system for a residence

Each residence may have a single four-pipe fan-coil unit to provide heating and cooling. The supply air is ducted to the different rooms, the air volumes of which are determined by variable volume terminals. Temperature control comes from a single thermostat. Outdoor air is generally ducted to each residence. Heating and cooling water is piped to each residence. The chillers and boilers can be installed on mechanical levels. The chilled-water temperature is

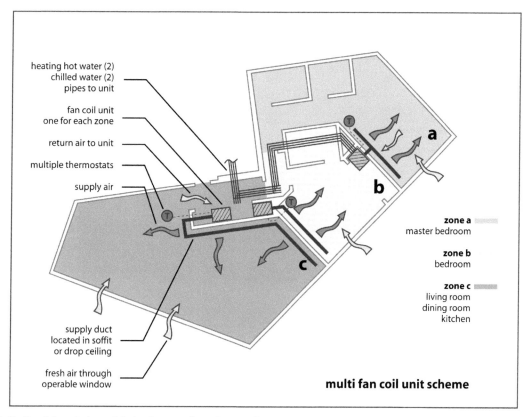

heating hot water (2)
chilled water (2)
pipes to unit

fan coil unit
one for each zone

return air to unit

multiple thermostats

supply air

a

b

zone a
master bedroom

zone b
bedroom

zone c
living room
dining room
kitchen

c

supply duct
located in soffit
or drop ceiling

fresh air through
operable window

multi fan coil unit scheme

Figure 16.2 Residential multiple fan-coil unit conditioning system.

often controlled to 55°F to 60°F (13°C to 15°C) to avoid having to install condensate drains from each fan-coil.

Toilet Exhaust

Each toilet will include an exhaust fan that exhausts vertically through a subduct system to an auxiliary fan with variable-frequency drive at the roof. The exhaust fan is operated via the toilet light switch.

Kitchen Hood Exhaust

Each kitchen hood will include an exhaust fan which will exhaust vertically through a subduct system to an auxiliary fan with variable-frequency drive at the roof. The exhaust fan is operated automatically when the kitchen hood is operated.

CONTROLS

High-rise residential dwellings thermostats must be in accordance with Section 120.2(c) 2016 Nonresidential Compliance Manual as follows (CEC 2015b):
"The energy standards require that thermostats in hotel and motel guest rooms have:

- Numeric temperature set points in °F and °C, and
- Set point stops that prevent the thermostat from being adjusted outside the normal comfort range (±5°F [±3°C]). These stops must be concealed so that they are accessible only to authorized personnel, and
- Setback capabilities with a minimum of four separate set points per 24-hour period; in additions, for nonresidential buildings,

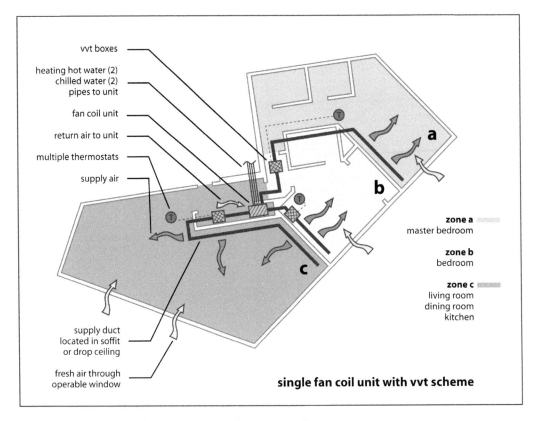

Figure 16.3 Residential single fan-coil unit with VVT conditioning system.

Most energy standards require that thermostats in high-rise residential dwelling units have setback capabilities with a minimum of four separate set points per 24-hour period."

Fan-Coil Unit Controls

Shutoff and Temperature Setup/Setback

For specific occupancies and conditions, each space-conditioning system must be provided with controls that comply with the following requirements (CEC 2015a, 2015b):

The control can automatically shut off the equipment during unoccupied hours and shall have one of the following:

- An automatic time switch device must have the same characteristics as lighting devices, as described in Chapter 16, and a manual override accessible to the occupants that allows the system to operate up to four hours. The manual override can be included as a part of the control device or as a separate override control.
- An occupancy sensor. Since a building ventilation purge is required prior to normal occupancy, an occupancy sensor may be used to control the availability of heating and cooling but should not be used to control the outdoor ventilation system.
- A four-hour timer that can be manually operated to start the system. As with occupancy sensors, the same restrictions apply to controlling outdoor air ventilation systems.

VENTILATION STANDARDS' CODE ENGINEERED PATH COMPLIANCE

ASHRAE 62.1 minimum ventilation requirements are determined, and the calculated airflow is compared to the minimum values. If the calculated airflow is lower than the minimum compliance airflow, then the openings need to be adjusted until minimum compliance values are achieved.

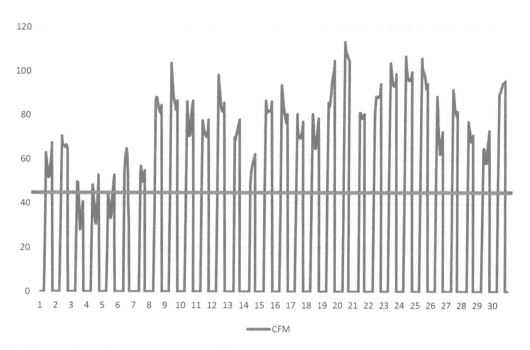

Figure 16.4 Natural-ventilation-created airflow versus ASHRAE 62.1 code-required minimum ventilation rate in September as a result of buoyancy-driven ventilation. Location: New York.

ASHRAE Standard 62.1: 4 persons at 5 cfm per person + 0.06 cfm/ft^2 × 400 ft^2 = 62 cfm
(4 persons at 2.5 L/s per person + 0.3L/s·m^2 × 40 m^2 = 22 L/s)
There are two types of natural ventilation: buoyancy driven and wind driven.

New York—Buoyancy Driven

Figure 16.4 shows ventilation requirements for a sample building located in New York City. 44 cfm (22 L/s) is required to comply with ASHRAE 62.1 ventilation requirements. In this location, there are only a few days when 44 cfm (22 L/s) cannot be provided by buoyancy-driven natural ventilation.

New York—Wind Driven

See Chapter 4, Climate Data, for more information on wind-driven ventilation.
Figures 16.4 and 16.5 show ventilation requirements for a sample building located in New York City. 44 cfm (22 L/s) is required to comply with ASHRAE 62.1 ventilation requirements, there are only a few days when 44 cfm (22 L/s) cannot be provided by wind-driven natural ventilation.

NATURAL CONDITIONING COMFORT STANDARDS COMPLIANCE ANALYSIS[2]

Interpreting Results for Decision to Proceed

Based upon the minimum ventilation air requirements, the user can see whether the minimum ventilation air is provided through natural ventilation to the space. A primary assessment of natural ventilation air to a space can be provided by a prescriptive model or for further accuracy a bulk air movement tool.

---

2. This section provides text originally published by Guyer (2012). To integrate smoothly into the book, the content has been updated to conform to this book's style; otherwise, the content is as originally published.

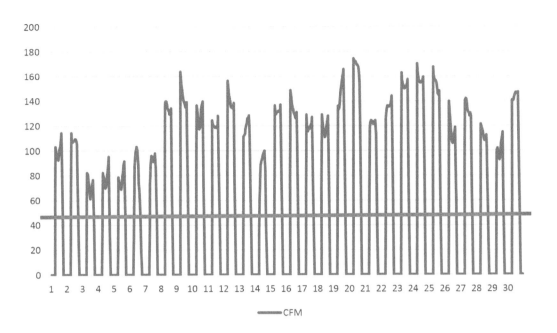

Figure 16.5 Natural-ventilation-created airflow versus ASHRAE 62.1 minimum code-required ventilation rate in September as a result of wind-driven ventilation. Location: New York.

The acceptable comfort zone shall be that prescribed by the ASHRAE Standard 55, *Thermal Environmental Conditions for Human Occupancy*. Eighty percent or more of the building occupants will find this zone thermally acceptable in still air and shade conditions. Figure 10 Acceptable Operative Temperature (to) Ranges for Naturally Conditioned Spaces shows the acceptable range of temperature and humidity conditions for persons in typical summer (0.35 to 0.6 clo) and winter (0.8 to 1.2 clo) clothing at near sedentary (less than 1.2 met) activity levels.

The Effect of Air Movement

Air movement influences the bodily heat balance by affecting the rate of convective heat transfer between the skin and air and the rate of bodily cooling through evaporation of skin moisture. The air velocity lines on show the extent to which increased air movement can increase the range of temperatures and humidity's in which people will feel comfortable.

Required Air Velocities for Human Comfort

Minimum rates of ventilation are based on requirements for health (oxygen supply and removal of contaminants). Ventilation, natural or mechanical, is always required. The maximum rates of interior air velocity are defined by factors other than human physiological comfort alone. The upper limit of indoor velocity depends on building type and use. For offices and commercial spaces, the limit is 160 fpm (0.8 m/sec), the point at which loose paper, hair and other light objects may be blown about. Maximum indoor air velocities for residential buildings are between these extremes. A practical upper limit is 197 fpm (1.0 m/sec).

APPLICABILITY[3]

The adaptive method defines acceptable thermal environments for a space where the following conditions are met:

---

3. This section provides text originally published in ANSI/ASHRAE Standard 55 (ASHRAE 2017b). To integrate smoothly into the book, the content has been updated to conform to this book's style; otherwise, the content is as originally published.

- Spaces are occupant-controlled and naturally conditioned.
- There is no mechanical cooling system (e.g., refrigerated air conditioning, radiant cooling, or desiccant cooling) installed. No heating system is in operation.
- Representative occupants have metabolic rates ranging from 1.0 to 1.3 met.
- Representative occupants are free to adapt their clothing to the indoor and/or outdoor thermal conditions within a range at least as wide as 0.5 to 1.0 clo.
- The prevailing mean outdoor temperature is greater than 50°F (10°C) and less than 92.3°F (33.5°C).

Occupant-controlled naturally conditioned spaces are those where the thermal conditions of the space is regulated primarily by the occupants through opening and closing of openings in the envelope. Field experiments have shown that occupants' thermal responses in such spaces depend in part on the outdoor climate and may differ from thermal responses in buildings with centralized HVAC systems primarily because of the different thermal experiences, changes in clothing, availability of control, and shifts in occupant expectations. This optional method is intended for such spaces.

For this optional method to apply, the space in question must be equipped with operable openings to the outdoors that can be readily opened and adjusted by the occupants of the space.

It is permissible to use mechanical ventilation with unconditioned air but opening and closing of windows must be the primary means of regulating the thermal conditions in the space. It is permissible for the space to be provided with a heating system, but this optional method does not apply when the heating system is in operation. It applies only to spaces where the occupants are engaged in near-sedentary physical activities, with metabolic rates ranging from 1.0 to 1.3 met. This optional method applies only to spaces where the occupants are free to adapt their clothing to the indoor and/or outdoor thermal conditions. The permitted range of acceptable clothing must be at least as broad as 0.5 to 1.0 clo.

DEFINITIONS OF COMFORT TEMPERATURE COMPLIANCE

General Requirements

Section 5 of ASHRAE Standard 55 outlines the core requirements of the Standard used to determine acceptable thermal environment for each representative occupant of a space. Section 5.2 provides necessary information to determine the characteristics (*met* and *clo*) of the representative occupants. Sections 5.3 and 5.4 describe the method used to determine thermal comfort for the representative occupants in the space.

Factors Affecting Determination of Thermal Comfort

Standard 55 uses six factors in determining acceptable thermal environment for the representative occupants in space in a steady state:

- Metabolic rate
- Clothing insulation
- Air temperature
- Radiant temperature
- Air speed
- Humidity

The first two factors are personal to the occupant and the remaining four factors are conditions of the thermal environment.

Personal Factors

Occupant activities and the associated metabolic rate are the personal factors addressed in Standard 55. The level of activity of the occupant is associated with their metabolic rate, which in turn affects the thermal conditions at which they are likely to be comfortable. Standard 55

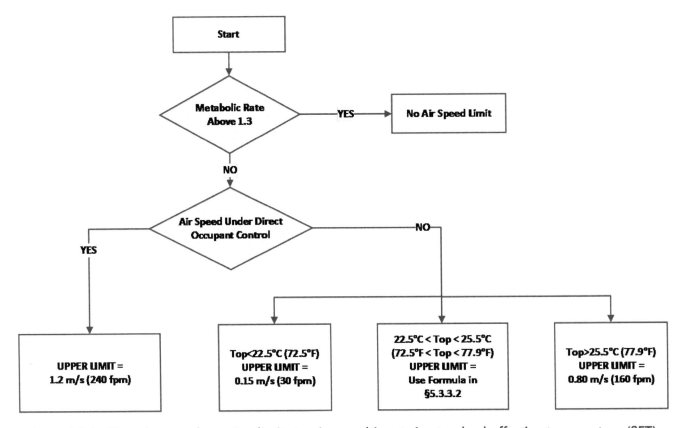

Figure 16.6 Flow chart to determine limits to air speed inputs in standard effective temperature (SET) model.
(ASHRAE 2017b).

does not regulate or in any way try to control occupant activities. Rather, the expected or observed activity is used as an input to thermal comfort determination.

Similar to occupant activities, Standard 55 also uses expected or observed occupant clothing insulation as an input to the determination of thermal comfort.

Environmental Factors

While many HVAC systems use closed-loop control for dry-bulb temperature alone, this is only one of four categories of environmental factors listed in the scope of the standard. The other three are thermal radiation, humidity, and air speed. In addition, there are four local factors that must also be considered.

Elevated Air Speed Comfort Zone Method (ASHRAE 2017b)

When using the elevated air speed approach outlined in Appendix D of Standard 55, the user is allowed higher operative temperatures and average air speeds, the exact amounts of which are dependent on whether the occupant has direct control over the increased air speed and their activity level (met rate) as shown in Figure 16.6.

Limits to Average Air Speed (V_a) with Occupant Control

When control of local air speed is provided to occupants, the air speed can be a maximum of 237 fpm (1.2 m/s). The same value applies as the maximum allowed in the analytical method embedded in the ASHRAE Thermal Comfort Tool (ASHRAE 2011).

Regardless of whether the user selects an analytical approach or uses the flow chart shown in Figure 16.6, Standard 55 requires that control should be directly accessible to occupants and be provided either for every six occupants or less or for every 900 ft² (84 m²) or less. Further,

Standard 55 requires that the range of control should encompass air speeds suitable for sedentary occupants. The air speed should be adjustable continuously or in maximum steps of 50 fpm (0.25 m/s) as measured at the occupant's location.

An exception to the control requirements is in multioccupant spaces where groups gather for shared activities, such as classrooms and conference rooms. In such instances, at least one control should be provided for each space, regardless of size. Multioccupant spaces that can be subdivided by movable walls should have one control for each space subdivision. The air speed control must extend to still air 40 fpm (0.2 m/s) as measured at the occupant's location and be adjustable continuously or in maximum steps of 50 fpm (0.25 m/s) as measured at the occupant's location. If the representative occupant is engaged in activities in excess of 1.3 met, there is no upper limit for average air speed.

Limits to Average Air Speed (V_a) without Occupant Control

If occupants do not have control over the local air speed meeting the requirements of Section 5.3.3.1 of ANSI/ASHRAE Standard 44, the following limits apply to the SET model and Figure 16.7.

For operative temperatures (t_o) above 77.9°F (25.5°C), the upper limit to average air speed (V_a) should be 160 fpm (0.8 m/s).

For operative temperatures (t_o) below 72.5°F (22.5°C), the limit to average air speed (V_a) should be 30 fpm[4] (0.15 m/s).

For operative temperatures (t_o) between 72.5°F and 77.9°F (22.5°C and 25.5°C), the upper limit to average air speed (V_a) should follow the approximate curve in I-P and SI units by the following equation:

$$V_a = 31375.7 - 857.295\, t_o + 5.86288(t_o)^2 \text{ (fpm, °F)} \tag{16.1a}$$

$$V_a = 50.49 - 4.4047\, t_o + 0.096425(t_o)^2 \text{ (m/s, °C)} \tag{16.1b}$$

Exception:

If the representative occupant is engaged in activities in excess of 1.3 met, there is no upper limit for average air speed (ASHRAE 2017b).

ACCEPTABLE THERMAL CONDITIONS IN OCCUPANT-CONTROLLED NATURALLY CONDITIONED SPACES

Standard 55 Appendix A establishes the indoor operative temperature via other means, which is then compared to a mathematical representation of the adaptive comfort model.

The Standard provides a method to specifically deal with those spaces where occupants are in direct control of their thermal environment. This method is also colloquially known as the *Adaptive Comfort Method*, and for the sake of brevity, this design guide will use the same term to describe this method.

Methodology

The Adaptive Method is based on statistical analysis of a large dataset of occupant comfort evaluations (21,000 sets of data compiled from thermal comfort field studies conducted in 160 buildings located on four continents in varied climate zones). Detailed physical measurements, along with responses to questions about thermal sensation, acceptability, and preference were analyzed to determine the relationship between optimum indoor temperature and outdoor temperature.

Based on this analysis, Standard 55 establishes criteria for 80% and 90% acceptability limits as shown in Figure 16.7

It is important to note that only the 80% acceptability limit is used when a user is to show compliance with the Adaptive Method. The 90% acceptability limits are for illustra-

---

4. The Standard 55 User's Manual states 30 fpm (0.15 m/s). Standard 55 states 40 fpm (0.2 m/s).

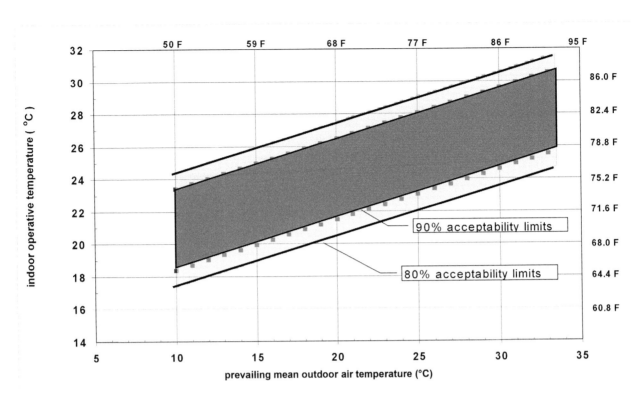

Figure 16.7 Acceptable operative temperature (t_o) ranges for naturally conditioned spaces.

tive purposes only but can be used on a voluntary basis if a designer or building owner chooses to provide higher level of acceptability. For any jurisdictions requiring compliance with Standard 55 though, compliance is only required at the 80% acceptability limits.

The allowable operative temperature (t_o) limits in may not be extrapolated to outdoor temperatures above and below the end points of the curves in Figure 16.7. If the prevailing mean outdoor temperature is less than 50°F (10°C) or greater than 92.3°F (33.5°C), this option may not be used, and no specific guidance for such conditions is included in this standard.

Figure 16.7 accounts for local thermal discomfort effects in typical buildings, so it is not necessary to address these factors when using this option. If there is reason to believe that local thermal comfort is a problem, it is acceptable to apply the criteria in Section 5.3.4 of Standard 55.

Figure 16.7 accounts for people's clothing adaptation in naturally conditioned spaces by relating the acceptable range of indoor temperatures to the outdoor climate, so it is not necessary to estimate the clothing values for the space. No humidity or air speed limits are required when this option is used.

Figure 16.7 includes the effects of people's indoor air speed adaptation in warm climates, up to 59 fpm (0.3 m/s) in operative temperatures (t_o) warmer than 77°F (25°C). In naturally conditioned spaces where air speeds within the occupied zone exceed 59 fpm (0.3 m/s), the upper acceptability temperature limits are increased by the corresponding Δt_o in Table 5.4.2.4 of the Standard (Table 16.2 in this document), which is based on equal SET values as illustrated in Section 5.3.3 of the Standard. For example, increasing air speed within the occupied zone from 59 to 118 fpm (0.3 to 0.6 m/s) increases the upper acceptable temperature limits in by a Δt_o of 2.2°F (1.2°C). These adjustments to the upper acceptability temperature limits apply only at $t_o > 77°F$ (25°C) in which the occupants are engaged in near sedentary physical activity (with metabolic rates between 1.0 met and 1.3 met).

Table 16.1 Increases in Acceptable Operative Temperature Limits (Δt_o) in Occupant-Controlled, Naturally Conditioned Spaces (Figure 16.10) Resulting from Increasing Air Speed above 0.3 m/s (59 fpm)

Average Air Speed (V_a), 118 fpm (0.6 m/s)	Average Air Speed (V_a), 177 fpm (0.9 m/s)	Average Air Speed (V_a), 236 fpm (1.2 m/s)
1.2°C (2.2°F)	1.8°C (3.2°F)	2.2°C (4.0°F)

Prevailing Mean Outdoor Air Temperature[5]

Note also that the adaptive method introduces a new definition—*Prevailing Mean Outdoor Air Temperature*. Prevailing Mean Outdoor Air Temperature ($t_{pma(out)}$) is based on the arithmetic average of the mean daily outdoor temperatures over some period of days. It represents the broader external climatic environment to which building occupants have become physiologically, behaviorally, and psychologically adapted. At its simplest, $t_{pma(out)}$ can be approximated by the climatically normal monthly mean air temperature from the most representative local meteorological station available. When being used in conjunction with dynamic thermal simulation software in which outdoor weather data is formatted as a TMY, the preferred expression for $t_{pma(out)}$ is an exponentially weighted, running mean of a sequence of mean daily outdoor temperatures prior to the day in question. Days in the more remote past have less influence on the building occupants' comfort temperature than more recent days, and this can be reflected by attaching exponentially decaying weights to the sequence of mean daily outdoor temperatures. This can be written as follows:

$$t_{pma(out)} = (1-\alpha)\,[t_{e(d-1)} + \alpha\,t_{e(d-2)} + \alpha^2\,t_{e(d-3)} + \alpha^3\,t_{e(d-4)} + ...] \qquad (16.2)$$

where α is a constant between 0 and 1 that controls the speed at which the running mean responds to changes in weather (outdoor temperature). Recommended values for α are between 0.9 and 0.6, corresponding to a slow- and fast-response running mean respectively. Adaptive comfort theory suggests that a slow-response running mean ($\alpha = 0.9$) could be more appropriate for climates in which synoptic-scale (day-today) temperature dynamics are relatively minor, such as the humid tropics. But for mid-latitude climates where people are more familiar with synoptic-scale weather variability, a lower value of $\alpha = 0.7$ could be more appropriate. In Equation 16.2, $t_{e(d-1)}$ represents the mean daily outdoor temperature for the previous day, $t_{e(d-2)}$ is the mean daily outdoor temperature for the day before that, and so on. The equation contains a sum to infinity, but is reducible to this more convenient form:

$$t_{pma(out)} = (1-\alpha)\,t_{e(n-1)} + \alpha\,t_{rm(n-1)} \qquad (16.3)$$

where $t_{e(n-1)}$ is the mean daily outdoor temperature for the day before the day in question, and $t_{rm(n-1)}$ is the running mean temperature for the day before the day in question ($n-1$). For example, if $\alpha = 0.7$, the prevailing mean outdoor temperature for today would be 30% of yesterday's mean daily outdoor temperature plus 70% of yesterday's running mean outdoor temperature. This form of the equation advances the value of the running mean from one day to the next and is convenient both for computer algorithms and for manual calculations. A value for running mean temperature has to be assumed for day one in order to "seed" the sequence, but from then onwards it can be calculated with Equation 16.3. The running mean may be initiated seven days prior to the start of the period of interest, and the actual daily mean outdoor temperature can be used for that first day to "seed" the sequence.

---

5. This section provides text originally published in ANSI/ASHRAE Standard 55 (ASHRAE 2017b). To integrate smoothly into the book, the content has been updated to conform to this book's style; otherwise, the content is as originally published.

COMPLIANCE ANALYSIS METHODOLOGY
ENGINEERED SYSTEM COMPLIANCE PATH[6]

Determining Acceptable Thermal Conditions in Occupant-Controlled Naturally Conditioned Spaces

This method defines acceptable thermal environments only for occupant-controlled naturally conditioned spaces that meet all the following criteria:

- There is no mechanical cooling system (e.g., refrigerated air conditioning, radiant cooling, or desiccant cooling) installed. No heating system is in operation.
- Representative occupants have metabolic rates ranging from 1.0 to 1.3 met.
- Representative occupants are free to adapt their clothing to the indoor and/or outdoor thermal conditions within a range at least as wide as 0.5 to 1.0 clo.
- The prevailing mean outdoor temperature is greater than 50°F and less than 92.3°F (10°C and 33.5°C).

Methodology. The allowable indoor operative temperatures to shall be determined from Figure 16.8 using the 80% acceptability limits or the equations in Section 5.4.2.2.

The prevailing mean outdoor air temperature $tpma_{out}$ shall be determined in accordance with all the following.

- It shall be based on no fewer than seven and no more than 30 sequential days prior to the day in question.
- It shall be a simple arithmetic mean of all the mean daily outdoor air temperatures $tmda_{out}$ of all the sequential days in Section 5.4.21.1.

Exception Weighting methods are permitted, provided that the weighting curve continually decreases toward the more distant days such that the weight applied to a day is between 0.6 and 0.9 of that applied to the subsequent day. For this option, the upper limit on the number of days in the sequence does not apply.

Mean daily outdoor air temperature for each of the sequential days in Section 5.4.2.1.1 shall be the simple arithmetic mean of all the outdoor dry-bulb temperature observations for the 24-hour day. The quantity of measurements shall be no less than two, and, in that case, shall be the minimum and maximum for the day. When using three or more measurements, the time periods shall be evenly spaced.

Observations shall be from the nearest approved meteorological station, public or private, or Typical Meteorological Year (TMY) weather file.

When the weather data to calculate the prevailing mean outdoor air temperature are not available, it is permitted to use as the prevailing mean the published meteorological monthly means for each calendar month. It is permitted to interpolate between monthly means

It shall be permitted to use the following equations which correspond to the acceptable operative temperature to ranges:

- Upper 80% acceptability limit (°F) = 0.31 $t_{pma(out)}$ + 60.5
- Upper 80% acceptability limit (°C) = 0.31 $t_{pma(out)}$ + 21.3
- Lower 80% acceptability limit (°F) = 0.31 $t_{pma(out)}$ + 60.5
- Lower 80% acceptability limit (°C) = 0.31$t_{pma(out)}$ + 14.3

---

6. This section provides text originally published in ANSI/ASHRAE Standard 55 (ASHRAE 2017b). To integrate smoothly into the book, the content has been updated to conform to this book's style; otherwise, the content is as originally published.

If $t_o > 77°F$ (25°C), then it shall be permitted to increase the upper acceptability temperature limits in Figure 16.8 and the equations in Section 5.4.2.2 by the corresponding Δt_o in Table 5.4.2.4.

Methodology

A Description of Flat mean and Prevailing Mean Assessment Methods

Space dry-bulb and operative temperatures as well as airflow through the space are calculated by a simulation program (or manually). The temperatures and airflow are calculated for each hour of the month. The data is sorted in workdays and occupation hours.

The assumed external dry-bulb to seed the random number generating algorithm was calculated from the first 24 hours of the outside air dry-bulb temperature for the natural ventilation analysis. The mean for the last 24 hours is calculated.

Determination of Upper and Lower 80% Limits

The flat mean temperature is the mean monthly temperature. There is an 80% lower limit that is calculated from lower 80% acceptability limit (°F) = 0.31 (mean outdoor monthly air temperature) + 47.9°F (14.3°C). The flat mean 80% upper limit is calculated from upper 80% acceptability limit (°F) = 0.31 (mean outdoor monthly air temperature) + 60.5°F (21.3°C).

The results from a bulk air analysis are fed into a spreadsheet. The spreadsheet bins the data into the following groups:

- Workday
- Occupied hour
- Ventilation cfm per ft^2 (m^3/h·m^2)
- Ventilation cfm (L/s)
- ASHRAE Standard 62.1 threshold cfm (L/s)
- ASHRAE Standard 62.1 compliance true/false
- Operative temperature (from simulation results)
- Flat mean 80% lower limit: no air speed (from Figure 16.9)
- Flat mean 80% upper limit: no air speed (from Figure 16.9)
- Comfort status: too cold/good/too hot
- Flat mean 80% upper limit: with air speed – 236 fpm (1.2 m/s) = flat mean 80% upper limit: no air speed (from Figure 16.9) +4°F (+2°C)
- Comfort status with 236 fpm (1.2 m/s) elevated air speed: too cold/good/too hot
- Assumed external dry-bulb to seed
- Mean for last 24 hours
- Running mean for last 168 hours (i.e., 7 days)
- $t_{pma(out)}$: this is = (1 – 0.7) × Mean for last 24 hours + 0.7 × Running Mean for last 168 hours (i.e., 7 days)
- Prevailing mean 80% lower limit = 0.31 × $t_{pma(out)}$ + 47.9
- Prevailing mean 80% upper limit: No air speed = 0.31 × $t_{pma(out)}$ + 60.5
- Comfort status against prevailing mean: too cold/good/too hot
- Prevailing mean 80% upper limit with air speed at 236 fpm (1.2 m/s): too cold/good/too hot = Prevailing mean 80% upper limit: no air speed +4°F (+2°C)

For the month of June, the 80% upper and lower limits are 70°F and 82.6°F (21°C and 28°C) respectively (Figure 16.8).

The next step was to bin all the hours of outdoor air between 70°F and 82.6°F(21°C and 28°C) and remove all hours outside of this temperature range. All weekend hours are also removed from the results. The total hours during which natural ventilation complies with both ASHRAE Standards 55 and 62.1 can then be provided. At present, humidity and possible air contaminants are not considered in this analysis (see Figures 16.9, 16.10, and 16.11).

Figure 16.8 Monthly 80% upper and lower temperature limits for natural ventilation compliance in New York, I-P and SI.

Figure 16.9 shows prevailing mean natural conditioning compliance hours during representative months. In March, the prevailing mean 80% lower limit is 55.68°F (13.1°C), the 80% upper limit is 69.28°F (20.7°C), and with elevated air speed is 73.28°F (22.9°C). There are 152 too cold hours, 199 hours that are good, and 45 hours that are good with elevated air speed.

In June, the prevailing mean 80% lower limit is 67.78°F (19.8°C), the 80% upper limit is 80.38°F (26.8°C), and with elevated air speed is 84.38°F (29.1°C). There are 138 too cold hours, 198 hours that are good, and 60 hours that are good with elevated air speed.

In September, the prevailing mean 80% lower limit is 70.88°F (21.6°C), the 80% upper limit is 83.48°F (28.6°C), and with elevated air speed is 87.48°F (30.8°C). There are 145 too cold hours,198 hours that are good, and 198 hours that are good with elevated air speed.

In December, the prevailing mean 80% lower limit is 60.82°F (16°C), the 80% upper limit is 73.42°F (23°C), and with elevated air speed is 77.42°F (25.4°C). There are 153 too cold hours, 191 hours that are good, and 187 hours that are good with elevated air speed.

Figure 16.10 shows adaptive comfort comparison of indoor operative temperature to flat mean and prevailing mean criteria in September. The flat mean 80% lower limit is 69.1°F (20.6°C), the 80% upper limit is 81.7°F (27.6°C), and with elevated air speed is 85.7°F. The prevailing mean 80% lower limit is 70.88°F, the 80% upper limit is 83.48°F, and with elevated air speed is 87.48°F. There are 145 too cold hours, 198 hours that are good, and 198 hours that are good with elevated air speed.

Figure 16.11 shows prevailing mean natural conditioning compliance hours during representative months. In March, the prevailing mean 80% lower limit is 55.68°F (13.1°C), the 80% upper limit is 69.28°F (20.7°C) and with elevated air speed is 73.28°F (22.9°C). There are no too cold hours, 179 hours that are good, 197 hours that are good with elevated air speed, and 28 hours when it is too hot.

In June, the prevailing mean 80% lower limit is 67.78°F (19.8°C), the 80% upper limit is 80.38°F (26.8°C), and with elevated air speed is 84.38°F (29.1°C). There are no too cold hours, 92 hours that are good, 198 hours that are good with elevated air speed, and 60 hours when it is too hot.

In September, the prevailing mean 80% lower limit is 70.88°F (21.6°C), the 80% upper limit is 83.48°F (28.6°C), and with elevated air speed is 87.48 °F (30.8°C). There are no too cold hours, 102 hours that are good, 197 hours that are good with elevated air speed, and 96 hours when it is too hot.

In December, the prevailing mean 80% lower limit is 60.82°F (16°C), the 80% upper limit is 73.42°F (23°C), and with elevated air speed is 77.42°F (25.23°C). There is 1 too cold hour, 176 hours that are good, 200 hours that are good with elevated air speed, and 29 hours when it is too hot.

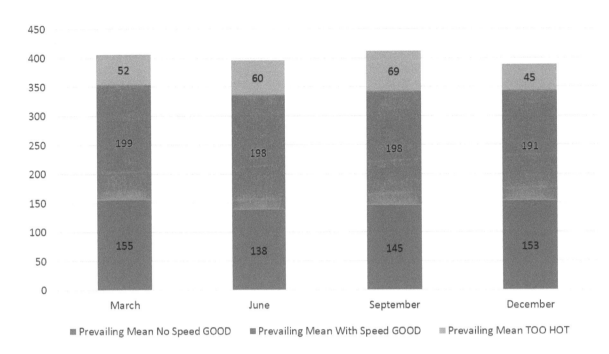

Figure 16.9 Standard 55 prevailing mean natural conditioning compliance hours for an office in New York due to buoyancy-driven ventilation.

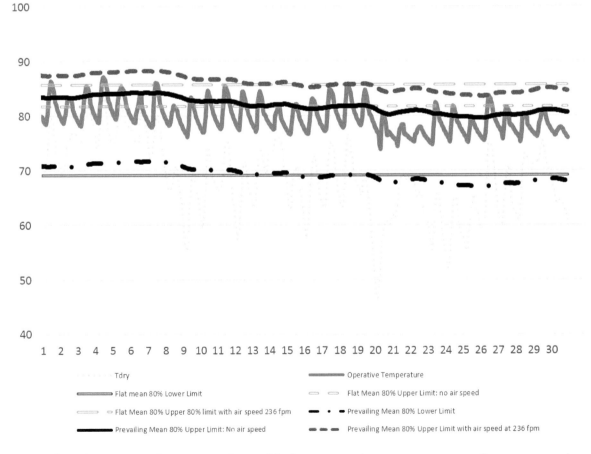

Figure 16.10 Adaptive comfort comparison of indoor operative temperature to flat mean and prevailing mean criteria. New York, buoyancy driven, September. α is 0.7 for prevailing mean.

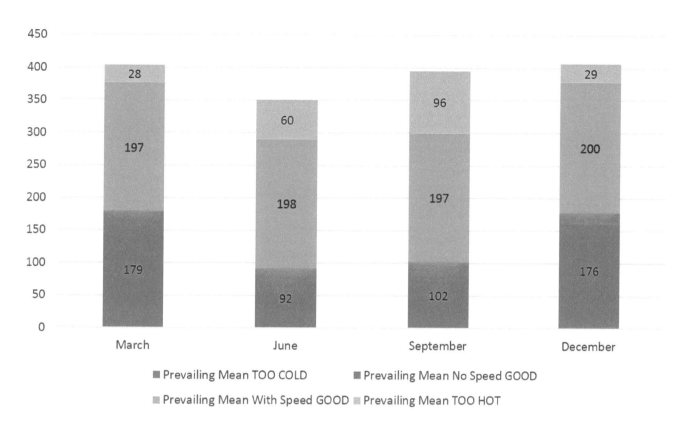

Figure 16.11 ASHRAE 55 prevailing mean natural conditioning compliance hours for an office in New York due to wind-driven ventilation.

CASE STUDY
Shanghai World Financial Center

Shanghai

Name: Shanghai World Financial Center/Park Hyatt Shanghai

Location: Shanghai, China

Description: Virtually a city within a city, this supertall structure houses a mix of office and retail uses, as well as the Park Hyatt Shanghai on the 79th to 93rd floors. Occupying the tower's uppermost floors, the SWFC Sky Arena offers visitors aerial views of the historic Lujiazui and winding river below and the chance to walk almost 1640 ft (500 m) above the city via the 100th floor sky walk.

A square prism, the symbol used by the ancient Chinese to represent the earth, is intersected by two cosmic arcs, representing the heavens, as the tower ascends in gesture to the sky. The interaction between these two realms gives rise to the building's form, carving a square sky portal at the top of the tower that lends balance to the structure and links the two opposing elements, the heavens and the earth.

In collaboration with the project's structural engineer, Leslie E. Robertson Associates, the team arrived at an innovative structural solution that abandoned the original concrete frame structure in favor of a diagonal-braced frame with outrigger trusses coupled to the columns of the mega-structure. This enabled the weight of the building to be reduced by more than 10%, consequently reducing the use of materials and resulting in a more transparent structure in visual and conceptual harmony with the tower's elegant form

Building Function: Headquarters for CITIC Group and CITIC Bank, as well as tenant occupied office spaces and a multipurpose business center.

Building Height: 1621 ft (494.3 m)

Building Floor Area: 4,107,500 ft^2 (381,600 m^2)

Architects: Kohn Pedersen Fox Associates, Mori Building, and Irie Miyake Architects and Engineers (Design); East China Architectural Design and Research Institute, Shanghai Modern Architectural Design Company (Architects of Record)

Structural Engineer: Leslie E. Robertson (Design)

MEP Engineer: Kenckiku Setsubi Sekkei Kenkyusho (Design)

Adapted from a report originally published on archello.com
https://archello.com/project/shanghai-world-financial-center.

CHAPTER 17
Electrical System Interfaces

Typical supertall and megatall buildings have multiple electrical feeds, with a normal power supply from the local utility company and an emergency supply from standby generator sets or standby power from batteries. For many modern buildings, tenants often require space for their own standby generators.

Bendix (2007) describes typical arrangements, in which the utility company provides medium- or high-voltage power (typically 11 kV to 66 kV) to substations. Multiple substations are used to provide power from multiple sources within the building to provide redundancy. Utility power can be metered at substations, with main switchgear usually placed in basement areas. It is normal to have multiple main switchgear isolated from each other, usually in different fire compartments.

Utility companies can have specific requirements for substations and switchgear. In some instances, there are no specific requirements, whereas in other cases there can be many specific requirements determined by the utility company, such as for installing substations and switchgear against outside walls.

To facilitate utility power connections, it is advisable to contact the utility as soon as possible in the design process. Specifics for service equipment, location, and access can also be defined during this period. Local codes and standards need to be studied at this stage.

In the United States, Canada, and Europe, the utility supply voltage is transformed down to the required building voltage (480 V in the United States, 600 V in Canada, and 400 V or 380 V in much of Europe and Asia) (Bendix 2007). In most buildings, transformers are located at basement level, but in supertall and megatall buildings, multiple transformers are required. Transformers are therefore installed at positions throughout the building to optimize the voltage drop. The location and size of the required electrical rooms must be coordinated between the architect and the engineers. Electrical rooms must be easily accessed for maintenance and operation; there must be sufficient room to remove and replace equipment if required. There is always a trade-off between the space requirements for equipment and an efficient floor design.

Typically, medium- and low-voltage cables are separated and routed in fire-rated spaces that are accessible for maintenance. Cables are installed and supported so that they are not stressed and movement under short-circuit events is limited.

In the event of a power outage, emergency power is provided by the standby generator sets. The duration of standby power must be sufficient for the buildings life safety systems. Where elevators can be used for egress in emergencies, there must be sufficient emergency power available. In some cases, emergency power can be used for noncritical power requirements.

Low- or medium-voltage emergency generators may be selected. If medium-voltage generators are selected, then fewer, larger units can be installed at low level. However, the transfer and synchronization of medium-voltage generator sets can be more costly than for low-voltage generator sets. In some jurisdictions, medium-voltage generators are not permitted. If low-voltage generators are used, then more units will be required, and the distance between the generators must be controlled because of voltage drop. Regardless of which emergency power voltage is used, the synchronization and activation of emergency power systems must be carefully designed.

Electrical generator rooms are also subject to code requirements for makeup and exhaust air, as well as fuel storage and generator cooling systems.

SERVICE SPACES

Coordinating mechanical, electrical, and plumbing equipment space in buildings always presents a challenge, not only between electrical and mechanical engineers, who often compete for the same space, but also with the architect in balancing the space required for MEP systems and the optimum lease area. This discourse will run throughout the whole building design phase. Not only must the equipment fit in the rooms provided, it must be freely accessible for maintenance. Especially in supertall and megatall buildings, the offsets required when transferring shafts, chutes, and risers from one zone to another can present obstacles. It is very common that the initial spaces provided for electrical rooms are inadequate for the proposed electrical systems.

Electrical rooms are needed for many different systems, including power distribution panels, feeder and plug-in busways, lighting control panels, emergency lighting, systems supply panels, fire alarm panels and their associated emergency power battery cabinets, building security system equipment, voice and data distribution racks and cabinets, building management system panels, and cable and conduit risers. Spreading the equipment among several floors and serving multiple floors with one piece of equipment can help minimize space usage, but these strategies are not practical for all equipment types (Bendix 2007). Local codes may require segregation between normal power and emergency power.

Service spaces in the core may be adjacent to an elevator shaft or riser shafts for air distribution or linen or garbage chutes. However, service raceways are not permitted to penetrate such risers, and service rooms may also be surrounded by structural shear walls, with limited opportunities for penetrations. These raceways are typically routed into a public area, above a ceiling, and therefore may be limited in size, resulting in the need for additional service risers.

The length of power distribution conductors is limited by overall voltage drop. Horizontal copper telecommunication cables (categories 5 and 6) can have a maximum length of 295 ft (89 m) to comply with most standards (Bendix 2007). Some networking standards further limit distance to allow for higher data throughput. Telecommunications cabling may also require segregation of 1 to 3 ft (0.3 to 0.9 m) from electrical power cables and conduits, which can further complicate the layout of communications and electrical rooms in a building's core.

The architect and electrical engineer will need to cooperate and compromise to ensure that electrical equipment is accommodated with adequate clearance to be safely serviced and with minimum loss of usable space.

STRUCTURAL CONSIDERATIONS

Especially in very tall buildings, embedding electrical conduits in a concrete structure creates challenges for the structural engineer. The electrical and structural engineers must consult to determine the maximum size and concentration of conduits that may be safely embedded in the slab; the results depend on the type and thickness of slab construction.

Supertall and megatall building structures usually include deep transfer beams. The structural engineer will typically allow limited, minor penetrations through structural elements; however, for more numerous and/or large penetrations, careful coordination and planning is required. Large penetrations and openings should be discussed early in the design process so that they can be integrated into the structure. The later in the process these openings are identified, the more likely are unsatisfactory results and project delays.

LIGHTING

Lighting for most supertall and megatall buildings is usually designed by a specialist who provides dedicated designs as requested by the architect and owner. As for other systems, the lighting design must be coordinated with the electrical and mechanical engineers. The electrical engineer is responsible for the correct wiring and operation of lighting system and the mechanical engineer must ensure that the lighting thermal load is accounted for in the cooling load calculations.

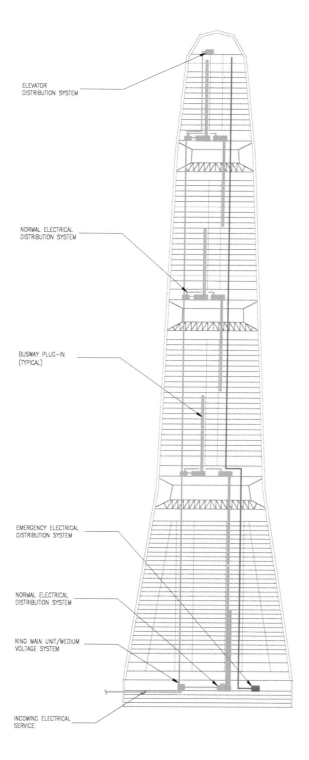

ELEVATOR
DISTRIBUTION SYSTEM

NORMAL ELECTRICAL
DISTRIBUTION SYSTEM

BUSWAY PLUG-IN
(TYPICAL)

EMERGENCY ELECTRICAL
DISTRIBUTION SYSTEM

NORMAL ELECTRICAL
DISTRIBUTION SYSTEM

RING MAIN UNIT/MEDIUM
VOLTAGE SYSTEM

INCOMING ELECTRICAL
SERVICE

Figure 17.1 A typical electrical distribution for a megatall building.

An energy-efficient lighting design reduces the building cooling load, and the energy requirements of a high-performance lighting system should be reflected in the energy modeling of the building and its systems.

Owners and design teams have used natural daylighting and its documented benefits as prescribed in many energy standards, such as ANSI/ASHRAE/IES Standard 90.1. When harvesting natural daylight, photosensors measure the available light levels in a space, and the lighting controls adjust the artificial lighting system to provide the designed lighting levels (Chow and Noschang 2013). Light contrast ratios and glare should be carefully assessed. Dedicated lighting controls should be set to optimize the use of artificial lighting.

High-performance lighting systems using daylight harvesting can reduce a building's energy consumption, mostly in the perimeter zone. If a building's lighting system consumes a minimum of energy, the building's cooling load and energy consumption is reduced compared to a code-compliant minimum design. This can result in a reduction of cooling equipment size. However, the heating energy consumption is slightly increased, because less heat released from the lighting system to heat the building.

If the lighting system can be simulated in the energy model, the cooling load can be optimized, and the resulting system's energy consumption will be minimized (Rush 2015).

With modern control systems, it is possible to integrate systems to control the lighting system as well as the HVAC system. Open protocols such as BACnet®, LonWorks, and Modbus enable products from different manufacturers to work together (Chow and Noschang 2013).

Aircraft Warning Lights

Aircraft warning lights are an essential requirement on any tall building. Usually, these systems must comply with Federal Aviation Administration (FAA) and International Civil Aviation Organization (ICAO) requirements. The required warning lights should be integrated into the building's design and aesthetics.

LIGHTNING PROTECTION

Supertall and megatall buildings are subject to lightning strikes, and they require lightning protection systems. The type of system needed for each building depends on local code requirements.

There are typically two types of lightning protection systems:

- Attraction-based systems (e.g., Faraday cages, lightning rods)
- Charge-dissipative systems, which prevent lightning strikes

The design of the system must be coordinated with the architect and structural engineer. In cases where a Faraday cage is designed around the building, copper conductors can be used to direct the energy to the earth. However, this is usually an unnecessary expense, because the reinforcing steel in the building's structure already is a good conductor and is often used for this purpose (Bendix 2007).[7]

SMART GRID BASICS

This section provides the basis for understanding changes occurring in the electric grid infrastructure and how buildings now and in the future interact with the grid. Because this is a rapidly evolving topic area, readers are encouraged to seek additional information on the latest changes and future directions. For additional resources and information, refer to the U.S. Department of Energy's SmartGrid.gov (http://smartgrid.gov) and Energy.gov (http://energy.gov /oe/technology-development/smart-grid/smart-grid-primer-smart-grid -books) web pages.

---

7. The following section provides partial text from Chapter 63, Smart Building Systems, in *ASHRAE Handbook—HVAC Applications* (2019a). To integrate smoothly into this chapter, the figure and table numbering have been modified from the original; otherwise the content remains as originally published.

Electric Power Grid Operational Characteristics

The modern electric grid is modeled as three interconnected domains (Figure 17.2). The **generation system** produces electric energy. This domain contains a set of power stations and distributed energy generators (e.g., residential solar photovoltaic systems). The electricity generated is conditioned to reduce losses and is then transmitted over long distances across the **transmission system**. The transmission system typically consists of high-voltage wires that distribute electricity hundreds of miles. When needed to power loads within a region, the electricity is reconditioned (i.e., converted and/or stepped down in voltage) and distributed to customers over the **distribution system**. The distribution system is ordinarily a network of medium-voltage wires that distribute energy across a metropolitan area. The distribution system also includes electrical substations that transform the energy to the low voltages needed by customer loads and transmit it over the wires connected to the customer.

A **transmission grid** is a network of power stations, transmission lines, and substations. Electricity is usually transmitted within a grid as three-phase alternating current (ac). Single-phase ac is used only for distribution to end users, because it is not suitable for large, polyphase induction motors. In the 19th century, two-phase transmission was used but required either four wires or three wires with unequal currents. Higher-order-phase systems require more than three wires, but deliver marginal benefits.

The capital cost of electric power stations is so high, and electric demand so variable, that it is often less expensive to import some portion of the needed power than to generate it locally. Because nearby loads are often correlated (e.g., hot weather in the Southwestern United States might cause many people to use air conditioners simultaneously), electricity often comes from distant sources. Because of the economics of load balancing, wide-area transmission grids now span across countries and even large portions of continents. The web of interconnections between power producers and consumers ensures that power can flow, even when a few links are inoperative.

The unvarying (or slowly varying over many hours) portion of the total electric system demand is known as the **base load** and is generally served by large generation facilities (which are efficient for this purpose because of economies of scale) with low variable costs for fuel and operations. Such facilities might be nuclear, natural-gas, or coal-fired power stations or, in some locations, hydroelectric plants. Variable renewable energy sources, such as solar photovoltaics, wind, and wave power, because of their intermittency, are not considered base-load capable (unless firmed by storage) but can still add power to the grid. The remaining power demand is supplied by intermediate load-following plants and peaking-power plants, which are

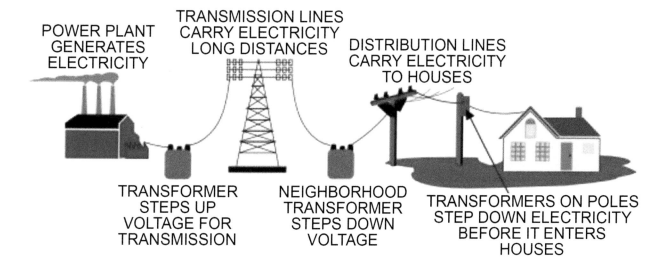

Figure 17.2 Electric power grid.

typically smaller, faster-responding, and higher-cost sources, such as combined-cycle or combustion turbine plants fueled by natural gas.

Subtransmission is part of an electric power transmission system that runs at relatively lower voltages. It is uneconomical to connect all distribution substations to the high main transmission voltage, because the equipment is larger and more expensive. Typically, only larger substations connect with this high voltage. The electric power is stepped down and sent to smaller substations in towns and neighborhoods. Subtransmission circuits are usually arranged in loops so that a single line failure does not cut off service to a large number of customers for more than a short time. Although subtransmission circuits are usually carried on overhead lines, buried cable is also used in urban areas.

The amount of power that can be sent over a transmission line is limited. These limits vary depending on the length of the line and can depend on the ambient temperature. For a short line, heating of conductors because of line losses sets a thermal limit. If too much current is drawn, conductors may sag too close to the ground or other obstructions (e.g., trees), or conductors and equipment may be damaged by overheating. For intermediate-length lines on the order of 62 mi (100 km), the limit is set by the voltage drop in the line. For longer ac lines, system stability limits the power that can be transferred. Approximately, the power flowing over an ac line is proportional to the cosine of the phase angle of the voltage and current at the receiving and transmitting ends. This angle depends on system loading and generation, and it is undesirable for the angle to approach 90°. Very approximately, the allowable product of line length and maximum load is proportional to the square of the system voltage. Series capacitors or phase-shifting transformers are used on long lines to improve stability. High-voltage DC lines are restricted only by thermal and voltage drop limits, because the phase angle is not material to their operation.

To ensure safe and predictable operation, the components of the transmission system are controlled with generators, switches, circuit breakers, and even loads. The voltage, power, frequency, load factor, and reliability capabilities of the transmission system are designed to provide reliable, cost-effective performance for customers.

The transmission system provides for base- and peak-load capability, with safety and fault tolerance margins. The peak-load times vary by region largely because of differences in the industry mix. In very hot and very cold climates, home air-conditioning and heating loads can have a significant effect on the overall load at times. These loads are typically highest in the late afternoon in the hottest part of the year, and in mid-mornings and mid-evenings in the coldest part of the year. This variability makes the power requirements differ by season and the time of day. Distribution system designs take the base and peak loads into consideration.

Electricity produced by the generation system has to match the energy consumed by the loads, or the system becomes unstable. The transmission system usually does not have a large storage capability to match the varying energy consumed by loads. Thus, fast-acting balancing generation units (known as spinning reserves) are connected to the transmission system and kept matched to the load to prevent overloading failures of the generation equipment.

Typical Building Load Profile

Figure 17.3 depicts a typical commercial building load profile in relation to the utility system load profile. The profile reflects the building's individual characteristics, including building use, occupancy and equipment schedules, equipment characteristics, and building control strategies used. In contrast, the utility system load is the aggregate of all the individual loads, including commercial facilities, but also includes residential, industrial, and public facilities. Although individual commercial facility electric loads may have the same general shape as the utility system load, they may not have an identical shape and may peak at different times given the aggregation of the many loads that make up the system load. Understanding the relationship between the load profile of an individual facility and the overall system profile provides the basis for optimizing electricity use and costs to the mutual benefit of the grid and the customer.

Utility Demand Response Strategies

Demand response is the change in electric usage by end-use customers from their normal consumption patterns in response to changes in the price of electricity over time, or to incentive payments designed to induce lower electricity use at times of high wholesale market prices or when system reliability is jeopardized (DOE 2006).

Flexible load shape attempts to achieve a load shape composed of end-use services with varying degrees of reliability, allowing the utility the flexibility to control/adjust end-use demand in accordance with supply capability. In exchange for accepting a lower level of reliability, a customer receives some financial incentive. A flexible load shape may be achieved using interruptible loads, energy management systems, or individual customer load control devices imposing service constraints.

Peak shaving reduces the amount of energy purchased from a utility company during the peak. Many businesses pay for their electricity consumption on a time-of-use basis. Peak demand charges typically apply to electricity consumed within the peak hours, whereas lesser charges apply to the remainder of the day.

Direct load control involves the utility disabling and enabling consumer end uses. A communication system between the utility and the customer transmits control instructions to a receiver and control actuator on the customer's premises that enables activation/deactivation of customer loads. Many utilities use direct load control to reduce peaking requirements, and consider control only during the most probable days of the system peak. Other utilities use direct load control to reduce operating cost and dependence on critical fuels.

Valley filling involves increasing energy consumption in a time period when the electric system is under used. Valley filling may be particularly desirable where the long-run marginal cost of electricity is less than the average price of electricity. Properly priced off-peak load can decrease the average price for the customer and provide cost or capacity benefits to the utility. Valley filling can be accomplished in several ways, including using thermal energy storage (water or space heating or cooling).

Load shifting moves energy consumption to another time period, typically when prices are lower. Common options include storage water heating, storage space heating, cool storage, and time-of-use or other special rates. The shifting usually occurs within a 24 h period. The total energy used by a customer needs not be significantly affected by load shifting.

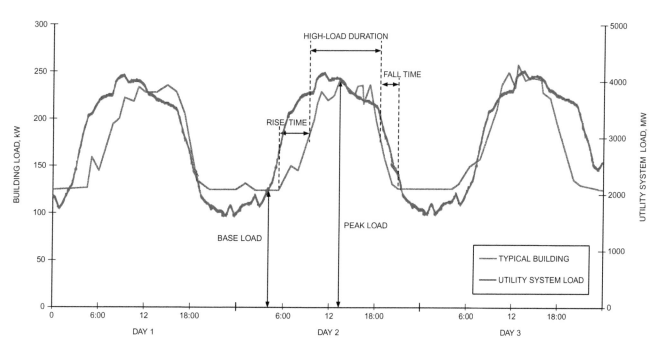

Figure 17.3 Example commercial building load profile in relation to utility system load.
(Adapted from Price 2010)

Strategic conservation is directed at reducing end-use consumption, often through increased efficiency. The change reflects a reduction in sales and a change in the use pattern. Examples include weatherization and appliance efficiency improvement.

Strategic load growth increases end-use consumption by increasing energy sales beyond the valley-filling strategy. The emphasis is often on increasing total sales without regard to the seasonal or daily timing of the load. Strategic load growth may involve area development, electrification, and increased market share of loads that are or can be served by competing fuels.

Utility Rate Options and Strategies

Public regulatory bodies provide incentives to drive customer behaviors using electric tariff design. To increase the reliability and use of existing generation assets or reduce the need for additional generation/transmission assets, there are two methods to reduce customer demand during peak consumption times. Utility customers can be induced to provide demand response either through **dynamic pricing tariffs**, retail electric rates that reflect short-term changes in wholesale electricity costs (e.g., hourly pricing or critical-peak pricing), or through **demand response programs** that offer customers payments in return for reducing consumption when called upon to mitigate high market prices or reserve shortfalls. Table 17.1 shows common types of demand response programs.

Modern Smart-Grid Strategy

The smart grid represents a modern grid concept that would replace dated infrastructure with currently available and future technologies that enable safe and secure two-way flows of electricity and information between customers and their electricity providers. In the typical grid configuration, energy predominately flows one way, from utilities to consumers, and information flows almost exclusively one-way, from consumers' power meters to grid operators. However, with the smart grid, energy and information would flow easily from the grid to customers, and vice versa, in real time.

The vision for the modern electric grid is one that

- Motivates and includes the consumer
- Accommodates all generation and storage options
- Enables markets
- Provides power quality for 21st-century needs
- Resists attacks
- Self heals
- Optimizes assets and operates efficiently
- Provides less expensive electric power more cleanly

Two-way flows of energy and information would provide customers with valuable information about their electricity prices and consumption patterns. This would enable customers to better manage their electricity use. On the utility side, the grid could be more accurately balanced, brownouts or blackouts could be avoided, and outages could be quickly mitigated. Advantages of the smart grid to the utility and to consumers are compared in Figure 17.4.

Investments in the smart grid are expected to yield the following four long-lasting effects (Lott et al. 2011):

- Next-generation electric power grid infrastructure that replaces the existing grid
- Substantial improvements in energy efficiency that bring financial and environmental benefits
- Greater use of renewable generation
- Widespread use of distributed generation

This smart-grid strategy is intended to enable a new kind of load response, in which loads and generation are on an equal footing with equal visibility of the value of electricity in real time. It includes use of automation and other tools to enable even small customers to manage load in response to the real-time value of energy. It focuses on integrating renewables and higher reliability and resiliency, as well as distributed energy (customer-owned generation and storage) and advancing the regulatory framework to enable customers (and small generators) to manage the distributed energy resources and load in a variable-price environment.

Relevance to Building System Designers

As the modern grid develops, buildings will need grid communications to know the condition of the grid and to determine how to respond to it. Facilities can be operated in ways that support grid reliability while potentially lowering their costs of operation by managing loads and storage to contribute to balancing grid-wide demand and changes to the generation mix. An example is Open Automated Demand Response (OpenADR™), a research and standards development collaboration for power demand management. Typically, OpenADR is used to communicate data and signals that turn off powered devices when electrical demand is high. See OpenADR Alliance (n.d.) for more information.

Buildings and facilities should be designed for operation in an environment where electricity is valued in real time, varying throughout the day. Building owners, managers, and designers should consider incorporating automation to allow shifting and shedding loads, as well as planning to allow for thermal energy storage and renewable energy generation systems integration. Further, there should be some consideration of microgrid operations, with additional fossil-fuel-based distributed generation (fuel cells, diesel generators, etc.) and electrical storage capability on site.

In the future, not only will electricity costs become more dynamic, energy prices will continue to rise. Controlling energy costs begins with energy efficiency as the cornerstone of an overall energy management plan. Strategies for developing a site-specific plan can be found in the EPA ENERGY STAR Guidelines (n.d.).

The success of the smart grid depends on interoperability and communication between energy service providers and facility energy management systems to effectively manage supply and demand. Proposed ASHRAE *Standard* 201P, Facility Smart Grid Information Model (under development), would define an abstract, object-oriented information model to enable appliances and control systems in homes, industrial facilities, and other buildings to manage electrical loads and generation sources in response to communication with a smart electrical grid and to communicate information about those electrical loads to the utility and other electrical service providers. This model defines a comprehensive set of data objects and actions that support a wide range of energy management applications and electrical service provider interactions, including on-site generation, demand response, electrical storage, peak-demand management, direct load control, and other related energy management functions. This standard will become part of the Smart Grid Interoperability Panel Catalog of Standards recommended for adoption by utilities and energy service providers (NIST 2017).

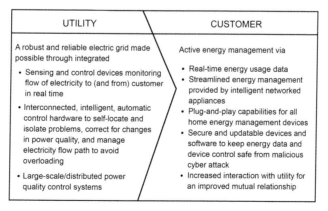

Figure 17.4 Benefits of Smart Grid as Viewed by utilities and customers.
(Lott et al. 2011)

Table 17.1 Common Types of Demand Response (DR) Programs: Price Options and Incentive- or Event-Based Options

Price-Based DR Programs: Higher Prices Used to Induce Demand Reduction	
Time of use (TOU) rates	Rates with fixed price blocks that differ by time of day.
Critical peak pricing (CPP)	Rates include a prespecified, extra-high rate that is triggered by the utility and is in effect for a limited number of hours.
Real-time pricing (RTP)	Rates vary continually (typically hourly) in response to wholesale market prices.
Incentive- or Event-Based Programs: Incentives Provided to Induce Demand Reduction	
Direct load control	Customers receive incentive payments for allowing utility a degree of control over certain equipment.
Demand bidding/ buyback programs	Customers offer bids to curtail load when wholesale market prices are high or identify how much they would be willing to curtail at posted prices.
Emergency demand response programs	Customers receive incentive payments for load reductions when needed to ensure reliability, but curtailments are voluntary.
Capacity market programs	Customers receive incentive payments or rate discounts/bill credits for providing load reductions as substitutes for system capacity.
Interruptible/curtailable programs	Customers receive a discounted rate or bill credit for agreeing to reduce load upon request. If participants do not curtain when requested, they can be penalized.
Ancillary services market programs	Customers receive payments from a grid for ancillary services provided. Require that customers are able to adjust load quickly.

Sources: FERC (2006), Goldman et al. (2010).

CHAPTER 18
Intelligent Building and Controls

When designing tall, supertall, and megatall buildings, it is essential to operate the building's systems so the least amount of energy is consumed. The integration of smart building systems will increase the building's efficiency and also provide more insight into the operation characteristics of the building. Maintenance of these large buildings can also be reduced by the introduction of automated fault detection and diagnostics (AFDD) in the building management system.[8]

Smart building systems are building components that exhibit characteristics analogous to human intelligence. These characteristics include drawing conclusions from data or analyses of data rather than simply generating more data or plots of data, interpreting information or data to reach new conclusions, and making decisions and/or taking action autonomously without being explicitly instructed or programmed to take the specific action. These capabilities are usually associated with software, but they can also be possessed by hardware with embedded software code, or firmware. The line between systems that are "smart" and "not smart" is blurry, and, for purposes of this chapter, does not need to be absolutely defined. The purpose of this chapter is to introduce readers to emerging technologies that possess some of these smart characteristics.

Smart technologies offer opportunities to reduce energy use and cost while improving the performance of HVAC systems to provide better indoor environmental quality (IEQ). This chapter covers smart systems and technologies in the fields of AFDD, sensors and actuators, and the emerging modernized electric power grid and its relationship to buildings and facilities.

AUTOMATED FAULT DETECTION AND DIAGNOSTICS

Many buildings today use sophisticated building automation systems (BASs) to manage a wide and varied range of building systems. Although the capabilities of BASs have increased over time, many buildings still are not properly commissioned, operated, or maintained, which leads to inefficient operation, excess expenditures on energy, poor indoor conditions at times, and reduced lifetimes for equipment. These operation problems cause an estimated 15 to 30% of unnecessary energy use in commercial buildings (Katipamula and Brambley 2005a, 2005b). Much of this excess consumption could be prevented with widespread adoption of AFDD. In the long run, automation even offers the potential for automatically correcting problems by

---

8. The following chapter provides partial text from Chapter 63, Smart Building Systems, in *ASHRAE Handbook—HVAC Applications* (2019a). To integrate smoothly into this book, the figure and table numbering have been modified from the original; otherwise, the content is as originally published.

reconfiguring controls or changing control algorithms dynamically (Brambley and Katipamula 2004; Fernandez et al. 2009, 2010; Katipamula and Brambley 2007; Katipamula, Brambley, and Luskay 2003).

AFDD is an automatic process by which faulty operation, degraded performance, and failed components are detected and understood. The primary objective is early detection of faults and diagnosis of their causes, enabling correction of the faults before additional damage to the system, loss of service, or excessive energy use and cost result. This is accomplished by continuously monitoring the operations of a system, using AFDD processes to detect and diagnose abnormal conditions and the faults associated with them, then evaluating the significance of the detected faults and deciding how to respond. For example, the temperature of the supply air provided by an air-handling unit (AHU) might be observed to be chronically higher than its set point during hot weather. This conclusion might be drawn by a trained analyst visually inspecting a time series plot of the supply air temperature. Alternatively, a computer algorithm could process these data continuously, reach this same conclusion, and report the condition to operators or interact directly with a computer-based maintenance management system (CMMS) to automatically schedule maintenance or repair services.

Automated diagnostics generally goes a step further than simply detecting for out-of-bounds conditions. In this air-handler example, an AFDD system that constantly monitors the temperature and humidity of the outdoor, return, mixed, and supply air, as well as the status of the supply fan, hot-water valve, and chilled-water valve of the air handler, might conclude that the outdoor-air damper is stuck fully open. As a result, during hot weather, too much hot and humid outdoor air is brought into the unit, increasing the mechanical cooling required and often exceeding the capacity of the mechanical cooling system. As a result, the supply air temperature is chronically high. This is an example of how an AFDD system can detect and diagnose this fault.

Over the past two decades, fault detection and diagnostics (FDD) has been an active area of research among the buildings and HVAC&R research communities. Isermann (1984), Katipamula and Brambley (2005a, 2005b), and Rossi and Braun (1997) described an operations and maintenance (O&M) process using AFDD that can be viewed as having four distinct functional processes, as shown in Figure 18.1. With only a few exceptions, most AFDD systems for building applications existing today lack the evaluation process (Katipamula and Brambley 2005a, 2005b). Automated correction after detection and diagnostics also has been an active area of research in the past decade (Brambley and Katipamula 2004; Fernandez et al. 2009, 2010; Katipamula and Brambley 2007; Katipamula, Brambley, and Luskay 2003; Katipamula. Brambley, Bauman, and Pratt 2003).

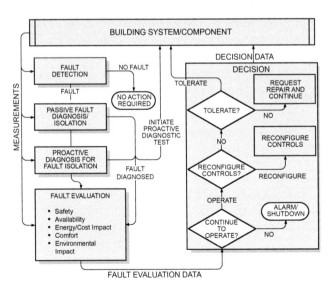

Figure 18.1 Generic process for using AFDD in ongoing operation and maintenance of building systems. (Adapted from Katipamula and Brambley 2005a).

As shown in Figure 18.1, the first functional step of an AFDD process is to monitor the building systems and detect abnormal (faulty) conditions. This step is generally referred to as the **fault detection** phase. If an abnormal condition is detected, then the **fault diagnosis** process identifies the cause. If the fault cannot be diagnosed using passive diagnostic techniques, proactive diagnostics techniques may be required to isolate the fault (Katipamula, Brambley, and Luskay 2003). Following diagnosis, **fault evaluation** assesses the impact (energy, cost, and availability) on system performance. Finally, a decision is made on how to react to the fault. In most cases, detection of faults is easier than diagnosing the cause or evaluating the effects of the fault. Detailed descriptions of the four processes are provided in Katipamula and Brambley (2005a, 2005b) and Katipamula, Brambley, and Luskay (2003).

Applications of AFDD in Buildings

AFDD has been successfully applied to critical systems such as aerospace applications, nuclear power plants, automobiles, and process controls, in which early identification of malfunctions could prevent loss of life, environmental damage, system failure, and/or damage to equipment. In these applications, AFDD **sensitivity**, the lowest fault severity level required to trigger the correct detection and diagnosis of a fault, is a vital feature; **false-alarm rate** is the rate at which faults are incorrectly indicated when no fault has actually occurred. A high false-alarm rate could result in significant economic loss associated with investigation of nonexistent faults or unnecessary stoppage of equipment operation.

The ability to detect faults in HVAC&R systems has existed for some time, and has been used primarily to protect expensive equipment from catastrophic failure, ensure safety, and provide alarms when a measured variable goes outside its acceptable operating range. In recent years, the motivation for development and use of AFDD has expanded to include expectations of improved energy efficiency and IAQ, as well as reduced unscheduled equipment downtime (Braun 1999). Developers expect that AFDD will someday be applied ubiquitously, leading to prolonged equipment life for everything from large equipment (e.g., chillers) to small components (e.g., individual actuators).

The need for AFDD capabilities has been established by surveys, site measurements, and commissioning assessments that have documented a wide variety of operational faults in common HVAC&R equipment and systems.

AFDD shows promise in three areas of building engineering: (1) commissioning, (2) operation, and (3) maintenance.

Commissioning of existing buildings involves in part ensuring that systems are installed correctly and that they operate properly. Faults found during commissioning include installation errors (e.g., fans installed backward), incorrectly sized equipment, and improperly implemented controls (e.g., schedules, set points, algorithms). Most commissioning actions that discover these faults, which include visual inspections and functional testing, are performed manually. Data are collected during some tests using automated data loggers, and analysis might be done with computers, but the process of interpreting the data and evaluating results is performed manually. AFDD methods could automate much of the functional testing and interpretation of test results, ensuring completeness of testing, consistency in methods, records of all data and processing, increased cost effectiveness, and the ability to continuously or periodically repeat the tests throughout the life of the facility (Katipamula, Brambley, and Luskay 2003; PECI and Battelle 2003). AFDD methods applied during initial building start-up differ from those applied later in a building lifetime. At start-up, no historical data are available, whereas later in the life cycle, data from earlier operation can be used. Selection of methods must consider these differences; however, automated functional testing is likely to involve short-term data collection, whether performed during initial building commissioning or during routine operation later in the building's lifetime, and therefore, the same methods can be used regardless of when the functional tests are performed. Such a short time period is generally required for functional testing to eliminate the possibility that the system being tested changes (e.g., performance degrades) during the test itself. Besides use in functional testing, AFDD methods could be used to verify the proper installation of equipment without requiring visual inspection. Labor intensity could be minimized by only performing visual inspections to confirm installation problems after they have been detected automatically.

During **building operation**, AFDD tools can detect and diagnose performance degradation and faults, many of which go undetected for weeks or months in most commercial buildings. Many building performance problems are automatically compensated by controllers so occupants experience no discomfort, but energy consumption and operating costs often increase. For example, when the capacity of a packaged rooftop air conditioner decreases because of refrigerant loss, the unit runs longer to meet the load, increasing energy use and costs, and occupants experience no discomfort (until design conditions are approached). AFDD tools can detect these, as well as more obvious, faults.

AFDD tools not only detect faults and alert building operation staff to them, but also identify causes of faults so that **maintenance** efforts can be targeted, ultimately lowering maintenance costs and improving operation. By detecting performance degradation rather than just complete failure of physical components, AFDD tools can also help prevent catastrophic failures by alerting building operation and maintenance staff to impending failures before failure occurs. This condition-based maintenance allows convenient scheduling of maintenance, reduced downtime from unexpected faults and failures, and more efficient use of maintenance staff time.

Future for Automated Fault Detection and Diagnostics

The commercial availability of AFDD tools is increasing, although somewhat slowly, demonstrating some recognition of their value. As market penetration and experience in use increase, the need for improvements will accumulate. Key technical issues still to be completely addressed include the following (Katipamula and Brambley 2005b):

- Eliminating the need to handcraft and configure AFDD systems
- Automatic generation of AFDD systems
- Identifying the best AFDD method for each HVAC&R application
- Developing decision-support tools for using AFDD in operation and maintenance
- Developing prognostic tools to transform HVAC&R maintenance from corrective and preventive to predictive, condition-based maintenance
- Lowering the cost of obtaining data for AFDD and O&M support

Some AFDD tools require users to implement data collection from building automation systems, which is often difficult, costly, and beyond the capabilities of many end users. Other tools require the input of values or selections for many configuration parameters (e.g., the specific method used to control an economizer). Solutions for these problems include (1) developing AFDD tools that include databases sufficient to cover many equipment models, (2) delivering AFDD as part of equipment control packages, and (3) developing methods for automatically generating AFDD tools. The first approach was introduced in a hand tool for air-conditioning service providers more than a decade ago. The second approach of embedding AFDD onboard equipment controls has started to be used by some manufacturers of equipment and equipment controls (e.g., chillers). The third approach, involving rapid automatic generation of AFDD, requires research before it emerges in products.

Use of open communication standards for BAS (e.g., BACnet®) is increasing, and use of Internet and intranet technologies is pervasive. These developments make integration of third-party software with AFDD features that use BAS data easier, lowering the cost-to-benefit ratio of deploying AFDD systems. To benefit from these changes, facility managers, owners, operators, and energy service providers need the capabilities and resources to better manage this information and, as a result, their buildings and facilities.

SENSING AND ACTUATING SYSTEMS

Sensors

The typical sensors used in smart building systems are not far different from those used in all buildings. Smart building systems rely on sensors to measure quantities such as temperature, humidity, pressure, occupancy, electric power and energy use, fossil fuel energy use, light levels, air speeds, carbon dioxide, and electric harmonics. See Chapter 37, Measurement and Instruments, of the 2017 *ASHRAE Handbook—Fundamentals* for in-depth discussion of measurement techniques for such quantities.

Traditional sensors are connected to control systems via twisted pairs of wires, which conduct voltage or current signals. Sensor calibration (i.e., mapping from electronic signals back to measured physical quantities) can be complicated by nonlinear and/or time-varying functions, which are often implemented in software code by field engineers. The calibration process is time consuming and error prone. In practice, sensors are subject to various defects; therefore, sensor data should not be used without validation. Under certain conditions, multiple physical sensors of different kinds should be used for reliable measure of a physical quantity. Truly smart buildings require pervasive use of smart sensors that possess intelligence and memory to identify, recalibrate, and repair defective sensors.

The intelligence of smart sensors can be described in four categories, discussed in the following paragraphs.

Local Intelligence. In local intelligence, the signal and data-processing capability reside at the local sensor node. For example, some fire detectors are equipped with multiple physical sensors to reduce false alarms and increase reliability, using complicated algorithms. Other sensors may be equipped with flash memory to store historical data. Another type of local intelligence is the ability to compute information based on raw sensor measurements. For instance, a photoresistor can be used to measure luminance, but the mapping from voltage across the resistor in the meter to luminance is not linear. A smart sensor is equipped with circuitry that calculates the desired quantity onboard, either through analog or digital approaches.

Networking Intelligence. Sensors with networking intelligence allow bidirectional communications via scalable, secure, and robust computer networks. Traditional sensors are connected to ports on panels via twisted pairs of wires. While implementing control sequences, engineers must embed the port number and detailed sensor characteristics to calculate the physical quantity of measurement from electronic signals. In practice, there is usually only one quantity that is measured by each sensor, and the direction of information flow is always in one direction from the sensor to control panels. As shown in Figure 18.2, smart sensors support bidirectional communications, are individually addressable, and form scalable, reliable, and robust networks. Networked sensors can be integrated by either wired or wireless approaches:

- *Wired sensors.* Some sensors are equipped with network ports and can be plugged directly into building control networks. They may support protocols including BACnet (ASHRAE *Standard* 135 [ASHRAE 2012]), LonWorks® (ISO 2012), Modbus® (Modbus 2012), etc.
- *Wireless sensors.* Wireless protocols, such as ZigBee® (ZigBee Alliance 2008), Z-Wave® (Z-Wave® Alliance 2014), and WirelessHART® (IEC *Standard* 62591 [2010]) are

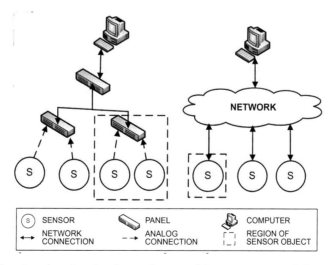

Figure 18.2 Traditional twisted-pair wired sensing architecture transmitting analog signals (left) versus computer network architecture capable of exchanging digital information (right).

designed for low-energy, low-data-rate sensors. Wi-Fi (IEEE *Standard* 802.11 [2016]), WiMax (IEEE *Standard* 802.16 [2017]), Bluetooth® (Bluetooth SIG 2013), and GSM cellular protocols (Eberspächer et al. 2009) are also found in different types of sensors.

Data Object Intelligence. In this approach, structured data and commands are encapsulated within sensor data objects. Traditional sensors do not have computation capabilities to process high-level commands from control systems. For sensors with data object intelligence, sensor vendors ship sensors with detailed data sheets and sophisticated instructions on diagnostics. It is nontrivial work for field engineers to understand the detailed differences between hundreds of sensors and to implement proper sensor-handling logic in control systems; this type of intelligence automates those tasks. BACnet (ASHRAE *Standard* 135 [2012]) and IEEE *Standard* 1451 (2007) are representative standards that support object models:

- *BACnet.* This protocol supports data objects in traditional system architectures. In addition to reading from sensors, a controller can send commands/messages to sensors. Note that commands are not sent to physical sensors, where information flow is always from sensor to panel. For example, the panel can receive a "who-is" query from other BACnet devices and respond accordingly to describe its attached sensors.
- *IEEE* Standard *1451.* This smart sensor standard has been adopted by the automobile industry for test data acquisition. It features **transducer electronic data sheets (TEDS)**, which make plug-and-play operation feasible. Because sensor data, including calibration parameters, are embedded in TEDS, calibration can be conducted automatically. Numerous IEEE *Standard* 1451 vendors provide smart sensors for HVAC systems. However, the technology has not yet been widely adopted by the building industry, partially because of its high device cost.

Web Automation Intelligence. With this approach, sensor data objects are exposed as web services and integrated with web applications. Today, many sensors are connected to the Internet and expose web services via standard or proprietary application programming interfaces (APIs). These devices are often referred as the "Internet of things," or IoT. For example, a personal weather station can measure and submit air quality data to the cloud, where the data are shared with the world through the Internet. Various vendors collect building performance data from customer sites via the Internet, process the raw data in the cloud, and expose results of business analysis to the web for applications of weather monitoring, lighting control, remote FDD, and IEQ monitoring. Some web data object standards including XML standards, such as Sensor Model Language (SensorML) (OGC® *Standard* 12-000), Transducer Markup Language—TransducerML (retired) (OGC® *Standard* 06-010r6), and numerous OASIS standards for smart grid and security.

The four levels of intelligence for smart sensors are interdependent. Local intelligence is the foundation for the entire architecture. Networking intelligence enables bidirectional data exchange and shields users from the detailed data transportation mechanism. Data object intelligence offers an abstracted and concise sensor data interface for effective software integration and serves as the enabling technology for plug-and-play sensors. As the result, engineers are liberated from tedious work such as manual sensor calibration. The web automation intelligence is the most advanced form of "smart" for sensors. Propelled by increasing applications in cloud computing, smart grid, and mobile devices, smart sensors with web automation intelligence could be widely used to enable smart building systems.

Actuators

The typical actuators used in smart buildings are similar to those used in all buildings. Smart buildings rely on actuators to, among other tasks, modify air flows through damper control and other means, modify chilled-water flow, adjust steam flows, shut off electrical devices, and adjust shading devices. Refer to Chapter 7 of the 2017 *ASHRAE Handbook—Fundamentals* for in-depth discussion of control actuation approaches for building systems.

A smart actuator is one that can correct itself and is possibly self powered. It can also have some sort of display showing the status of the actuator, either on the actuator itself, or on monitoring software having data sent to it directly from the actuator.

Smart actuators are relatively new and are still in the research phase. Not many commercially available smart actuator technologies are currently on the market. Research is ongoing to develop self-correcting HVAC actuators that detect soft faults (e.g., problems in computer software, incorrect set points) and automatically correct to the proper operating condition, as well as to develop ways to automatically correct hard faults (e.g., bent damper linkages) by adjusting actuator response to compensate for the faults (Fernandez et al. 2009; Siemens VAI 2008). Other efforts have pursued developing self-powered actuators that communicate using wireless mechanisms. These devices can control valves and dampers and are powered through harvested thermal or vibrational energy. Because actuators require more energy than sensors, power management is critical in such devices to ensure that they function as desired.

As smart actuators mature, the HVAC field could benefit from this new technology through potential energy savings (e.g., preventing energy waste from faulty actuators and by using self-powered actuators) and through potential maintenance cost savings (e.g., from automated calibration).

Sensor and Actuator Integration

To achieve truly smart buildings, smart sensors and actuators must take advantage of all data obtained throughout the building. Communication between devices is therefore critical. With the large number of sensing and actuating points, conventional sensor wiring may become impractical, especially when attempting to implement these systems on existing buildings. For these reasons, communication (via wireless means and power lines) is a vital technique to integrate smart devices to make a complete building network.

Chapter 41 of *ASHRAE Handbook—Fundamentals* (ASHRAE 2017a) provides an in-depth discussion of wireless technologies, suitable applications for wireless devices, and selection of wireless systems. For smart sensing and actuating, low-data-rate technologies are most appropriate, though radios based on IEEE *Standard* 802.11 (2016) could be used because of their large market. Although reliable communications are of paramount importance when considering wireless communications, low maintenance becomes critical when many devices are present in a building. One of the key maintenance concerns is the need to replace batteries, because many of these devices may not have convenient access to line power. Protocols for low-data-rate applications attempt to minimize energy consumption of these devices by taking steps such as putting the devices to sleep when they are not actively taking measurements, performing actions, or transmitting or receiving commands. IEEE *Standard* 802.15.4 (2003) is one such protocol that specifies the physical layers and media access control of radios appropriate for low-data-rate applications. This standard forms the basis of specifications such as ZigBee (ZigBee Alliance 2008), ISA *Standard* 100.11a (2011), WirelessHART (IEC *Standard* 62591 [2010]), and proprietary protocols, such as MiWi™, which add upper layers to IEEE *Standard* 802.15.4 to increase usability.

Reliability of Wireless Communications in Buildings. Attenuation of signals by building materials and interference from other devices make long-distance signal travel difficult. To overcome these problems, different network topologies can be implemented to make the network more robust. For example, a mesh network can allow each device to transmit and receive, communicating with other devices to relay messages through the network to their intended destinations or to enable direct communication between devices without the need for central control equipment. The intelligence can, therefore, be moved down to specific portions of the building.

Wired Power Line Communications (PLC). Power line communication can also be used to reduce the cost and effort in deploying smart sensors and actuators throughout a building. In this type of communication, signals are sent over the same wires that carry alternating current (ac) electric power in a building. This approach reduces the need to run dedicated control system wiring and is especially useful in existing buildings. Some installation of wiring may still be needed to connect the sensor or actuator to the nearest electrical outlet. Modulated signals are typically sent at frequencies away from the common 50 to 60 Hz frequency of ac electricity. Bandwidth that is appropriate for streaming Internet traffic can be achieved, but noise on the lines and components of the electrical system (e.g., transformers) can make the signal unavailable in certain installations. IEEE *Standard* 1901 (2010) provides specifications for providing high-speed broadband networking over power lines using frequencies below 100 MHz. A variety of commercial protocols are available to provide a suite of products that can communicate with each other.

Physical integration of the sensors and actuators is not the final step in developing the components of a smart building; integrating the data streams seamlessly is a challenge, considering the potentially large number of devices. IEEE *Standard* 1451 provides guidance that aims to create plug-and-play devices that automatically report key operating parameters to other devices connected to them. Standards such as these will help to ease the burden in configuring sensing and actuating systems in buildings.

CASE STUDY
One Vanderbilt

Name: One Vanderbilt

Location: New York, New York

Description: Set to become the tallest office tower in Midtown, One Vanderbilt will meet the market demands of Midtown East as it transforms the civic experience of the Grand Central District. Following the layered architectural language of neighboring New York City icons, One Vanderbilt joins the Chrysler Building and Empire State Building as one of three-point towers to define the city's renowned skyline.

One Vanderbilt fits into the city's network of public transport more than any other building, blending private enterprise and the public realm. The base of the building will be part of the spatial sequence of Grand Central and a doorstep to the city, greeting thousands of commuters daily. An integrated complex of below-grade conditions offers connections to the terminal, the new East Side Access, and an active urban base.

The building's massing is made up of four interlocking and tapering volumes that spiral toward the sky, in sympathetic proportion to the nearby Chrysler Building. At the base, a series of angled cuts organize a visual procession to Grand Central, revealing the Vanderbilt corner of the terminal's cornice—a view that has been obstructed for nearly a century.

Building Function: Contains TD Bank offices

Building Height: 1401 ft (427 m)

Building Floor Area: 1,750,212 ft^2 (162,600 m^2)

Architect: Kohn Pedersen Fox Associates (Design)

Structural Engineer: Severud Associates Consulting Engineers (Design)

MEP Engineer: Jaros, Baum and Bolles (Design)

Report courtesy of KPF.

APPENDIX A
Climatic Calculation Examples for Four Cities

For the following calculation examples[9], four cities were selected, each with its own unique climate characteristics: Beijing (cold, dry), Bangkok (hot, humid), Dubai (hot, arid), and Copenhagen (cold, humid). Because stack effect has different influences on buildings of different heights, in each city, buildings of various heights were calculated.[10]

For each city, climate data (acquired from a climate consultant) show the average winter and summer temperature and humidity, which can be used to calculate stack effect in different ASHRAE climate zones (Figure A.1). The lighter shade indicates the averages, and the darker shade shows the summer and winter temperature extremes.

The building type is residential. Outdoor temperature and humidity levels are equal to the heating or cooling seasons' average temperature. Indoor temperature is 70°F (38°C), height above sea level is 0 ft (0 m), wind speed is 5 mph (8 km/h), typical building floor height is 14 ft (4.3 m), air pressure is 29.92 in. Hg (101.3 kPa), and results are per square foot (meter) of envelope area.

Beijing. Table A.1 gives the example parameters, and Table A.2 shows the calculation results. As shown in Figure A.2, the biggest difference between internal pressure occurs in winter, when internal pressure increases along the building height; in summer, it decreases along the height. In addition, when the building gets taller, its NPL on the windward side rises: the extreme is for a building height of 1969 ft (600 m), for which the NPL on the windward side is almost on the top of the building. For a 328 ft (100 m) building, the windward-side pressure is almost the same as the stack pressure.

For the climate in Beijing, which is cold and dry in the winter and warm and humid in summer, stack effect is much more intense than in warmer climates. Stack effect during cold outdoor conditions may cause problems, such as elevator doors not closing properly because of the pressure differential across the doors, causing the doors to stick in their guideways enough that the closing mechanism cannot overcome it.

Another difference of Beijing compared with other cities is that the wintertime NPL is slightly lower, or below the middle of the building. During winter in a 1969 ft (600 m) building in Beijing, the NPL is slightly below 984 ft (300 m), which means the indoor air pressure is much higher at the upper level of the building than in the following cities. Therefore, for upper levels of the building, air leakage is much greater in Beijing than other, warmer cities, the air-

---

9.   This appendix provides partial text from Chapter 4, Tall Buildings, in *ASHRAE Handbook—HVAC Applications* (2019a). For this information to integrate smoothly into this book, the figure and table numbering have been modified from the original; otherwise the content remains as originally published.

10.   Please refer to the spreadsheets available at https://www.ashrae.org/tallbuildings.

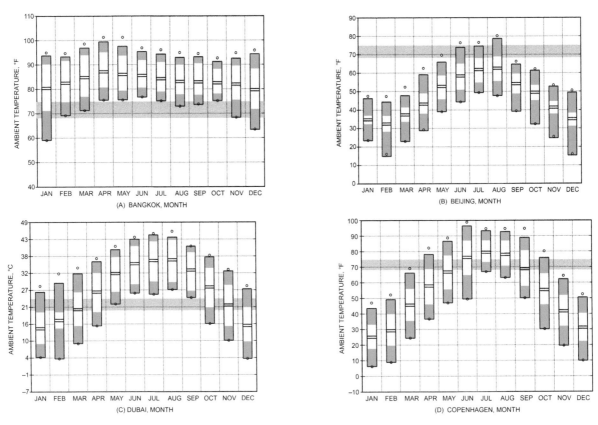

Figure A.1 Climate data for (A) Bangkok, (B) Beijing, (C) Dubai, and (D) Copenhagen, I-P.

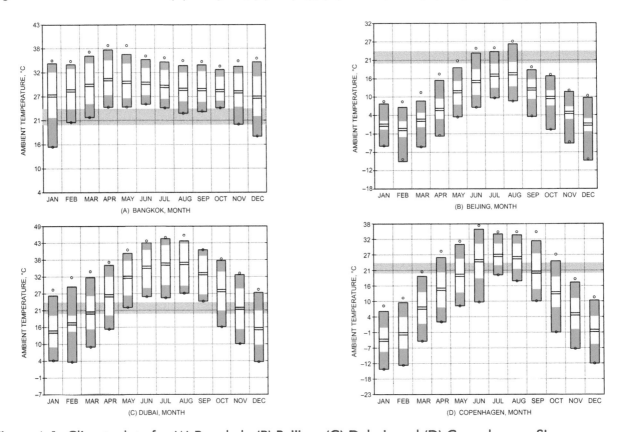

Figure A.1 Climate data for (A) Bangkok, (B) Beijing, (C) Dubai, and (D) Copenhagen, SI.

flow rate is higher, the building function is significantly affected. Address stack effect during design. Architects and engineers must pay close attention to solving the problems associated with stack effect, which are exacerbated in extremely cold climates.

Bangkok. Bangkok has a hot and humid climate throughout the year (Table A.3); therefore, in winter, the leeward- and windward-side pressures on the Bangkok building change more from the bottom to the top than those on the Beijing building (Figure A.3 and Table A.4). Also, because even in winter outdoor air is warmer than the indoor air, internal pressure decreases along the building height.

Because Bangkok's climate is humid and hot throughout the year, winter and summer temperatures are similar (average winter temperature is approximately 80°F (27°C), and average summer temperature is approximately 84°F [29°C]). Stack effect on the building in summer and winter is therefore approximately the same.

Figures A.4 and A.5 show air density and wind speed changes along the building height. According to the calculation, wind speed increases from 5 mph (8 km/h) at ground level to 22 mph (35 km/h) at the top (i.e., more than four times greater at the upper level). In contrast, air density decreases drastically as building height increases, from 0.0737 lb/ft^3 (1.18 kg/m^3) to

Table A.1 Parameters for Beijing Example Building

	Summer	Winter
Outdoor temperature, °F (°C)	94.9 (34.9)	15.6 (−9.1)
Indoor temperature, °F (°C)	75 (24)	68 (20)
Relative humidity, %	54	15
Height above sea level, ft (m)	180 (54)	180 (54)
Wind speed, mph (km/h)	14.9 (23.98)	14.9 (23.98)
Air pressure, in. Hg (kPa)	29.77 (101)	29.77 (101)

Table A.2 Stack Effect Calculations for Beijing Example Buildings (I-P)

	Height, ft						
	0	328	668	988	1308	1648	1968
Outdoor air temperature, °F	94.90	92.44	89.90	87.50	85.11	82.56	80.16
Air pressure, in. of water	405.16	399.74	394.18	389.00	383.88	378.50	373.49
Air density, lb/ft^3	0.07	0.07	0.07	0.07	0.07	0.07	0.07
Stack pressure difference, in. of water	0.00	−0.08	−0.17	−0.25	−0.32	−0.40	−0.48
Wind pressure, in. of water	1.07E-02	2.30E-02	2.95E-02	3.46E-02	3.91E-02	4.35E-02	4.73E-02
Total pressure, in. of water	405.14	399.64	394.00	388.75	383.56	378.10	373.02
Airflow rate, ft^3/s	828.08	826.17	824.18	822.30	820.42	818.41	816.52
Internal pressure, in. of water	389.08	389.08	389.08	389.08	389.08	389.08	389.08
Wind speed, mph	14.90	21.97	24.99	27.18	29.03	30.76	32.23
Windward side, in. of water	421.19	415.70	410.06	404.81	399.62	394.16	389.08
Leeward side, in. of water	389.08	383.59	377.95	372.70	367.50	362.05	356.97

Table A.2 Stack Effect Calculations for Beijing Example Buildings (SI)

	Height, m						
	0	100.0	203.7	301.2	398.8	502.4	600.0
Outdoor air temperature, °C	34.94	33.58	32.17	30.84	29.51	28.09	26.76
Air pressure, kPa	100.58	99.23	97.85	96.57	95.30	93.96	92.72
Air density, kg/m^3	1.14	1.13	1.12	1.11	1.10	1.09	1.08
Stack pressure difference, kPa	0.00	−0.04	−0.08	−0.12	−0.16	−0.20	−0.24
Wind pressure, kPa	8.14E-03	1.75E-02	2.25E-02	2.63E-02	2.98E-02	3.31E-02	3.61E-02
Total pressure, kPa	100.58	99.20	97.78	96.46	95.16	93.78	92.51
Airflow rate, m^3/s	23.45	23.39	23.33	23.28	23.22	23.17	23.11
Internal pressure, kPa	96.41	96.37	96.33	96.29	96.25	96.21	96.17
Wind speed, km/h	23.98	35.36	40.23	43.74	46.71	49.50	51.86
Windward side, kPa	104.12	102.74	101.32	100.00	98.69	97.32	96.04
Leeward side, kPa	96.41	95.03	93.62	92.30	90.99	89.62	88.34

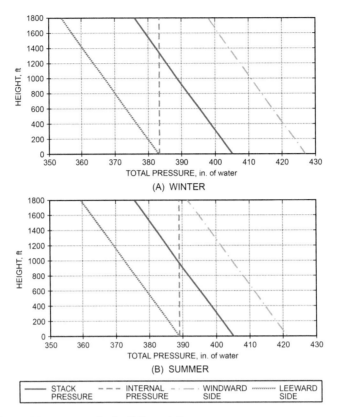

Figure A.2 Stack effect for Beijing example building, I-P.

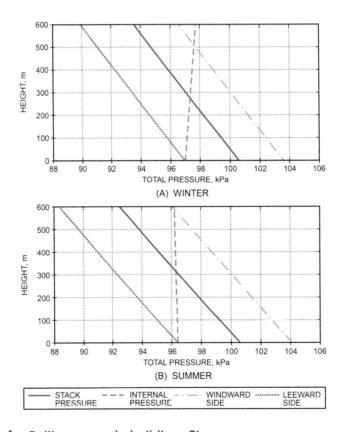

Figure A.2 Stack effect for Beijing example building, SI.

0.0696 lb/ft^3 (1.115 kg/m^3). Because the wind speed increase along the building height is so great, the airflow rate is much higher at the upper level compared to the lower level. It is crucial for architects and engineers to consider the high wind pressure on the building façade's upper levels.

Dubai. Because Dubai is in a hot and arid climate area (Table A.5), the summertime decrease of leeward-side, windward-side, and internal pressures is more obvious, and the NPL on the windward side almost reaches the top of the building (Figure A.6 and Table A.6). This means the windward side continuously admits air from the outdoors. Even though the temperature in summer is extremely high in Dubai, its winter temperature is lower than Bangkok's and below the building's internal temperature, which means the internal pressure decreases along the building height.

The biggest problem in Dubai is the ambient humidity. In summer, humidity is extremely low, averaging approximately 9% rh, which significantly influences the stack effect. As shown in Figure A.6, when the relative humidity increases from 9% to 60%, the air temperature at the top level of a 1969 ft (600 m) building changes from 79°F (26°C) to 82°F (28°C). Air temperature is the most significant factor that affects stack effect. Therefore, architects and engineers should also consider the consequences of humidity on stack effect when designing a building.

Table A.3 Parameters for Bangkok Example Building

	Summer	Winter
Outdoor temperature, °F (°C)	96.7 (35.9)	67.4 (19.7)
Indoor temperature, °F (°C)	75 (24)	68 (20)
Relative humidity, %	56	56
Height above sea level, ft (m)	13 (4)	13 (4)
Wind speed, mph (km/h)	10 (16.1)	10 (16.1)
Air pressure, in. Hg (kPa)	29.77 (101)	29.77 (101)

Table A.4 Stack Effect Calculations for Bangkok Example Buildings (I-P)

	Height, ft						
	0	328	668	988	1308	1648	1968
Outdoor air temperature, °F	96.70	94.26	91.73	89.35	86.98	84.45	82.07
Air pressure, in. of water	407.95	402.49	396.90	391.69	386.54	381.13	376.09
Air density, lb/ft^3	0.07	0.07	0.07	0.07	0.07	0.07	0.07
Stack pressure difference, in. of water	0.00	−0.09	−0.18	−0.27	−0.35	−0.44	−0.52
Wind pressure, in. of water	4.83E-03	1.40E-02	1.92E-02	2.33E-02	2.71E-02	3.09E-02	3.42E-02
Total pressure, in. of water	407.91	402.38	396.70	391.41	386.18	380.69	375.57
Airflow rate, ft^3/s	829.41	827.51	825.53	823.66	821.78	819.78	817.90
Internal pressure, in. of water	391.74	391.74	391.74	391.74	391.74	391.74	391.74
Wind speed, mph	10.00	17.07	20.09	22.28	24.13	25.86	27.33
Windward side, in. of water	424.09	418.55	412.87	407.58	402.35	396.86	391.74
Leeward side, in. of water	391.74	386.21	380.53	375.24	370.01	364.52	359.40

Table A.4 Stack Effect Calculations for Bangkok Example Buildings (SI)

	Height, m						
	0	100.0	203.7	301.2	398.8	502.4	600.0
Outdoor air temperature, °C	35.94	34.59	33.19	31.87	30.55	29.14	27.82
Air pressure, kPa	101.27	99.92	98.53	97.24	95.96	94.61	93.36
Air density, kg/m^3	1.14	1.13	1.12	1.11	1.10	1.09	1.08
Stack pressure difference, kPa	0.00	−0.05	−0.09	−0.13	−0.18	−0.22	−0.26
Wind pressure, kPa	3.68E-03	1.06E-02	1.46E-02	1.78E-02	2.07E-02	2.35E-02	2.60E-02
Total pressure, kPa	101.27	99.87	98.44	97.11	95.79	94.41	93.12
Airflow rate, m^3/s	23.49	23.43	23.37	23.32	23.26	23.20	23.15
Internal pressure, kPa	97.06	97.02	96.97	96.93	96.88	96.84	96.80
Wind speed, km/h	16.09	27.48	32.34	35.85	38.83	41.61	43.98
Windward side, kPa	104.84	103.45	102.02	100.69	99.37	97.98	96.70
Leeward side, kPa	97.06	95.67	94.24	92.91	91.59	90.20	88.92

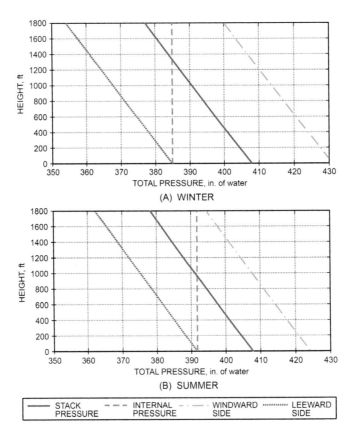

Figure A.3 Stack effect for Bangkok example building, I-P.

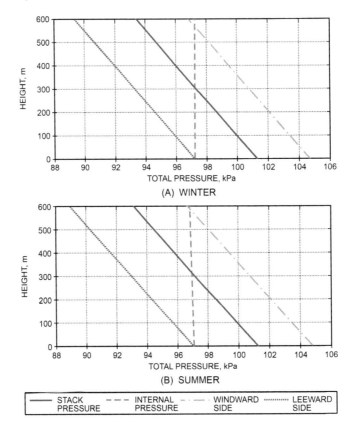

Figure A.3 Stack effect for Bangkok example building, SI.

Copenhagen. Table A.7 gives the parameters for the Copenhagen example building. Stack effect is shown in Figure A.8, and the calculations are shown in Table A.8.

Stack effect exists in almost every tall building higher than 100 m. Its effect on the building's interior environment or façade is significant because the increased difference between indoor and outdoor air pressure and increased wind speed on the building envelope's exterior cause problems that considerably affect building function. For example, elevator doors may not close because of pressure differences across the door; heating load may be increased by a substantial influx of cold air entering the building through openings at the lower levels. An extreme example would be an extremely tall commercial building whose lower portion is occupied while the top of the building is still under construction. A

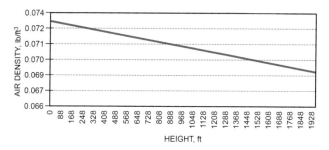

Figure A.4 Air density for Bangkok example building, I-P.

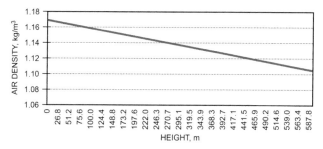

Figure A.4 Air density for Bangkok example building, SI.

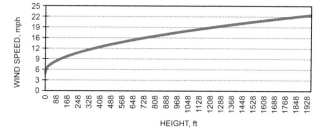

Figure A.5 Wind speed for Bangkok example building, I-P.

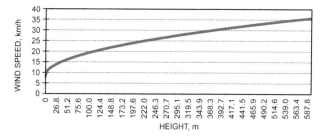

Figure A.5 Wind speed for Bangkok example building, SI.

tall building with an open top has the NPL shifted to the top of the building. This shift causes an extremely high outdoor air pressure on the building at the lower floors, which could result in malfunction of the revolving entry doors.

As demonstrated by the example buildings, it is important to pay attention to the windward and leeward sides of the building, because each side has different pressure differentials between indoors and outdoors. These differences cause different airflow directions in the building, especially in windy areas like Chicago, where wind can place huge pressures on the building façade.

It is therefore, mandatory that stack effect gain enough attention from both architects and engineers when designing high-rise buildings to ensure tight envelopes and means to deal with stack effect infiltration and exfiltration. Knowing its mechanism and calculation requirements can help improve understanding of the distribution of ambient air pressure and temperature, and identify potential problems so that they can be avoided when the building is occupied.

Climate (especially temperature and pressure) also significantly influences stack effect in and on the building. Figure A.9 shows the pressure difference in the example cities used previously. In Beijing or Copenhagen, the temperature is extremely low during the winter; the temperature change along building height can cause pressure to change from 407.5 in. of water to

Table A.5 Parameters for Dubai Example Building

	Summer	Winter
Outdoor temperature, °F (°C)	109.2 (42.9)	57 (13.9)
Indoor temperature, °F (°C)	75 (24)	68 (20)
Relative humidity, %	38	45
Height above sea level, ft (m)	33 (10)	33 (10)
Wind speed, mph (km/h)	16.4 (26.4)	16.4 (26.4)
Air pressure, in. Hg (kPa)	29.77 (101)	29.77 (101)

Table A.6 Stack Effect Calculations for Dubai Example Buildings (I-P)

	Height, ft						
	0	328	668	988	1308	1648	1968
Outdoor air temperature, °F	109.20	106.60	103.91	101.38	98.85	96.16	93.62
Air pressure, in. of water	407.61	402.16	396.57	391.37	386.22	380.82	375.78
Air density, lb/ft³	0.07	0.07	0.07	0.07	0.07	0.07	0.07
Stack pressure difference, in. of water	0.00	−0.14	−0.28	−0.41	−0.54	−0.68	−0.80
Wind pressure, psi	1.27E-02	2.58E-02	3.25E-02	3.78E-02	4.25E-02	4.70E-02	5.09E-02
Total pressure, psi	407.59	402.01	396.29	390.96	385.69	380.15	375.00
Airflow rate, ft³/s	838.69	836.64	834.50	832.49	830.47	828.31	826.28
Internal pressure, in. of water	391.29	391.29	391.29	391.29	391.29	391.29	391.29
Wind speed, mph	16.40	23.47	26.49	28.68	30.53	32.26	33.73
Windward side, in. of water	423.89	418.31	412.58	407.26	401.98	396.45	391.29
Leeward side, in. of water	391.29	385.71	379.99	374.66	369.39	363.85	358.70

Table A.6 Stack Effect Calculations for Dubai Example Buildings

	Height, m						
	0	100.0	203.7	301.2	398.8	502.4	600.0
Outdoor air temperature, °C	42.89	41.45	39.95	38.55	37.14	35.65	34.24
Air pressure, kPa	101.19	99.83	98.45	97.16	95.88	94.54	93.29
Air density, kg/m³	1.12	1.11	1.10	1.09	1.08	1.07	1.06
Stack pressure difference, kPa	0.00	−0.07	−0.14	−0.21	−0.27	−0.34	−0.40
Wind pressure, kPa	9.67E-03	1.96E-02	2.48E-02	2.88E-02	3.23E-02	3.58E-02	3.88E-02
Total pressure, kPa	101.19	99.78	98.32	96.97	95.63	94.22	92.91
Airflow rate, m³/s	23.75	23.69	23.62	23.56	23.50	23.44	23.38
Internal pressure, kPa	96.92	96.85	96.78	96.71	96.65	96.58	96.52
Wind speed, km/h	26.39	37.78	42.64	46.15	49.13	51.91	54.28
Windward side, kPa	104.83	103.42	101.96	100.61	99.27	97.86	96.55
Leeward side, kPa	96.92	95.51	94.05	92.70	91.36	89.95	88.64

377.4 in. of water (101.5 kPa to 94 kPa). However, in Dubai, which averages higher temperatures during the year than Beijing or Copenhagen, the temperature change along building height causes pressure to decrease from 407.5 in. of water to 375.4 in. of water (101.5 kPa to 93.5 kPa). In Bangkok, the pressures change from 407.5 in. of water to 374.1 in. of water (101.5 kPa to 93.2 kPa). This phenomenon must be addressed by architects and engineers when designing tall buildings in warmer cities, where building façades experience greater pressure changes. The upper levels of the building might experience significantly more infiltration (reverse stack effect), which may cause greater heat loss and consequently higher energy consumption.

A high-rise building in Bangkok is more likely to have reduced pressure on the upper levels, which means more infiltration from the external environment to the inside of the building, resulting in higher energy consumption. In Bangkok, it is important to improve the building's tightness to minimize air leakage into the upper levels of the building.

In cities like Beijing and Copenhagen, where tall buildings experience high pressures at upper levels, the opposite of the Bangkok situation occurs in the winter; therefore, when designing the building, increasing indoor pressure is important.

Essentially, in cold climates, designers need to reduce the high pressure at upper levels of a high-rise building, and in warm climates, which have lower pressure at the top level, it is crucial to minimize infiltration by increasing the internal pressure.

Table A.7 Parameters for Copenhagen Example Building

	Summer	Winter
Outdoor temperature, °F (°C)	77.8 (25.4)	21.2 (–6)
Indoor temperature, °F (°C)	75 (24)	68 (20)
Relative humidity, %	58	75
Height above sea level, ft (m)	16 (4.8)	16 (4.8)
Wind speed, mph (km/h)	22.9 (36.9)	22.9 (36.9)
Air pressure, in. Hg (kPa)	29.77 (101)	29.77 (101)

Table A.8 Stack Effect Calculations for Copenhagen Example Buildings

	Height, ft						
	0	**328**	**668**	**988**	**1308**	**1648**	**1968**
Outdoor air temperature, °F	77.80	75.38	72.87	70.51	68.15	65.64	63.27
Air pressure, in. of water	407.89	402.44	396.85	391.64	386.50	381.08	376.05
Air density, lb/ft^3	0.07	0.07	0.07	0.07	0.07	0.07	0.07
Stack pressure difference, in. of water	0.00	–0.01	–0.02	–0.04	–0.05	–0.06	–0.07
Wind pressure, in. of water	2.62E-02	4.45E-02	5.35E-02	6.02E-02	6.61E-02	7.18E-02	7.67E-02
Total pressure, in. of water	407.89	402.44	396.84	391.63	386.48	381.06	376.02
Airflow rate, ft^3/s	815.23	813.39	811.48	809.67	807.86	805.93	804.11
Internal pressure, in. of water	391.95	391.95	391.95	391.95	391.95	391.95	391.95
Wind speed, mph	22.90	29.97	32.99	35.18	37.03	38.76	40.23
Windward side, in. of water	423.82	418.37	412.78	407.57	402.41	397.00	391.95
Leeward side, in. of water	391.95	386.51	380.91	375.70	370.55	365.13	360.09

Table A.8 Stack Effect Calculations for Copenhagen Example Buildings

	Height, m						
	0	**100.0**	**203.7**	**301.2**	**398.8**	**502.4**	**600.0**
Outdoor air temperature, °C	25.44	24.10	22.71	21.40	20.08	18.69	17.38
Air pressure, kPa	101.26	99.90	98.52	97.22	95.95	94.60	93.35
Air density, kg/m^3	1.18	1.17	1.16	1.15	1.14	1.13	1.12
Stack pressure difference, kPa	0.00	–0.01	–0.01	–0.02	–0.02	–0.03	–0.03
Wind pressure, kPa	2.00E-02	3.39E-02	4.07E-02	4.59E-02	5.04E-02	5.47E-02	5.84E-02
Total pressure, kPa	101.27	99.92	98.54	97.24	95.96	94.62	93.37
Airflow rate, m^3/s	23.09	23.03	22.98	22.93	22.88	22.82	22.77
Internal pressure, kPa	97.20	97.19	97.18	97.18	97.17	97.17	97.16
Wind speed, km/h	36.85	48.24	53.10	56.61	59.59	62.37	64.74
Windward side, kPa	104.71	103.37	101.98	100.69	99.41	98.06	96.81
Leeward side, kPa	97.20	95.85	94.46	93.17	91.89	90.55	89.29

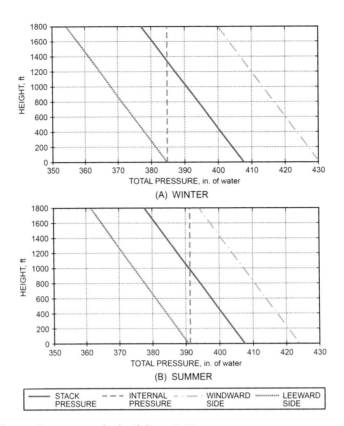

Figure A.6 Stack effect for Dubai example building (I-P).

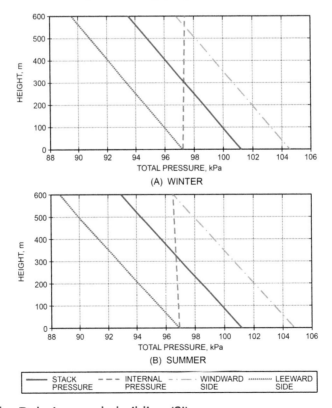

Figure A.6 Stack effect for Dubai example building (SI).

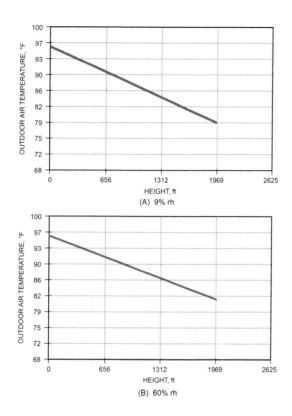

Figure A.7 Atmospheric temperature for Dubai example building, I-P.

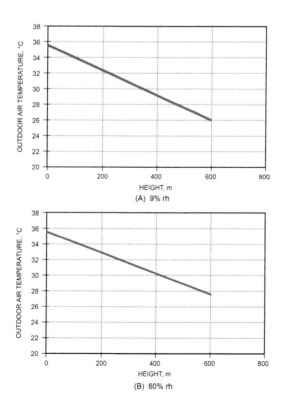

Figure A.7 Atmospheric temperature for Dubai example building, SI.

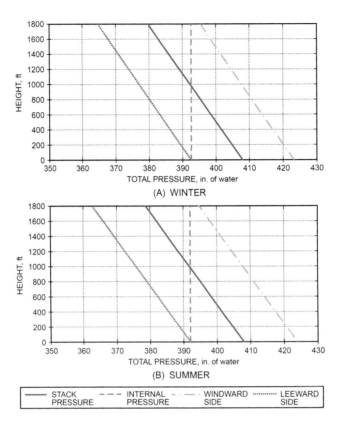

Figure A.8 Stack effect for Copenhagen example building, I-P.

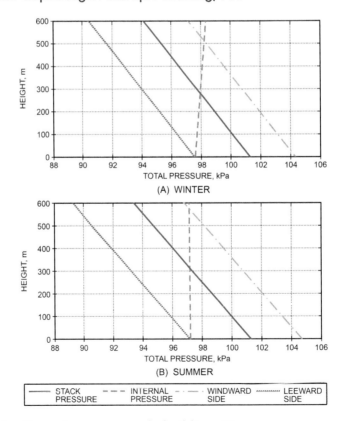

Figure A.8 Stack effect for Copenhagen example building, SI.

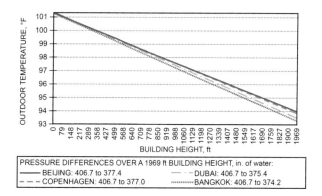

Figure A.9 Air pressure difference over a 1969 ft building height in four example cities, I-P.

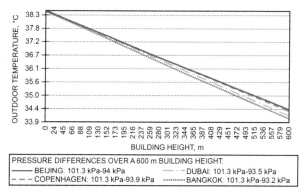

Figure A.9 Air pressure difference over a 600 m building height in four example cities, SI.

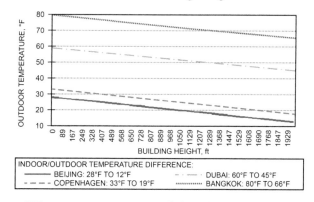

Figure A.10 Air temperature difference over a 1969 ft building height in four example cities, I-P.

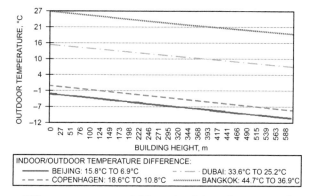

Figure A.10 Air temperature difference over a 600 m building height in four example cities, SI.

The ambient temperature difference along the building height varies from city to city (Figure A.10), and interacts with stack effect to influence infiltration/exfiltration. In Beijing, the temperature is low around the top levels of the building, which, combined with a higher pressure, causes increased air infiltration from the outdoors, resulting in increased heating and higher energy consumption. However, in warmer cities like Bangkok and Dubai, the upper-level temperature is warm during most of the year. In winter, this warmth is beneficial; however, in summer, the warmer air can infiltrate into the upper levels of the building, increasing the building's cooling load. It is therefore always beneficial to seal the building tightly to avoid the stack effect.

APPENDIX B
Energy Analysis

BASIC CONDITIONS

In this study, DesignBuilder is selected as the simulation tool to analyze energy performance in high-rise buildings. Three basic cases are developed, including 328, 984, and 2000 ft (100, 300, and 600 m) tall buildings. The location is in Shanghai, meeting the requirement of GB 50189-2005, *Design Standard for Energy Efficiency of Public Buildings* (PRC 2005), as baseline.

SIMULATION PROGRAM INPUT

Table B.1 Characteristics of Each Floor

Item	Detail
Location	Shanghai
Height	328, 984, 2000 ft (100, 300, 600 m)
Floors	24, 72, 143
Floor to floor height	13 ft 9 in. (4.2 m)
Total floor area	24,122 ft^2 (2241 m^2)
Core area	328 ft^2 (100 m^2)
Perimeter area	23,045 ft^2 (2141 m^2)
Window height	10 ft 6 in. (3.2 m)

Table B.2 Building Envelope Parameters

Element	Value	Reference Standard
Wall U-factor	0.264 Btu/h·ft^2·°F (1.5 W/m^2·K)	
Roof U-factor	0.159 Btu/h·ft^2·°F (0.9 W/m^2·K)	
Window window-to-wall area ratio (WWR)	0.6	PRC 2005
Window U-factor	0.528 Btu/h·ft^2·°F (3.0 W/m^2·K)	
Window solar heat gain coefficient (SHGC)	E,S,W – 0.35, N – 0.45	

Table B.3 Office and Circulation—Summer and Winter

Zone	Summer		Winter	
	Temperature, °F (°C)	RH (%)	Temperature, °F (°C)	RH (%)
Office	78.8 (26)	≤60	64.4 (18)	≥30
Circulation	82.4 (28)	≤65	68 (20)	≥30

* The indoor temperature is 82.4°F (28°C) within 1 hour before and after work (design standard for energy efficiency in public buildings).

Table B.4 Indoor Heat Gains

Element	Zone	Value	Reference Standard
Lighting power density	Office	3.49 Btu/h·ft²·°F (11 W/m²)	
	Circulation	1.59 Btu/h·ft²·°F (5 W/m²)	
Occupancy density	Office	2.54 Btu/h·ft²·°F (8 W/m²)	PRC 2005
	Circulation	15.85 Btu/h·ft²·°F (50 W/m²)	
Equipment density	Office	4.12 Btu/h·ft²·°F (13 W/m²)	
	Circulation	0 Btu/h·ft²·°F (0 W/m²)	

Table B.5 HVAC

Element	Value	Reference Standard
System	Overhead VAV	PRC 2005
Centrifugal chiller COP	5.5	

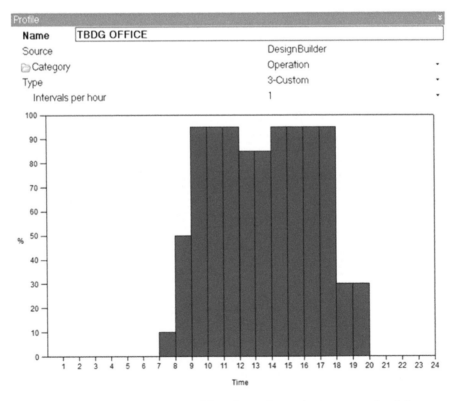

Figure B.1 Customized schedule in DesignBuilder (based on design standard for energy efficiency in public buildings).

Results

Two methods are used to develop the physical model. One is built for each floor or multiple floors with no simplification; another one is built using a multiplier and adiabatic blocks.

Base Case

Model is developed floor by floor, which means it is more time-consuming when running a simulation. Three models are shown in Figure B.2. On the left is Method 1; Method 2 is shown on the right.

Alternative 1

As suggested in the DesignBuilder tutorial, the multiplier (in the Activity Tab) and adiabatic block can also be used for high-rise building modeling as a simple way to accelerate simulation.

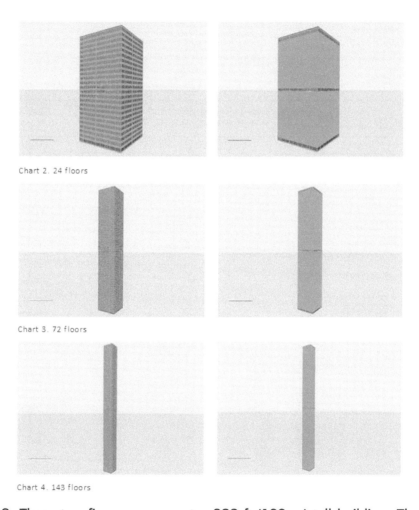

Chart 2. 24 floors

Chart 3. 72 floors

Chart 4. 143 floors

Figure B.2   Chart 2: These two figures represent a 328 ft (100 m) tall building. The figure on the left shows the simulation model, modeled using 24 individual floors. The figure on the right shows the simulation model, modeled from a single floor with a floor multiplier.
Chart 3: These two figures represents 984 ft (300 m) supertall building. The figure on the left shows the simulation model, modeled using 72 individual floors. The figure on the right shows the simulation model, modeled from a single floor with a floor multiplier
Chart 4: These two figures represent a 2000 ft (600 m) megatall building. The figure on the left shows the simulation model, modeled using 143 individual floors. The figure on the right shows the simulation model, modeled from a single floor with a floor multiplier.

Table B.6 EUI Result

Case	Floor	Area, ft² (m²)	Total EUI		Heating, kWh/m²	Cooling, kWh/m²	Lighting, kWh/m²	Equipment, kWh/m²	DHW, kWh/m²
			kWh/m²	kBtu/ft²					
1-Original	24	578,937 (53,785)	258.54	81.96	0.33	70.84	107.52	76.39	3.33
2-Original	72	1,735,950 (161,275)	257.18	81.53	0.23	69.61	107.57	76.43	3.33
3-Original	143	3,447,800 (320,311)	255.99	81.15	0.33	68.32	107.57	76.43	3.33
1-Multiplier	24	578,937 (53,785)	237.71	75.35	**0.55**	**49.83**	107.57	76.43	3.33
2-Multiplier	72	1,735,950 (161,275)	204.21	64.73	**0.23**	**16.65**	107.57	76.43	3.33
3-Multiplier	143	3,447,800 (320,311)	195.84	62.08	**0.15**	**8.35**	107.57	76.43	3.33

DHW = domestic hot water

Table B.7 Total Energy Consumption Result

Case	Floor	Area, ft² (m²)	Heating, kWh	Cooling, kWh	Lighting, kWh	Equipment, kWh	DHW, kWh
1-Original	24	578,937 (53,785)	17,740	3,810,223	5,782,941	4,108,719	179,206
2-Original	72	1,735,950 (161,275)	37,468	11,226,827	17,348,823	12,326,159	537,620
3-Original	143	3,447,800 (320,311)	106,381	21,885,071	34,456,691	24,481,123	1,067,774
1-Multiplier	24	578,937 (53,785)	**29,435**	**2,678,834**	5,782,941	4,108,719	179,206
2-Multiplier	72	1,735,950 (161,275)	**36,341**	**2,685,460**	17,348,823	12,326,159	537,620
3-Multiplier	143	3,447,800 (320,311)	**47,232**	**2,676,027**	34,456,691	24,481,123	1,067,774

DHW = domestic hot water

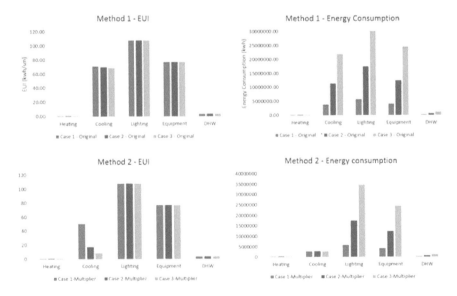

Figure B.3 The difference in EUI and energy consumption between method 1 (individual floors) and method 2 (floor multiplier).

Figure B.4 Activity template.

Results

With both methods, the lighting, equipment, and domestic hot-water (DHW) annual EUI are the same, which means the total energy consumption for these systems increased with the floors and total area.

However, for heating and cooling, the results show the following:

1. The result from Method 1 is similar to other systems. Cooling EUI slightly decreased with the increase of floors, but the total cooling increased with the increase of floors. Heating is similar to cooling.
2. The result from Method 2 is unstable. Although the results for method differ, the total cooling load remains virtually the same, even though the floors are doubled, while the heating load increased only slightly. This results in a decrease in the EUI.

DISCUSSION AND TIPS

1. All six models already have simulation results, which can be seen by clicking the "Simulation" tab directly. Any change made in input will result in rerunning the simulation and generating new results.
2. Method 1 is better and more practical at this stage, because no solution was found for the unstable result generated by using method 2.
3. The result covers annual and monthly energy data, which can be showed by charts, tables, and sheets for further analysis.

APPENDIX C
HVAC Design Criteria and Systems Description for a Multiple-Tenant Office Building

---

1. **General**

   The entire installation will comply with all applicable governmental codes and local regulations.

2. **Design Criteria**

   Temperature and Humidity Conditions

   Outdoor Design Conditions

Winter	0°F (–18°C) db
Summer	95°F (35°C) db

   Indoor Design Conditions

   Heating

All occupied spaces	72°F (22°C) db maximum*
Storage/Mechanical Areas	
Electrical Equipment Areas	65°F (18°C) db
Elevator Machine Rooms	65°F (18°C) db

   * No humidification will be provided.

   Cooling

All occupied spaces	75°F (24°C) db ± 2°F (1°C)
	50% rh maximum ±5%
Storage/Mechanical Areas	Ventilated only
Electrical Equipment Rooms	Ventilated or air conditioned to 85°F (30°C) db minimum
Elevator Machine Rooms	Air conditioned to 80°F (27°C) db minimum

   Internal Heat Loads

   Office Spaces

Lighting	1.2 W/net ft^2 (12 W/net m^2)
Equipment (Small Power)	2 W/net ft^2 (20 W/net m^2)
People	1 person/100 net ft^2 (9.3 net m^2)

Retail Spaces

Lighting and Equipment (Small Power) 17 W/net ft^2 (180 W/net m^2)

People 1 person/50 net ft^2 (4.6 net m^2)

Lobby Spaces

Lighting and Equipment (Small Power) 10 W/net ft^2 (100 W/net m^2)

People 1 person/100 net ft^2 (9.3 net m^2)

Minimum Outdoor Air Quantity

Office Spaces 20 cfm (9.44 L/s)/person

Retail Spaces 20 cfm (9.44 L/s)/person with a 50% occupancy diversity factor applied to the population

Acoustical Design Criteria

Office Spaces Noise levels will conform to a noise criteria of NC 35, except that within 10 ft (3 m) of the local floor fan room, NC 40 will result.

Retail Spaces Noise levels will conform to NC 35, subject to a review of the tenant architectural and engineering design details

3. **Special Design for Supplementary Cooling**

In addition to the capacity to handle the previously mentioned cooling loads as well as the cooling needs of the building façade, the condenser water delivered to each office floor will have the capacity to provide an additional 2 W/net ft^2 (22 W/net m^2) to be used by each tenant for supplemental cooling loads. Tenants using this capacity will provide their own air-handling units and extend the condenser water from valved connections provided in the local fan room.

4. **Air-Conditioning Systems (see Chapter 6)**

5. **Heating Systems**

The system will be fed by supply and return loops serving water risers at the perimeter columns and will be piped in a reverse return arrangement.

6. **Miscellaneous Systems**

Core toilets on each floor will be exhausted at a ventilation rate of 2 cfm/ft^2 (10 L/s·m^2) via duct risers located in the building core. Supply air will be provided at a rate of 1 cfm/ft^2 (5 L/s·m^2).

7. **Building Automation and Temperature Control System**

The building energy management system will be microprocessor based with distributed direct digital processing. It will incorporate the use of direct digital controls (DDC) for all central mechanical equipment. Local zone (VAV box) control will be direct digital control type with electric actuators. Final output to terminal devices (valves, damper operators, etc.) serving central mechanical equipment will be pneumatic. It will be completely stand-alone as a system. Each local floor-by-floor and main air-handling systems and each water system will be provided with a separate DDC unit. The automation system will provide the ability to monitor, control, and optimize the operations of all building HVAC systems and to provide the necessary interfaces to allow proper operation of the building life safety systems. The system will also include a freeze protection sequence to automatically circulate chilled water when the outdoor air temperature drops below an adjustable value.

REFERENCES AND BIBLIOGRAPHY

REFERENCES

AIVC. 1996. *A guide to energy efficient ventilation*. Coventry, UK: Air Infiltration and Ventilation Centre. https://www.aivc.org/sites/default/files/members_area/medias/pdf/Guides/GU03%20GUIDE%20TO%20ENERGY%20EFFICIENT%20VENTILATION.pdf

Akin R.E., J.A. Peterka. and J.E. Cermak. 1979. Averaged pressure coefficients for rectangular buildings. Proc. 5th Inst. Conf. Wind Engineering, Fort Collins, USA 1979. Pergamon Press,.

Al-Sharif, L. 1996. Lift and escalator energy consumption. *Proceedings of the CIBSE/ASHRAE Joint National Conference*, 231–39. England: Harrogate.

ASCE. 2010. Minimum design loads for buildings and other structures. Standard ASCE/SEI 7-10. Reston, VA: American Society of Civil Engineers.

ASHRAE. 2009. *Indoor Air Quality Guide: Best Practices for Design, Construction, and Commissioning*. Atlanta: ASHRAE.

ASHRAE. 2011. *ASHRAE Thermal Comfort Tool*, version 2. Atlanta: ASHRAE.

ASHRAE. 2012. ANSI/ASHRAE Standard 135-2012, *BACnet®—A data communication protocol for building automation and control networks*. Atlanta: ASHRAE.

ASHRAE. 2015a. *Active and Passive Beam Application Design Guide*. Atlanta: ASHRAE.

ASHRAE. 2016a. ANSI/ASHRAE/IES Standard 90.1-2016, Energy Standard for Buildings Except Low-Rise Residential. Atlanta: ASHRAE.

ASHRAE. 2016b. *ASHRAE Handbook—HVAC Systems and Equipment*. Atlanta: ASHRAE.

ASHRAE. 2017a. *ASHRAE Handbook—Fundamentals*. Atlanta: ASHRAE.

ASHRAE. 2017b. ANSI/ASHRAE Standard 55-2017, *Thermal Environmental Conditions for Human Occupancy*. Atlanta: ASHRAE.

ASHRAE. 2018. *ASHRAE Handbook—Refrigeration*. Atlanta: ASHRAE.

ASHRAE. 2019a. *ASHRAE Handbook—HVAC Applications*. Atlanta: ASHRAE.

ASHRAE. 2019b. ANSI/ASHRAE Standard 62.1-2016, *Ventilation for Acceptable Indoor Air Quality*. Atlanta: ASHRAE.

ASME. 1996a. ASME B16.34-1996, *Valves-Flanged, Threaded and Welding End*. New York: American Society of Mechanical Engineers.

ASME. 1996b. ASME B31.9-1996, *Building Services Piping*. New York: American Society of Mechanical Engineers.

ASME. 2013. ASME A17.1-2013/CSA B44-13, *Safety Code for Elevators and Escalators*. New York: American Society of Mechanical Engineers.

ASME. 2015. *Boiler and Pressure Vessel Code*. New York: American Society of Mechanical Engineers.

AWE. 2010. Condensate water introduction. Resource Library, Alliance for Water Efficiency. http://www.allianceforwaterefficiency.org/Condensate_Water_Introduction.aspx.

Bahnfleth, W.P., G.K. Yuill, and B.W. Lee. 1999. Protocol for field testing of tall buildings to determine envelope air leakage rate. ASHRAE Transactions 105(2).

Barrington, T. 2014. Multiple-car elevator systems on the rise. *High Rise Facilities*.

BBRI. 2002. *Source book for a better understanding of conceptual and operational aspects of active façades*. Brussels: Belgian Building Research Institute.

Bendix, M. 2007. Electrical design for tall buildings. *Consulting-Specifying Engineer*. http://www.csemag.com/single-article/electrical-design-for-tall-buildings/7260d7da4cb0d3d74 7af4483a76acb2b.html.

Bluetooth SIG. 2013. *Specification of the Bluetooth® system: Core specification 4.1, volume 0: Master table of contents & compliance requirements*. Bluetooth Special Interest Group, Kirkland, WA.

Bowen A.J. 1976. *A wind tunnel investigation using simple building models to obtain mean surface wind pressure coefficients for air infiltration estimates*. Report LTR LA 20N National Aeronautical Establishment NRCC 1976 Canada.

Brambley, M.R., and S. Katipamula. 2004. Beyond commissioning. *Proceedings of 2004 ACEEE Summer Study on Energy Efficiency in Buildings*. August 22-27, 3-14–3-51. American Council for Energy Efficient Economy, Washington, DC.

Braun, J.E. 1999. Automated fault detection and diagnostics for the HVAC&R industry. *International Journal of Heating, Ventilating, Air-Conditioning and Refrigerating Research* (now *Science and Technology for the Built Environment*) 5(2):85–86.

Calinoiu, D., M. Paulescu, I. Ionel, N. Stefu, N. Pop, R. Boata, A. Pacurar, P. Gravila, E. Paulescu, and G. Trif-Tordai. 2013. Influence of aerosols pollution on the amount of collectable solar energy. *Energy Conversion and Management,* 70:76–82.

Chow, M., and J. Noschang. 2013. Incorporate lighting controls with BAS to save energy. *Consulting-Specifying Engineer*. http://www.csemag.com/single-article/incorporate-ligh ting-controls-with-bas-to-save-energy/656ac830f7020a2e975f45c54552dc4a.html.

CIBSE. 2005. CIBSE AM10-2005, *Natural ventilation in non-domestic buildings*. London: Chartered Institution of Building Services Engineers.

CIBSE. 2015. CIBSE Guide A: Environmental design 2015. London: Chartered Institution of Building Services Engineers.

CEC. 2015a. 2016 Building Energy Efficiency Standards for Residential and Nonresidential Buildings for the 2016 Building Energy Efficiency Standards: Title 24, Part 6, and associated Administrative Regulations in Part 1, CEC-400-2015-037-CMF. California Energy Commission. www.energy.ca.gov/2015publications/CEC-400-2015-037/CEC-400-2015-037-CMF.pdf.

CEC. 2015b. 2016 Nonresidential Compliance Manual for the 2016 Building Energy Efficiency Standards: Title 24, Part 6 and associated Administrative Regulations in Part 1, CEC-400-2015-033-CMF. California Energy Commission. www.energy.ca.gov/2015publications/CEC-400-2015-033/CEC-400-2015-033-CMF.pdf.

CEC. 2015c. 2016 Nonresidential Alternate Calculation Method Compliance Manual for the 2016 Building Energy Efficiency Standards: Title 24, Part 6, and associated Administrative Regulations in Part 1, CEC-400-2015-025-CMF-REV. www.energy.ca.gov/2015publications/CEC-400-2015-025/CEC-400-2015-025-CMF.pdf.

CEN. 2007. EN 15251-2007, *Indoor Environmental Input Parameters for Design and Assessment of Energy Performance of Buildings—Addressing Indoor Air Quality, Thermal Environment, Lighting and Acoustics*. Brussels: CEN.

CMC. 2015. 2016 California mechanical code. Title 24, Part 4. http://epubs.iapmo.org/2016/CMC/mobile/index.html#p=1.

CTBUH. 2015. CTBUII Height Criteria. http://www.ctbuh.org/HighRiseInfo/TallestDatabase /Criteria/tabid/446/language/en-GB/Default.aspx.

CTBUH. 2019. The Skyscraper Center. http://www.skyscrapercenter.com/. Accessed on July 18, 2019.

Davenport, A.G., and H.Y.L. Hui. 1982. External and internal wind pressures on cladding of buildings. BLWT-820133. University of Western Ontario. London, Ontario, Canada: Boundary Layer Wind Tunnel Laboratory.

Deaves, D.M., and R.I. Harris. 1978. A mathematical model of the structure of strong winds. Report 76. Construction Industry Research and Information Association (U.K.).

DOE. 2006. *Benefits of demand response in electricity markets and recommendations for achieving them: A report to the United States Congress pursuant to Section 1252 of the Energy Policy Act of 2005* (February 2006 DOE EPAct Report). U.S. Department of Energy, Washington, DC.

Eberspächer, J., H-J Vögel, C. Bettstetter, and C. Hartmann. 2009. *GSM: Architecture, protocols and services*. Wiley, West Sussex, UK.

Egan, W. 1994. Radiative Transfer Properties of the Sahara Region. *Remote Sensing of Environment* 50:82–193.

Ellis, P.G. and P.A. Torcellini. 2005. Simulating Tall Buildings Using EnergyPlus. Proceedings of the Ninth International Building Performance Simulation Association (IBPSA). QC: Montreal.

Emmerich, S., and A.K. Persily. 2001. NISTIR 6729, *State-of-the-Art Review of CO_2 Demand Controlled Ventilation Technology and Application*. Gaithersburg, MD: National Institute of Standards and Technology.

Emmerich, S.J., and A.K. Persily. 2011. U.S. Commercial Building Airtightness Requirements and Measurements. Proceedings of the 32nd Air Infiltration and Ventilation Centre Conference, Air Infiltration and Ventilation Centre, Belgium.

Energy Design Tools. 2015. *Climate Consultant*, 6.0 Beta. Los Angeles: UCLA.

EPA. n.d. *The ENERGY STAR guidelines for energy management*. U.S. Environmental Protection Agency, Washington, D.C. Available from http://www.energystar.gov/buildings/tools-and-resources/energy-star-guidelines-energy-management.

Faure, L.E. 2018. Minimum Ventilation Requirements for Wind-Pressure-Exposed Environmental Enclosures. Aberdeen Proving Ground, MD: Edgewood Chemical Biological Center.

FERC. 2006. *Assessment of demand response and advanced metering staff report. Docket Number AD06-2-000*, Revised 2008. Federal Energy Regulatory Commission, Washington, DC.

Fernandez, N., M.R. Brambley, and S. Katipamula. 2009. *Self-correcting HVAC controls: Algorithms for sensors and dampers in air-handling units*. PNNL-19104. Pacific Northwest National Laboratory, Richland, WA.

Fisk, W.J. 2008. Personal communication with Leon Alevantis. June 2007–November 2008.

Fisk, W.J., D. Faulkner, and D.P. Sullivan. 2005. An evaluation of three commercially available technologies for real-time measurement of rates of outdoor airflow into HVAC systems. *ASHRAE Transactions* 111(2):443–55.

Fisk, W.J., D. Sullivan, S. Cohen, and H. Han. 2008. *Measuring outdoor air intake rates using electronic velocity sensors at louvers and downstream of airflow straighteners*. Report 1250. Berkeley, CA: Lawrence Berkeley National Laboratory.

Goldman, C., M. Reid, R. Levy, and A. Silverstein. 2010. *Coordination of energy efficiency and demand response*. LBNL-3044E. Lawrence Berkeley National Laboratory, Berkeley, CA.

Gowri, K., D.W. Winiarski, and R.E. Jarnagin. 2009. Infiltration modeling guidelines for commercial building energy analysis. Richland, WA: Pacific Northwest National Laboratory.

Guyer, J.P. 2012. An introduction to cooling buildings by natural ventilation. Fairfax, VA: PDH Center. https://pdhonline.com/courses/m441/m441content.pdf.

Hang, J., and Y. Li. 2010. Ventilation strategy and air change rates in idealized high-rise compact urban areas. *Building and Environment* 45:2754–67.

Hayakawa, S., and S. Togari. 1988 Study on the stack effect of tall office building (part 1). *Journal of Architectural Institute of Japan* 387: 42-52.

Hayakawa, S., and S. Togari. 1990. Simple test method for evaluating exterior wall airtightness of tall office buildings. ASTM STP 1067, Air Change Rate and Airtightness in Buildings. M.H. Sherman, ed. Philadelphia: American Society for Testing and Materials.

Hoyt, T., S. Schiavon, F. Tartarini, T. Cheung, K. Steinfeld, A. Piccoli, and D. Moon. 2009. CBE Thermal Comfort Tool. Berkeley, CA: Center for the Built Environment, University of California Berkeley.

Hunt, C.M. 1986 Some induced-pressure measurements in a high-rise office building. ASTM STP 904, Measured Air Leakage of Buildings. H.R. Trechsel and P.L. Lagus, eds. Philadelphia: American Society for Testing and Materials.

ICC. 2012a. International Energy Conservation Code. Country Club Hills, IL: International Code Council.

ICC. 2012b. International Building Code. Country Club Hills, IL: International Code Council.

ICC. 2018a. IgCC/189.1. *International green construction code® powered by ANSI/ASHRAE/ICC/USGBC/IES Standard 189.1.* Washington, DC: International Code Council.

ICC. 2018b. *International mechanical code®.* Washington, DC: International Code Council.

IEC. 2010. Standard 62591:2010, *Industrial communication networks—Wireless communication network and communication profiles—WirelessHART™.* International Electrotechnical Commission, Geneva, Switzerland.

IEEE. 1990. ANSI/IEEE Standard 241-1990, *IEEE Recommended Practice for Electric Power in Commercial Buildings—Gray Book.* Piscataway, NJ: The Institute of Electric and Electronic Engineers, Inc.

IEEE. 2003. IEEE Standard 802.15.4, Part 15.4, *Wireless medium access control (MAC) and physical layer (PHY) specifications for low-rate wireless personal area networks (LR-WPANs).* Institute of Electrical and Electronics Engineers, New York.

IEEE. 2007. IEEE Standard 1451.0-2007, *IEEE Standard for a Smart Transducer Interface for Sensors and Actuators—Common Functions, Communication Protocols, and Transducer Electronic Data Sheet (TEDS) Formats.* New York: Institute of Electrical and Electronics Engineers.

IEEE. 2010. IEEE Standard 1901-2010, *IEEE Standard for Broadband over Power Line Networks: Medium Access Control and Physical Layer Specifications.* New York: Institute of Electrical and Electronics Engineers.

IEEE. 2016. Standard 802.11-2016, *Wireless LAN Medium Access Control (MAC) and Physical Layer (PHY) Specifications.* IEEE Institute of Electrical and Electronics Engineers, New York.

IEEE. 2017. IEEE Standard 802.16-2017, *IEEE Standard for Air Interface for Broadband Wireless Access Systems.* Institute of Electrical and Electronic Engineers, New York.

ISA. 2011. ANSI/ISA Standard 100.11a-2011, *Wireless Systems For Industrial Automation: Process Control and Related Applications.* International Society of Automation, Research Triangle Park, NC.

Isermann, R. 1984. Process fault detection based on modeling and estimation methods—A survey. *Automatica* 20(4):387–404.

Jacob, E. 2018. Smart elevators—Six major trends for 2019. Dedham, MA: ARC Advisory Group. https://www.arcweb.com/blog/smart-elevators-six-major-trends-2019

Jo, J.H, H.T. Seok, M.S. Yeo, and K.W. Kim. 2009. Simplified prediction method of stack-induced pressure distribution in high-rise residential buildings. *Journal of Asian Architecture and Building Engineering* 8(1):283–90.

Jordan, C. 1989. Central vs. local HVAC fan systems for high-rise office buildings. ASHRAE Journal September, 48–46.

Katipamula, S., and M.R. Brambley. 2005a. Methods for fault detection, diagnostics and prognostics for building systems—A review, part I. *HVAC&R Research* (now *Science and Technology for the Built Environment*) 11(1):3–25.

Katipamula S., and M.R. Brambley. 2005b. Methods for fault detection, diagnostics and prognostics for building systems—A review, part II. *HVAC&R Research* (now *Science and Technology for the Built Environment*) 11(2):169–187.

Katipamula, S., and M. Brambley. 2007. Automated proactive fault isolation: A key to automated commissioning. *ASHRAE Transactions* 113(2): 40-51.

Katipamula S., M.R. Brambley, and L. Luskay. 2003. Automated proactive techniques for commissioning air-handling units. *Journal of Solar Energy Engineering* 125(3):282-291.

Katipamula, S., M.R. Brambley, N.N. Bauman, and R.G. Pratt. 2003. Enhancing building operations through automated diagnostics: Field test results. *Proceedings of the Third International Conference for Enhanced Building Operation*, Texas A&M University, College Station, TX.

Klote, J.H. 1993. Design of Smoke Control Systems for Areas of Refuge. ASHRAE Transactions 99(2).

Klote, J.H. 2014. Elevator pressurization in tall buildings. Lehigh University, Bethlehem, Pennsylvania: Council on Tall buildings and Urban Habitat.

Klote, J.H., and J.A. Milke. 2002. Principles of smoke management. Atlanta: ASHRAE.

Klote, J.H., and G.T. Tamura. 1986. Smoke Control and Fire Evacuation by Elevators, ASHRAE Transactions 92(1):231–45.

Klote, J.H., James A. Milke, Paul G. Turnbull, Ahmed Kashef, and Michael J. Ferreira. 2012. Handbook of Smoke Control Engineering. Atlanta: ASHRAE.

Larson, P. 2007. How to properly size a domestic water pressure booster system. http://www.pmengineer.com/articles/86275-how-to-properly-size-a-domestic-water-pressure-booster-system. *PM Engineer*.

LBNL. 2005. *DOE-2*, Version 2.2. Berkley, CA: Lawrence Berkeley National Laboratory.

Lawson. R.M. 1987. Design for openings in the webs of composite beams. CIRIA Special Publication 51, SCI Publication 068. The Steel Construction Institute, Ascot.

Leung, L., and P. Weismantle. 2008. Sky-sourced sustainability—How super tall buildings can benefit from height. Proceedings of the Council on Tall Buildings and Urban Habitat 8th World Congress, Dubai, UAE.

Leung L., and S.D. Ray. 2013. Low energy tall buildings? Room for improvement as demonstrated by New York City energy benchmarking data. *International Journal of High-Rise Buildings* 2(4):285–91. Council on Tall Buildings and Urban Habitat: Seoul.

Liu, J., F. Qiao, and L. Chang. 2010. The hybrid predictive model of elevator system for energy consumption. *Proceedings of the 2010 International Conference on Modeling, Identification and Control*, Okayama, Japan.

Loncour, X., A. Deneyer, M. Blasco, G. Flamant, and P. Wouters. Ventilated Double façades. *Proceedings of 2nd Biennial of the "Ventilated Double façades" Project*, Belgium: Belgian Building Research Institute.

Lovatt, J.E., and A. G. Wilson. 1994. Stack effect in tall buildings. ASHRAE Transactions 100(2).

Maddox, J.A. 2004. Smoke control and high rise office buildings with operable windows: Two case studies. ASHRAE Transactions 110(1).

Mass, M., M. Maybaum, and R. Haughney. 2001. High-rise HVAC. Consulting-Specifying Engineer, October:60–66.

McGuire, J.H., G.T. Tamura, and A.G. Wilson. 1970. Factors in controlling smoke in high buildings, Presented at the Symposium on Fire Hazards in Buildings, ASHRAE Annual Meeting, San Francisco, California, January.

Megri, A.C. 2011. Teaching high-rise plumbing design for engineers. Presented at the ASEE 2011 Annual Conference. Vancouver, BC: Canada

Mims, N., S. Schiller, E. Stuart, et al. 2017. Evaluation of U.S. building energy benchmarking and transparency programs: attributes, impacts, and best practices. Berkeley, CA: Lawrence Berkeley National Laboratory.

Modbus. 2012. *MODBUS application protocol specification v1.1b3*. Modbus Organization, Inc., Hopkinton, MA.

Modera, M.P., and D.J. Wilson. 1990. The effects of wind on residential building leakage measurements. ASTM STP 1067, *Air Change Rate and Airtightness in Buildings*. M.H. Sherman, ed. Philadelphia: American Society for Testing and Materials.

NFPA. 2008. *Fire protection handbook*, 20th ed. Quincy, MA: National Fire Protection Association.

NFPA. 2018a. NFPA 90A-2002, *Standard for the installation of air conditioning and ventilation systems*. Quincy, MA: National Fire Protection Association.

NFPA. 2018b. NFPA 92, *Standard for smoke-control systems*. Quincy, MA: National Fire Protection Association.

NFPA. 2018c. NFPA 5000, *Building Construction and Safety Code.* Quincy, MA: National Fire Protection Association.

NFPA. 2018d. NFPA 101, *Life safety code.* Quincy, MA: National Fire Protection Association.

NFPA. 2019. NFPA 13, *Standard for the Installation of Sprinkler Systems.* Quincy, MA: National Fire Protection Association.

NFPA. 2020. NFPA 70, *National electrical code*®. Quincy, MA: National Fire Protection Association.

NFRC. 2017. *Procedure for determining fenestration product U-factors.* Greenbelt, MD: National Fenestration Rating Council.

Ng, L.C., A. Musser, A.K. Persily, and S.J. Emmerich. 2013. Multizone airflow models for calculating infiltration rates in commercial reference buildings. *Energy and Buildings* 58:11–18.

NIST. 2017. Smart Grid Interoperability Panel, Catalog of Standards. https://www.nist.gov/programs-projects/smart-grid-national-coordination/catalog-standards.

NOAA. 2013. Weather balloon data. National Oceanic and Atmospheric Administration. Accessed on September 20, 2013. www.ncdc.noaa.gov/data-access/weather-balloon-data.

O'Connor, J., and J. Ellowitz. n.d. Multifamily residential HVAC systems: How do you decide? Burlington, MA: Erland. https://www.erland.com/articles/HVAC.pdf.

OGC®. 2007. OGC Standard 06-010r6 (retired), *OpenGIS*® *Transducer Markup Language (TML) Implementation Specification.* Open Geospatial Consortium, Wayland, MA.

OGC®. 2014. OGC Standard 12-000, *SensorML: Model and XML Encoding Standard.* Open Geospatial Consortium, Wayland, MA.

OpenADR Alliance. n.d. The OpenADR primer. Available at http://www.openadr.org/assets/docs/openadr_primer.pdf.

PECI and Battelle. 2003. *Method for automated and continuous commissioning of building systems.* ARTI-21CR/610-30040-01. Portland Energy Conservation, Inc. and Battelle Northwest Division. Air Conditioning and Refrigeration Technology Institute, Arlington, VA.

Pérez-Lombard, L., J. Ortiz, J.F. Coronel, and I.R. Maestre. A review of HVAC systems requirements in building energy regulations. *Energy and Buildings* 43:255–268.

Persily, A. 1997 Evaluating building IAQ and ventilation with indoor carbon dioxide. *ASHRAE Transactions* 102(2).

Persily, A., and R.A. Grot 1985. Accuracy in pressurization data analysis. ASHRAE Transactions 91 (2):105–16.

Persily, A., and R.A. Grot. 1986. Pressurization testing of federal buildings. ASTM STP 904, Measured Air Leakage of Buildings. H.R. Trechsel and P.L. Lagus, eds. Philadelphia: American Society for Testing and Materials.

Phoenix Energy. 2019 A complete guide to NYC local lawas: LL87, LL84, LL133, LL33. Brooklyn, NY: Phoenix Energy Group.

Poirazis, H. 2006. *Double skin façade.* A report of IEA SHC Task 34 ECBCS. Annex 43. Lund University, Lund Institute of Technology.

PRC. 2005. GB 50189-2005, *Design Standard for Energy Efficiency of Public Buildings.* Beijing: Ministry of Housing and Urban-Rural Development, People's Republic of China.

Price, P. 2010. *Methods for analyzing electric load shape and its variability.* LBNL-3713E. Lawrence Berkeley National Laboratory, Berkeley, CA.

Popp, J. 2013. Elevator design in modern residential high-rises. *High Rise Facilities.*

Ross, D. 2004. An HVAC design guide for tall buildings. Atlanta: ASHRAE.

Rossi, T.M., and J.E. Braun. 1997. A statistical, rule-based fault detection and diagnostic method for vapor compression air conditioners. *International Journal of Heating, Ventilating, Air-Conditioning and Refrigerating Research* (now *Science and Technology for the Built Environment*) 3(1):19-37.

Rush, C. 2013. Integration: Lighting and HVAC systems. *Consulting-Specifying Engineer.* http://www.csemag.com/single-article/integration-lighting-and-hvac-systems/6cdbfda10abe16e4770416fd60235987.html. (18 May 2015).

Sachs, H.M. 2005. Opportunities for elevator energy efficiency improvements. *Proceedings of the American Council for an Energy-Efficient Economy (ACEEE).* Washington, DC.

SA/SNZ. 2002. Structural design actions—Part 2: Wind actions. Standard AS/NZS 1170.2:2002. Sydney, AUS: Standards Australia International Ltd.

Schwartz, T. 2018. Innovations and new technology in elevators. Weston, FL: Connections Elevator. www.connectionselevator.com/innovations-and-new-technology-in-elevators/.

Siemens VAI. 2008. *Precision flatness control for SIROLLCIS CM: Highly improved flatness in cold rolling*. Metals Technologies GmbH & Co., Linz, Austria.

Simmonds P., and R. Zhui. 2014. Stack effect guidelines for tall, mega tall and super tall buildings. International Journal of High-Rise Buidlings 2(4).

Steele, A. 1984. *Advanced plumbing technology*. Construction Industry Press.

Tamblyn, R.T. 1991. Coping with air pressure problems in tall buildings, ASHRAE Transactions 97(1).

Tamblyn, R.T. 1993. HVAC system effects for all tall buildings. ASHRAE Transactions 99(2) 789–92.

Tamura G.T. 1994. Fire tower tests on vestibule pressurization for protection of stairshafts. ASHRAE Transactions 100(2).

Tamura, G.T., and C.Y. Shaw. 1976. Air leakage data for the design of elevator and stair shaft pressurization systems. ASHRAE Transactions 82(2):179–90.

Tamura, G.T., and A.G. Wilson. 1967a. Pressure differences for a nine-story building as a result of chimney effect and ventilation system operation. *ASHRAE Transactions*. 72(1).

Tamura, G.T., and A.G. Wilson. 1967b. Building pressures caused by chimney action and mechanical ventilation. *ASHRAE Transactions*. 72(2).

Wang, Y., and F. Gao. 2004. 2004. Tests of stairwell pressurization systems for smoke control in a high rise building. ASHRAE Transactions 110(1).

Webb, W. 2011. Supertall buildings—Special smoke control requirements. ASHRAE Transactions 117(1).

Willmert T. 2001. The return of natural ventilation. *Architectural Record* 7:137–40.

White, A., and M. Holmes. 2009. Advanced simulation applications using ROOM. Eleventh International IBPSA Conference, Glasgow, Scotland, July 27–30. https://pdfs.semantic-scholar.org/fa25/d13d24646f31711277d4d7b7268fda445547.pdf.

Wilson, A.G., and G.T. Tamura. 1970. Stack effect in buildings. *Canadian Building Digest*.

WRF. 2012. *Weather Research and Forecasting Model*. Boulder, CO.

Yeang, K. 1999. *The Green Skyscraper: The Basics for Designing Sustainable Intensive Buildings*. Munich, Germany: Pertel Velag.

Yuill, G.K., and K.H. Haddad. 1994. Effect of opening stairwell doors on the performance of a stairshaft pressurization system. ASHRAE Transactions 100(1).

ZigBee Alliance. 2008. *ZigBee specification*. Document 053474r17. Zigbee Alliance, San Ramon, CA.

Z-Wave® Alliance. 2014. *About Z-Wave® technology*. https://z-wavealliance.org/about_z-wave_technology/.

BIBLIOGRAPHY

Aber, J.D. and R. Freuder. 2000. Variation Among Solar Radiation Data Sets for the Eastern US and Its Effects on Predictions of Forest Production and Water Yield. Durham, NH: Complex Systems Research Center, University of New Hampshire.

AHAM. 2008. ANSI/AHAM Standard RAC-1-R2008, *Room Air Conditioners*. Chicago: Association of Home Appliance Manufacturers.

AHRI. 2004. Standard 310/380-2004, *Packaged Terminal Air Conditioners and Heat Pumps*. Air-Conditioning, Heating, and Refrigeration Institute, Arlington VA.

AIC. 1983. Infiltration Technical Note AIC-TN-11-83, Air Infiltration Centre, September.

AIC Wind Pressure Workshop. 1984. Proceedings. Technical Note AIC-TN-13.1 - 84. Air Infiltration Centre, November.Ali, M., and P. Armstrong. 2010. Sustainability and the tall building: Recent developments and future trends. Presented at the AIA Illinois Central Symposium.

Allen, C. 1981. Reporting format for the measurement of air infiltration in buildings. Technical Note AIC-TN-6-81, Air Infiltration Centre.

ASCE. 1999. Wind tunnel studies of buildings and structures. ASCE Manuals and Reports on Engineering Practice 67. Reston, VA: American Society of Civil Engineers.

ASCE. 2004. Outdoor human comfort and its assessment: State of the art. Reston, VA: American Society of Civil Engineers.

ASCE. 2014. Wind-driven rain effects on buildings. Report, Task Committee on Wind-Driven Rain Effects Environmental Wind Engineering Committee-Technical Council on Wind Engineering. Reston, VA: American Society of Civil Engineers.

ASHRAE. 2000. ASHRAE/ANSI Standard 149, Laboratory Methods of Testing Fans Used to Exhaust Smoke in Smoke Management Systems. Atlanta: ASHRAE.

ASHRAE. 2012c. Guideline 5-1994 (RA 2012), The Commissioning Process for Smoke Control Systems. Atlanta: ASHRAE.

ASME. 2012. ASME A17.2-2012, Guide for Inspection of Elevators, Escalators, and Moving Walks. New York: American Society of Mechanical Engineers.

ASPE. 2000. ASPE Data Book: A Plumbing Engineer's Guide to System Design and Specifications. Rosemont, IL: American Society of Plumbing Engineers.

Bae, Si-Hwa, and Sung-Moon Jung. 2004. A study on the satisfaction with work space in high rise office building. CTBUH2004 October 10–13, Seoul, Korea.

Bauman, F. 2003. Underfloor air distribution design guide. Atlanta: ASHRAE

Bauman, F., and T. Webster. 2001. Outlook for underfloor air distribution. ASHRAE Journal 44(6).

Baumgartner, S., J. Coleman, and A. Aboff. 2014. Linking Tall Buildings Energy Use to Tenant Contribution to Economy. Philadelphia: Greenbuild.

Beveridge, J. 2007. Domestic Water System Design for High-Rise Buildings Volume 6.

Boyer, J. and A. Dang. 2005. Designing for Performance: A Case Study in the Applied Science of an Environmentally Responsive High-Rise Design. Proceedings of Building Simulation 2007.

BSI. 1980. BS5925, Code of Practice for the design of buildings: ventilation principles and designing for natural ventilation, British Standards Institution.City of Chicago. 2019. Chicago Municipal Code. http://www.amlegal.com/library/il/chicago.shtml.

Chandel, S.S. 2005. New correlation to estimate global solar radiation on horizontal surfaces using sunshine hour and temperature data for Indian sites, *Journal of Solar Energy Engineering* 127(3):417–420.

Chandra, S., K. Ruberg, and A. Kerestecioglu. 1983. Outdoor testing of small scale naturally ventilated models. *Building and Environment* 18(s1–2):45–53.

CIBSE. 2000. Mixed mode ventilation. CIBSE Applications Manual AM13:2000. London: Chartered Institute of Building Services Engineers.

CIBSE. 2005. Natural ventilation in non-domestic buildings, CIBSE Applications Manual AM10. London: Chartered Institute of Building Services Engineers.

Clawson, K., and D. O'Connor. 2011. Considerations and challenges for refuge areas in tall buildings. Presented at CTBUH 2011 9th World Conference, Seoul, Korea, October 10–12, 2011.

Connelly, D. 2007. High-rise plumbing design: It's all the same, right? Newcomb and Boyd. http://www.newcomb-boyd.com/publications-presentations-seminar-notes/high-rise-plumbing-design-its-all-the-same-right/.

Cote, R. 2000. Life safety code handbook, 8th ed. Quincy, MA.: National Fire Protection Association.

Cresci, R. J. 1973. Smoke and fire control in high-rise office buildings—Part II: Analysis of stair pressurization systems. ASHRAE Transactions 79(2):16–23.

Crow, L. 1984. Weather year for energy calculations. *ASHRAE Journal* 26(6) 42-7.

CTBUH. 1980. Planning and environmental criteria for tall buildings. Lehigh University, Bethlehem, Pennsylvania: Council on Tall buildings and Urban Habitat.

CTBUII. 1992. Life Safety in Tall Buildings. Lehigh University, Bethlehem, Pennsylvania: Council on Tall buildings and Urban Habitat.

CTBUH. 1995. Architecture in Tall Buildings. Council on Tall Buildings and Urban Habitat, Lehigh University, Bethlehem, Pennsylvania.

Daly, A. 2002. Underfloor air distribution: Lessons learned. ASHRAE Journal 44(5):21–24.

Department of the Navy. 1990. Military Handbook 1011/2, Cooling Buildings by Natural Ventilation. Alexandria, VA: Naval Facilities Engineering Command. http://www.civil.uwaterloo.ca/beg/ArchTech/Navy%20Natural%20Cooling%20Guide.pdf.

Doebelin, E.O. 1975. Measurement systems: Application and design. New York: McGraw Hill.

Duda, S.W. 2004. Atria smoke exhaust: 3 approaches to replacement air delivery. ASHRAE Journal 46(6):21–27.

EIA. 2003. Commercial buildings energy consumption survey (CBECS). U.S. Department of Energy. Washington, DC: United States Energy Information Administration.

EIA. 2013. Energy Star score for offices in the United States—Technical reference. United States Environmental Protection Agency. U.S. Department of Energy. Washington, DC: United States Energy Information Administration.EPMI. 2003. 2003 CBCS National Median Source Energy Use. EUI Percentiles and Mean.

Elmroth, A., and P. Levin. 1983, Air infiltration control in housing: Aguide to international practice. Swedish Council for Building Research, 02:1983.

Etheridge, D.W. 1980. The British Gas multi-cell model for calculating ventilation. ASHRAE Transactions 86(2).

Fernandez, N., M.R. Brambley, S. Katipamula, H. Cho, J.K. Goddard, and L.H. Dinh. 2010. Self-correcting HVAC controls project final report. PNNL-19074. Pacific Northwest National Laboratory, Richland, WA.

Fisk, W.J., D. Faulkner, and D.P. Sullivan. 2007. A pilot study of the accuracy of CO2 sensors in commercial buildings. Proceeding of the IAQ 2007 Healthy and Sustainable Buildings. MD: Baltimore.

Frechette, R.E., and R. Gilchrist. 2008 Towards zero energy—A case study of the Pearl River Tower, Guangzhou, China. Presented at the CTBUH 8th World Congress.

Giai-Miniet, L. 2013. Energy harvesting power for the Internet of things. Consulting-Specifying Engineer. http://www.csemag.com/single-article/energy-harvesting-power-for-the-internet-of-things/8e949599956201d39e7ec1cb4b9f9ec1.html. (18 May 2015).

Goodfellow, H, and E. Tahti, eds. 2001. Industrial ventilation design guidebook. New York: Academic Press.

Harris, D.A. 1991. Noise control manual. New York: Van Nostrand Reinhold.

Hitchin, E. 1983, The CIB example weather year. Building Services Engineering Research and Technology 4(3):119—25.

ISO/IEC. 2012. ISO/IEC Standard 14908-4:2012, Information technology—Control network protocol—Parts 1, 2, 3 and 4. International Standards Organization, Geneva, Switzerland.

Kim, H.I. Integration of Sustainable Technology and Form Generation of Tall Building CTBUH.

Kirkpatrick, A.T., and J.S. Elleson. 1996. Cold air distribution system design guide. Atlanta: ASHRAE.

Kohn, E.A., and P. Katz. 2002. Building type basics for office buildings. New York: John Wiley & Sons, Inc.

Kraut, P.A. n.d. High rise water distribution. Plumbing Engineer. http://www.plumbingengineer.com/content/high-rise-water-distribution.

Kronvall, J. 1980 Airtightness—Measurements and measurement methods. Stockholm, Sweden: Swedish Council for Research.

Ladd, J.S. 2005. An evaluation and pressure-driven design of potable water plumbing systems. Master's thesis.

Leonardelli, M.J. 1993. Water treatment constraints in commercial buildings: Specific problems and solutions. ASHRAE Transactions 99(2).

Lewis, W.S. 1986. Design of high-rise shuttle elevators. Elevator World 34:74–76, 78–80.

Liddament, M and Allen, C, 1983, The validation and comparison of mathematical models of air

Liddament, M and Thompson, C. 1983, Techniques and instrumentation for the measurement of air infiltration in buildings - a brief review and annotated bibliography. Technical Note AIC-TN-10-83, Air Infiltration Centre, 1983.

Linford, R.G., and S.T. Taylor. 1989. HVAC systems: central vs. floor-by-floor. HPAC July:43–49, 56–57, 84.

Loring, J.R. 1995. The 21st Century Office Building—How Smart Will It Be? Habitat and the High Rise, Council on Tall Buildings and Urban Habitat, 791–98.

Lorsch, H.G, ed. 1993. Air-conditioning systems design manual. Atlanta: ASHRAE.

Lott, M.C., T.B. Seaman, C.R. Upshaw, and E.G.K. Haron. 2011. The smart grid in Texas: A primer. Power Across Texas, Austin. Available from http://www.poweracrosstexas.org/the-smart-grid-in-texas-primer-now-available/.

Loudermilk, K.J. 2003. Temperature control and zoning in underfloor air distribution systems. ASHRAE Transactions 109(1).

Lugtenburg, A. 1972. Luchtbewging om gebowen: Drukmetingen aan afvoerkanalen IG-T Report C 302. (Dutch).

McKew, H. 1978. Double duct design—A better way. Heating/Piping/Air-Conditioning December.

Modera, M.P. 1995. Field comparison of alternative techniques for measuring air distribution system leakage. ASTM STP 1255, Airflow Performance of Building Envelopes, Components and Systems. 284–98. Philadelphia: American Society for Testing and Materials.

Nady, M. 1988. Review of smoke control models. ASHRAE Journal 30(4):36–40.

New York. 2013. Green Buildings & Energy Efficiency: Benchmarking Scores & Reports. Accessed on September 26, 2013.

New York City. 2013. New York City Local Law 84 Benchmarking Report. September 2013. The City of New York.

NERC. 2012. Regional entities. North American Electric Reliability Corporation, Atlanta, GA.

NEN. 1999. NPR 1088, Ventilation in dwellings (Ventilatie van woongebouwen) Nederlands Normalisatie- Institute. (Dutch).NFPA. 2019. NFPA 72, National Fire Alarm and Signaling Code. Quincy, MA: National Fire Protection Association.

NFPA. 2019. Standard for the Installation of Standpipe and Hose Systems. Quincy, MA: National Fire Protection Association.

NFPA. 2019. NFPA 110, Emergency and Standby Power Systems. Quincy, MA: National Fire Protection Association.

NFPA. 2019. NFPA 111, Stored Electrical Energy Emergency and Standby Power Systems. Quincy, MA: National Fire Protection Association.

NRC. 2010. National Building Code of Canada. Ottawa ON: National Research Council Canada.

NYCDCP. 2013. BYTES of the BIG APPLE[TM]. New York City Department of City Planning. http://www.nyc.gov/html/dcp/html/bytes/applbyte.shtml.

O'Connor, D., K. Clawson, and E. Cui. 2012. Considerations and challenges for refuge areas in tall buildings: An update. Proceedings of the CTBUH 9th World Congress, September 19–21, 516–525. China: Shanghai. Council on Tall Buildings and Urban Habitat.

Osada, W. 2008. Restoration of domestic water pipes in high-rise buildings. March 2008.

Phaff, J.C., and W. de Gids. 1980. Ventilatie van gebauwen. Onderjoek naar de gevolgen van het openen van een ram op het binnenjlimaat ven en kamer.Rapport C 448, IMG-TNO.

Plumbing Engineer. 2010. Hot Water Recirculation in High-Rise Buildings Plumbing Engineer. Plumbing Engineer February.

Potter, I N,1979, Effects of fluctuating wind pressures on natural ventilation rates, ASHRAE Trans., Vol 85, Part 2, 1979.Rishel, J.B. 1993. Pumping system design for tall buildings. ASHRAE Transactions 99(2).

Raymond, W.H. 2000. Estimating moisture profiles using a modified power law. *Journal of Applied Meteorology* 39(7):1059–1070.

Rishel, JB. 2000. 40 years of fiddling with pumps. *ASHRAE Journal* 3.

Roaf, S., D. Crichton, and F. Nicol. 2009. Adapting buildings and cities for climate change: A 21st century survival guide, 2nd ed. Oxford: Architectural Press.

Ross, D. E. (1996). Bank of China: An integration of architecture and engineering. Total Building Design Seminar, Chicago, Illinois.

Sandberg, M. 1983, Definition of ventilation efficiency and the efficiency of mechanical ventilation 3rd AIC Conference 'Energy efficient domestic ventilation systems for achieving acceptable indoor air quality' Proceedings, September 1983, UK.Shaw, C.Y., D.M. Sander, and GT. Tamura. 1973. Air leakage measurements of the exterior walls of tall buildings. ASHRAE Transactions 79(2):40–48.

Seemann, S. W., E.E. Borbas, J. Li, W.P. Menzel, and L.E. Gurley. 2006. Modis Atmospheric Profile Retrieval Algorithm Theoretical Basis Document. Madison, WI: Cooperative Institute for Meteorological Satellite Studies, University of Wisconsin-Madison.

Shaw, C.Y., S. Gasparetto, and J.T. Reardon. 1990. Methods for measuring air leakage in high-rise apartments. ASTM STP 1067, Air Change Rate and Airtightness in Buildings. M.H. Sherman, ed. Philadelphia: American Society for Testing and Materials.

Sherman, M.H., and D.T. Grimsrud. 1980. Measurement of infiltration using fan pressurisation and weather data, 1st AIC Conference "Air infiltration instrumentation and measurement techniques." Proceedings.

Sherman, M., and L. Palmiter. 1995. Uncertainties in fan pressurization measurements. ASTM STP 1255, Airflow Performance of Building Envelopes, Components and Systems. 266–83. Philadelphia: American Society for Testing and Materials.

Shrestha, S., and G. Maxwell. 2009. An experimental evaluation of HVAC-grade carbon dioxide sensors—Part I: Test and evaluation procedures. ASHRAE Transactions 115(2):471–83.

Shrestha, S., and G. Maxwell. 2009. Wall-mounted carbon dioxide (CO_2) transmitters. National Building Controls Information Program, Iowa Energy Center, June.

Shrestha, S., and G. Maxwell. 2010. An experimental evaluation of HVAC-grade carbon dioxide sensors—Part 2: Performance test results. ASHRAE Transactions 115(2):471–83.

SMACNA. 2002. Fire, Smoke and Radiation Damper Installation Guide For HVAC Systems, 5th ed. Chantilly, VA: SMACNA.

Sommer, G.R. 1995. Simplified sizing of pressurized expansion tanks. ASHRAE Journal 37(10):40.

Steele, A. 1978. High rise plumbing design. Los Angeles: Miramar Publishing Co.

Stewart, W.E., Jr. 1998. Effect of air pressure differential on vapor flow through sample building walls. ASHRAE Transactions 104(2).

Strakosch, G.R. 2010. Vertical transportation: Elevators and escalators, 4th ed. New York: John Wiley & Sons.

Thompson, R. 2006. Design Considerations for Fire Pump Systems in High-Rise Buildings, Part 2. PME.

Thompson, T. 1984, A review of building airtightness and ventilation standards Technical Note AIC-TN-14-84, Air Infiltration Centre, 1984.

University of Wyoming. 2013. 72501 OKX Upton Observations. http://weather.uwyo.edu/cgi-bin/sounding?region=naconf&TYPE=TEXT%3AL-ST&YEAR=2013&MONTH=09&FROM=2900&TO=2900&STNM=72501. Accessed on September 29, 2013.

USGBC. 2013. LEED® Reference Guide for Building Design and Construction v4. U.S. Green Building Council.

Walton, G.N, and W. Dols. 2005. CONTAM 2.4 User Guide and Program Documentation, NISTIR 7251. Gaithersburg, MD: National Institute of Standards and Technology

Warren, P.R. and B.C. Webb. 1980. The relationship between tracer gas and pressurisation techniques in dwellings. AIC conference "Instrumentation and Measuring Techniques", Windsor, UK.

Watts, S., and N. Kalita. 2007. Cost model: Tall buildings. https://www.building.co.uk/data/cost-model-tall-buildings/3085522.article.

Wessel, D.J. 1991 Domestic water pumping considerations in a high-rise building. *ASHRAE Transactions* 97(1).

INDEX

R

raised floors, 16–17, 23, 111–112
refuge floors, 27, 73, 119, 214–216
residential 1, 25–26, 63, 75, 88, 124, 155–156, 171, 177, 186–188, 221–226, 228, 247–248, 263
    mechanical, electrical, and plumbing design, 17

S

service cores, 12
shading, 31, 33–36, 39, 64, 168, 258
smoke dampers, 126, 130
smoke detectors, 206–207, 218
stack effect, 27, 34, 66–68, 72, 75, 93, 95, 179, 188–189, 205, 209, 222, 263, 265–272, 274, 276
    reverse stack effect, 271
stairwell pressurization, 213
structural coordination, 17

T

tall building definitions, xviii, 8

U

underfloor air systems, 17, 111–112

V

ventilation
    mixed-mode ventilation, 92
    natural ventilation, xvi, 32, 33, 88, 92–95, 102–105, 115, 221–222, 227, 235–236
vertical transportation systems, 11, 13, 137, 179, 183, 188, 219
    double-deck elevators, 179, 182–184
    elevator recall system, 206, 218
    handling capacity, 180–181, 185, 187
    interval, 13, 180–181, 185, 187
    service elevator, 16, 185–186, 188
    sky lobby concept, 179, 181–183, 186
    system configurations, 179

W

water distribution systems, 157, 163, 194, 198–200